B.R. 229

ADMIRALTY HANDBOOK OF WIRELESS TELEGRAPHY

Volume I
Magnetism and Electricity

LONDON
PUBLISHED BY HIS MAJESTY'S STATIONERY OFFICE
To be purchased directly from H.M. STATIONERY OFFICE at the following addresses:
York House, Kingsway, London, W.C.2; 120 George Street, Edinburgh 2;
39–41 King Street, Manchester 2; 1 St. Andrew's Crescent, Cardiff;
80, Chichester Street, Belfast;
or through any Bookseller.

1938

Price 4s. 0d. net

March, 1938

The Lords Commissioners of the Admiralty have decided that a standard work on Wireless Telegraphy is required for the information and guidance of Officers and Men of H.M. Fleet; for this purpose the " Admiralty Handbook of Wireless Telegraphy, 1938 " has been prepared at H.M. Signal School.

This book, now in two volumes, supersedes " The Admiralty Handbook of Wireless Telegraphy, 1931."

By Command of Their Lordships,

First Published ...	...	...	1938
Reprinted	...	...	1939
Reprinted	...	...	1940
Reprinted	...	...	1941

PREFATORY NOTE.

This Handbook is now divided into two Volumes. Vol. I contains the basic " Magnetism and Electricity Theory " up to and including the " Oscillatory Circuit " ; Vol. II contains a treatment of " W/T Theory." The whole is intended to act as a companion book to various sets of purely technical instructions.

It will be found that certain paragraphs, or portions of paragraphs, are marked with an asterisk, and usually printed in smaller type, to indicate that they are of a more difficult nature than the rest of the book. Those who are unable to follow the treatment may omit them without much detriment to the sequence of the argument.

It will be noted that the various sections of Vol. II have been given characteristic reference letters. References in the index are given in terms of paragraph numbers and section letters.

In order to bring the unit of capacity into line with commercial practice, the use of the jar as the Service unit of capacity has been discontinued (A.F.O. 1552/37). It is to be considered as obsolescent for a few years, the farad and its sub-multiples gradually replacing it as the practical unit of capacity for standard use in the Service.

NOMENCLATURE OF WAVES.

In this Handbook, the range of frequencies of the æther waves used in wireless communication is sub-divided as follows :—

Below 100 kc/s.	..	..	..	Low Frequencies (L/F).
100-1,500 kc/s.	..	..	..	Medium Frequencies (M/F).
1,500-6,000 kc/s.	..	..	..	Intermediate Frequencies (I/F).
6,000-30,000 kc/s.	..	..	..	High Frequencies (H/F).
Above 30,000 kc/s.	..	..	..	Very high Frequencies (V.H/F).

It has been a common practice in the past to refer to the oscillatory currents produced by these waves in a receiving aerial as H/F currents, and to differentiate them from the currents of audible frequency produced after detection by using the term L/F for the latter. It is obvious that this usage conflicts with the nomenclature in the table above ; hence in this Handbook the term RADIO FREQUENCY (R/F) is applied to all currents directly produced by an incoming signal, and the currents flowing after detection are called AUDIO FREQUENCY (A/F) currents.

It also frequently happens that an oscillatory current whose frequency falls within the wireless range is generated by the action of a receiver, e.g., in superheterodyne and quench receivers. When describing the action of such receivers it is desirable to distinguish these currents from the R/F currents produced by an incoming signal. The designation of SUPERSONIC FREQUENCY (S/F) currents has therefore been adopted for these currents.

An International classification of frequencies would be very desirable. On the basis of a recent C.C.I.R. recommendation promulgated in French, a suitable nomenclature likely soon to be accepted internationally may be given in English as follows :—

Below 30 kc/s.	..	..	..	Very Low Frequencies (V.L/F).
30-300 kc/s.	..	..	..	Low Frequencies (L/F).
300-3,000 kc/s.	..	..	..	Medium Frequencies (M/F).
3-30 Mc/s.	..	..	..	High Frequencies (H/F).
30-300 Mc/s.	..	..	..	Very High Frequencies (V.H/F).
300-3,000 Mc/s.	..	..	..	Decimetre Waves (dc/W). (1 to 0·1 metre)
3,000-30,000 Mc/s.	..	..	..	Centimetre Waves (cm/W). (0·1 to 0·01 metre)

Since 1st January, 1938, the latter classification has been adopted for standard use in the Service.

CONTENTS

CHAPTER I.

Paragraph

General Introduction 1
Wave Motion—Sound Waves—Undamped and Damped Waves—The Æther—Wireless Systems.

CHAPTER II.

Electricity and Magnetism 23
Constitution of Matter—Atomic Structure—Electron Theory of Electricity—Units—Resistance—Lamps—Magnetism and Magnetic Fields—Electrostatics and Electric Fields—Primary Cells—Secondary Batteries.

CHAPTER III.

Electromagnetism, Inductance and Capacity 128
Electrodynamic Force—Self-Induction and Mutual Induction—Faraday's Law—Inductance—Capacity—D.C. Measuring Instruments.

CHAPTER IV.

Alternators, Generators and Motors 191
Alternating E.M.F.—Alternators—D.C. Generators—D.C. Motors—Starters—Motor Generators—Motor-Alternators, Boosters—Rotary Converter—Three-Phase Current—Induction Motor—Synchronous Motor.

CHAPTER V.

Alternating Currents 272
R.M.S. Value—Vector Diagram—Series A.C. Circuits—Resistive—Inductive—Capacitive—Combinations of These—Impedance—Resonance—Acceptor Circuits—Parallel Arrangements—Rejector Circuits—Power in A.C. Circuits—Coupled Circuits—The Operator " j."

CHAPTER VI.

The Transformer, Measuring Instruments, R/F Effects 349
Construction—Vector Diagrams for Various Loads—Equivalent Circuits—Auto-Transformer—A.C. Measuring Instruments—Variation of Electrical Quantities with Frequency—Resistance, Skin Effect—Inductance, Self-Capacity—Cores.

CHAPTER VII.

The Oscillatory Circuit : Damped Oscillations 387
The Oscillatory Circuit—Free Oscillations—Natural Frequency and Wavelength—Logarithmic Decrement—Closed and Open Oscillators—Tight and Loose Coupling—Double Frequency Effect—Forced Oscillations.

CHAPTER VIII.

Three-phase and Polyphase A.C. Systems 429
Disadvantages of single phase A.C. systems—Two-phase and Three-phase A.C. Systems with Phases separately Loaded and Balanced—Two-phase, Three-wire System—Three-phase, Four-wire Star Connection—Three-phase, Three-wire Star Connection—Relation between Line Current and Load Current with Mesh Connections—The Mesh Connection of Three Sources of Alternating Voltages-Power Supply with Three-phase Circuits—Use of Wattmeters in Three-phase Circuits—Three-phase Transformers—Three-phase Power Rectifiers—Unbalanced Three-phase Loads.

Appendix A—The Decibel and the Neper.
Appendix B—Conversion of mic. jars to kc./s.
Appendix C—Resuscitation from apparent death by electric shock.
Appendix D—W/T Text Books, works of reference and journals.

Index.

TABLE I.

The Greek Alphabet is here given for reference, as many Greek letters appear in the Text.

Letter.		Name.	English Equivalent.
Small.	Capital.		
α	Α	Alpha	a
β	Β	Beta	b
γ	Γ	Gamma	g
δ	Δ	Delta	d
ε	Ε	Epsilon	ĕ (as in " met ")
ζ	Ζ	Zeta	z
η	Η	Eta	ēē (as in " meet ")
θ	Θ	Theta	th
ι	Ι	Iota	i
κ	Κ	Kappa	k
λ	Λ	Lambda	l
μ	Μ	Mu	m
ν	Ν	Nu	n
ξ	Ξ	Ksi	x
ο	Ο	Omicron	ŏ (as in " olive ")
π	Π	Pi	p
ρ	Ρ	Rho	r
σ	Σ	Sigma	s
τ	Τ	Tau	t
υ	Υ	Upsilon	u
φ	Φ	Phi	ph
χ	Χ	Chi	ch (as in "school ")
ψ	Ψ	Psi	ps
ω	Ω	Ōmega	o (as in " broke ")

TABLE II.

Symbols for Quantities for Use in Electrical Equations, etc.

Number.	Quantity.	Sign.
1	Length	l
2	Mass	m
3	Time	t
4	Angles	α, θ, ϕ
5	Work or Energy	W
6	Power	P
7	Efficiency	η
8	Period	T
9	Frequency	f
10	$2\pi \times$ frequency	ω
11	Wavelength	λ
12	Phase displacement	ϕ
13	Temperature, centigrade	t or θ
14	Temperature, absolute	T or Θ
15	Quantity or charge of electricity	Q
16	Current	I
17	Voltage (E.M.F. or P.D.)	E or V
18	Resistance	R
19	Specific Resistance or Resistivity	ρ
20	Conductance	G
21	Specific Conductance or Conductivity	γ
22	Specific Inductive Capacity or Dielectric Constant	K
23	Electrostatic Field Strength	X
24	Electrostatic Displacement or Flux Density	D
25	Electrostatic Flux	ψ
26	Capacity	C
27	Magnetic Pole Strength	m
28	Permeability	μ
29	Magnetic Field Strength	H
30	Magnetic Induction or Flux Density	B
31	Magnetic Flux	Φ
32	Magnetic Reluctance	S
33	Magneto Motive Force	G
34	Self Inductance	L
35	Mutual Inductance	M
36	Reactance	X
37	Impedance	Z
38	Susceptance	B
39	Admittance	Y
40	Base of Naperian logs	e
41	Damping Factor	α
42	Logarithmic Decrement	δ
43	Aerial Capacity	σ
44	Valve mutual conductance	g_m
45	Valve A.C. resistance (impedance)	r_a
46	Valve amplification factor	m
47	Percentage modulation	N
48	Coil amplification factor ($\omega L/R$)	Q
49	Velocity of E.M. waves	C

TABLE III.

Distinguishing Symbols for Constant and Virtual Values of Quantities.

Number.	Quantity.		Constant Value.	Maximum Value.	Arithmetic Mean Value.	Virtual Value.	Instantaneous Value.
1	Potential Difference		V	$\mathcal{V}$	$\overline{V}$	V	v
2	E.M.F.		E	$\mathcal{E}$	$\overline{E}$	E	e
3	Charge		Q	$\mathcal{Q}$	$\overline{Q}$	Q	q
4	Current		I	$\mathcal{I}$	$\overline{I}$	I	i
5	Flux		Φ	Φ_m	$\overline{\Phi}$	Φ	ϕ
6	Magnetic Field		H	$\mathcal{H}$	$\overline{H}$	H	h
7	Electric Field		X	$\mathcal{X}$	$\overline{X}$	X	x

TABLE IV.

Prefixes for Multiples and Submultiples of Quantities.

Number.	Multiple or Submultiple.	Name.	Prefix.
1	10^6	Mega-	M
2	10^3	Kilo-	k
3	10^2	Hekto-	H
4	10^{-2}	Centi-	c
5	10^{-3}	Milli-	m
6	10^{-6}	Micro-	μ
7	10^{-9}	Millimicro-	mμ
8	10^{-12}	Micro-micro	μμ

TABLE V.

Signs for Units Employed after Numerical Values.

Number.	Unit.	Abbreviation.
1	Ampere	A
2	Volt	V
3	Ohm	Ω
4	Coulomb	C
5	Joule	J
6	Watt	W
7	Farad	F
8	Henry	H
9	Watt-hour	Wh
10	Volt-Ampere	VA
11	Ampere-hour	Ah
12	Kilowatt	kW
13	Kilo-volt-ampere	kVA
14	Kilowatt-hour	kWh
15	Decibel	db

TABLE VI.

(*See* paragraph 14.)

TABLE VII.

(*Cf.* paragraph 183.)

Quantity.	Symbol.	Practical Unit.	1 E.M.U.	1 E.S.U.	1 E.M.U. in E.S.U.
			In Practical Units.		
Energy	W	1 joule	$1 \text{ erg} = \dfrac{1}{10^7} \text{ joule}$		1
Power	P	1 watt	$1 \text{ erg per sec.} = \dfrac{1}{10^7} \text{ watt}$		1
Quantity of electricity	Q	1 coulomb	10	$\dfrac{1}{3 \times 10^9}$	3×10^{10}
Potential difference or E.M.F.	V or E	1 volt	$\dfrac{1}{10^8}$	3×10^2	$\dfrac{1}{3 \times 10^{10}}$
Electric field strength	X	1 volt per cm.	$\dfrac{1}{10^8}$	3×10^2	$\dfrac{1}{3 \times 10^{10}}$
Electric flux density	D	1 E.S.U.	3×10^{10}	1	3×10^{10}
Electric flux	Ψ	1 E.S.U.	3×10^{10}	1	3×10^{10}
Magnetic pole strength	m	1 E.M.U.	1	3×10^{10}	$\dfrac{1}{3 \times 10^{10}}$
Magnetic field strength	H	1 gauss (E.M.U.)	1	3×10^{10}	$\dfrac{1}{3 \times 10^{10}}$
Magnetic flux density	B	1 line per sq. cm. (E.M.U.)	1	3×10^{10}	$\dfrac{1}{3 \times 10^{10}}$
Magnetic flux	Φ	1 line (E.M.U.) or maxwell	1	3×10^{10}	$\dfrac{1}{3 \times 10^{10}}$
Magnetic reluctance	S	1 oersted (E.M.U.)	1	$\dfrac{1}{9 \times 10^{20}}$	9×10^{20}
Magneto Motive Force	G	1 gilbert (E.M.U.)	1	$\dfrac{1}{3 \times 10^{10}}$	3×10^{10}
Electric Current	I	1 ampere	10	$\dfrac{1}{3 \times 10^9}$	3×10^{10}
Resistance	R	1 ohm	$\dfrac{1}{10^9}$	9×10^{11}	$\dfrac{1}{9 \times 10^{20}}$
Capacity	C	1 farad $= 9 \times 10^8$ jars	10^9	$\dfrac{1}{9 \times 10^{11}}$	9×10^{20}
Inductance	L	1 henry	$\dfrac{1}{10^9}$	9×10^{11}	$\dfrac{1}{9 \times 10^{20}}$

TABLE VIII.
Operational Symbols.

Meanings.	Symbol.
"Is equal to"	$=$
"Is not equal to"	$\neq$
"Is approximately equal to"	$\vdots$
"Is the same thing as" or "denotes"	$\equiv$
"Difference" (*i.e.*, independent of sign)	$\sim$
"Varies as," or "Is proportional to"	∞
"Greater than"	$>$
"Not greater than"	$\not>$
"Less than"	$<$
"Not less than"	$\not<$
"The sum of"	Σ

CHAPTER I.

GENERAL INTRODUCTION.

1. In Wireless Telegraphy or Telephony we deal with the transmission, propagation and reception of Electromagnetic or Æther waves. It is the object of this book to explain this means of communication.

WAVE MOTION.

2. A " Wave " is a progressive disturbance in any medium, formed by the propagation of alternating pressures and tensions, without any permanent displacement of the medium itself in the direction in which these stresses are propagated.

The more concrete examples of wave motion, the waves of the sea, sound waves, &c., are very much more familiar than the wave motions associated with light, heat and wireless waves. This is because the media in which they are propagated are material. In such material media it is a movement of matter at the source which gives rise to the wave. A very simple example of this is given by the dropping of a large stone vertically into a pond of water. A wave motion is immediately produced on the surface by the impact, spreading out radially in all directions from the point where the stone strikes the water. Its form is due to alternate states of pressure and tension at the surface of the water, a crest corresponding to a pressure and a trough to a tension. It derives its energy from the loss of kinetic energy by the stone as its velocity is diminished on striking the surface.

Such a wave has certain characteristics, which we shall see later are more or less common to all types of wave motion.

(1) **The form of the wave** travels forward, although the water itself does not travel forward to any appreciable extent. Actually, the particles of water have approximately an up-and-down movement about their positions of equilibrium, and after a complete wave has passed they are in the same position as they were just before its arrival.

(2) **The energy** possessed by the wave on starting travels forward with it and is expended on the shore of the pond. During the passage of the wave some of this energy is lost through friction, and as a result the size of the wave diminishes the further it is from its source.

(3) **The speed** of the wave varies very little at different points along its direction of propagation. It depends primarily on the depth of the water in shallow water, and in deep water depends on surface tension, density of the water, and the length and size of the wave.

3. Any type of wave motion has four different quantities associated with it, its **Velocity, Frequency, Wavelength** and **Amplitude.**

The form of the wave and the energy which it is conveying travel outwards with a certain **Velocity.**

The Frequency is the number of waves that pass a fixed point in a given interval of time. For the type of wave motion associated with wireless the unit of time is one second, and the frequency is therefore the number of waves passing a given point per second. It is denoted by the symbol " f."

The Wavelength is the distance between one wave crest and the next, or, more generally, the distance between two consecutive points at which the moving particles of the medium have the same displacement from their mean position and are moving at every instant in the same direction. It is denoted by the symbol " λ."

The Amplitude is the maximum displacement of a moving particle of the medium from its mean position, BP or DQ in Fig. 1.

To these definitions may be added that of the **Period** of the wave, which is the time in which the waveform moves forward through one wavelength, or the interval of time between passage of successive waves past a given point.

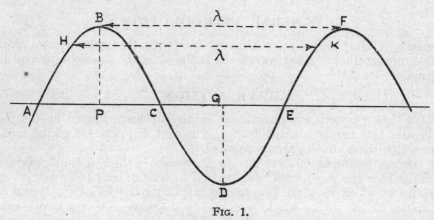

FIG. 1.

A **cycle** of a wave is one complete set of varying conditions, *i.e.*, in Fig. 1, the curve ABCDE. Portions of the wave above the mean line may be termed positive half cycles, below it, negative half cycles.

4. There are certain relationships between these quantities.

(*a*) The Period being the time between successive waves, and the Frequency the number of waves per second, Period $= \dfrac{1}{f}$ seconds.

(*b*) The Frequency being the number of waves per second, and the wavelength the distance between them, the product of these two quantities gives the speed at which the wave is travelling, *i.e.*, its velocity, written *c*.

As a formula, $f \times \lambda = c$.

$$f = \frac{c}{\lambda}.$$

$$\lambda = \frac{c}{f}.$$

5. The first elementary type of wave we took for illustrative purposes, that on the surface of water, is one in which the particles of the transmitting medium move at right angles to the direction of propagation. Such waves are called **Transverse Waves.**

Other examples of the above are the æther waves we shall be concerned with mainly in this book. There is another class of waves called **Longitudinal Waves,** in which the particles of the transmitting medium move to and fro in the same direction as the waves are propagated. The most common example is the sound wave.

SOUND WAVES.

6. When a bell rings, it vibrates at a rate depending on its mass, shape and material, and alternately presses forward and drags backward the particles of air immediately surrounding it. These particles communicate their motion to the particles adjacent to themselves, and the action is carried on, resulting in a wave motion being set up in the atmosphere. At any given instant there are alternate states of compression and rarefaction along any direction outwards from the source of sound, and these, impinging on the ear, make the ear drum vibrate backwards and forwards

at the same frequency as the source of sound. The particles of the transmitting medium, the air, which are set into vibration, move backwards and forwards in the same direction as the sound is going, *i.e.*, radially from the transmitter, and so this is a case of longitudinal vibration.

Just as in the case of visible waves on water, the frequency will be the number of waves passing per second—in this case, the number of states of compression passing a fixed point per second, and the wavelength will be the distance between states of maximum compression.

7. **Method of Representation.**—A transverse wave has a form that can be seen, but a longitudinal wave has not. If, however, we draw lines at right angles to the direction of propagation, and of lengths proportional to the amount of compression (drawn positively) or rarefaction (drawn negatively), and join up the ends of these lines, we shall get what looks like a transverse wave, and the definitions of the quantities associated with the wave may seem more obvious.

Such a waveform may be drawn as above with the horizontal axis an axis of distance, and the waveform representing an instantaneous set of conditions, or it might represent the variations in compression and rarefaction passing a fixed point, in which case the horizontal axis would be an axis of time.

8. The physiological sensation produced by a sound wave of a certain frequency is termed its "Pitch." Doubling the frequency of a sound wave raises its pitch one octave. For example, the pitch of middle C on a piano corresponds to a frequency of 256 cycles per second, the pitch of the next higher C to a frequency of 512 cycles per second, and so on.

It does not follow that all sound waves are **audible.** The best known form of sensitive receiver for sound waves is the human ear, but even this will only respond to a very limited range of pitch.

The lower limit of audibility is about 16 cycles per second. Below this frequency the ear separates the sound into its constituent parts, and the impression of a musical note is lost. In the same way the impression of continuity is lost if a cinema film is run at less than about 16 pictures per second. The upper limit of audibility varies from about 15,000 to 30,000 cycles per second, according to the person concerned.

The pipe organ usually ranges in frequency from 16 to 8,000.

The range of frequency for the human voice in singing is from 60 for a low bass voice to about 1,300 for a very high soprano. The average male speaking voice has a frequency of about 130, and the average female speaking voice is an octave higher, frequency about 260.

9. Applying the formula of paragraph 4 (*b*) to the case of sound waves, we can work out their wavelength given their velocity. Sound waves in air travel outwards in all directions from their source in three dimensions, with a velocity of about 1,130 ft. per second, or about 12·8 miles per minute, or about 770 miles per hour.

The wavelength of the note "middle C" would therefore be $\frac{1,130}{256}$ ft. = 4·4 ft., while that of the "treble C" would be $\frac{1,130}{512} = 2·2$ ft.

10. Sound signals produced in air are very erratic in their range and intensity, due to the fact that sound may be carried by the wind or reflected or refracted (bent from its course) by layers of air of different densities, so that a sound may be audible some distance away and yet be quite inaudible at points nearer the transmitting agency in the same straight line.

11. Sound waves may also be propagated through water, as is done by a "submarine bell." They travel at a higher speed in water, their speed in any medium being given by a formula involving the density and elasticity of the medium. For water this formula gives about four times the speed in air ; actually, 4,700 ft. per second in fresh water, 4,900 ft. per second in sea water.

The wavelength of "middle C" in sea water is $\frac{4,900}{256} = 19·14$ feet, and in fresh water, $\frac{4,700}{256} = 18·3$ feet.

Sound waves in water can be received on a suitable receiver, such as a hydrophone, an S/T oscillator, or even through the hull of a ship.

UNDAMPED AND DAMPED WAVES.

12. There is another method by which waves may be divided into two classes, viz. :—

(1) Continuous or " **undamped** " waves, represented graphically by Fig. 2 (a) below.

(2) " **Damped** " waves, represented by Fig. 2 (b).

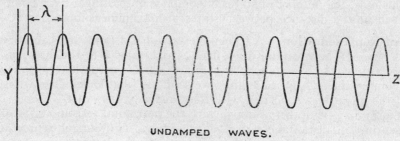

UNDAMPED WAVES.

(a)

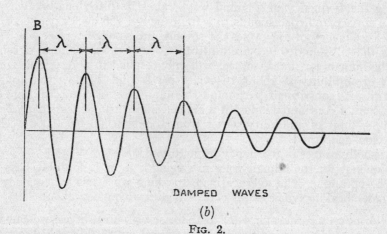

DAMPED WAVES

(b)

Fig. 2.

In these figures the horizontal axis is an axis of time, and the graphs represent amplitudes of waves passing a fixed point.

The essential feature of **undamped** or continuous waves is that the amplitude remains constant ; if we take a common type of wave motion, sound, such waves are the kind produced by an organ note, where a continuous force is applied to producing the note all the time the key is pressed down.

The **damped** wave, on the other hand, has a varying amplitude ; an example is the piano note, where the vibrating wire which produces the sound is set into agitation when the key is struck, and vibrates to and fro with less and less amplitude as time goes on. After the first impulse there is no steady supply of energy to it to overcome the " damping " effect of air resistance, etc., and so keep its amplitude of vibration constant.

The distinction between these types of wave is very important in wireless, because some types of transmitting apparatus produce undamped or continuous waves and some types damped waves. A group of waves as in Fig. 2 (b) is often called a wave **train.**

THE ÆTHER.

13. In the foregoing instances of wave motion, viz., surface sea waves and sound waves, the wave motion has depended on some movement of matter (paragraph 24) at the source.

There are other sorts of wave motion or vibration, called " æther waves," which are generated by the **movement of electrons** at their source.

Now we have seen that sound is conveyed from transmitter to receiver in the following manner : the transmitter is set in vibration ; the intervening medium is set in vibration ; the vibration of the medium sets the receiver in vibration.

We are led to believe in the existence of the medium we term the æther for the following reasons :—

The earth continually receives enormous quantities of energy from the sun in the form of light and heat, which travel through a space known to be empty of ordinary matter. Filaments of incandescent lamps give off light and heat, although the bulb contains practically no gas or air.

It is unreasonable to suppose that the energy in the sun or in an electric circuit disappears there and reappears at the earth (or the receiving circuit) without having been conveyed across the intervening space. It must be conveyed across either as an actual molecular movement, like the flow of a river, or as a wave motion, like the passage of sound through air.

All experience goes to show that light and electromagnetic energy generally are transmitted through space as a wave motion, and we are led to the supposition that all space is occupied by a medium which conveys the energy, and that this medium has properties different from those possessed by ordinary matter.

We call this medium " æther."

The medium called the æther must necessarily be universally diffused and must inter-penetrate all matter. It cannot be exhausted or removed from any place, because no material is impervious to it.

The presence of what we know as matter in its various forms may, however, modify the properties of æther so far as these æther waves are concerned. For example, a light wave can pass through a glass window, but cannot pass through a brick wall, while a wireless wave can pass through a brick wall, but cannot pass through a sheet of copper.

The æther must possess in great degree some form of **elasticity**—that is ,resistance to any change of state produced in it—and it must also possess **inertia,** or a quality in virtue of which a change so made in it tends to persist.

It is clear that it has the property of being capable of storing up energy in large quantities and transmitting it from one place to another, as shown by the fact that enormous amounts of energy are hourly being transmitted from the sun to the earth.

Vibrations of the æther are *only* produced by the electric and magnetic fields associated with electrons in motion. (*See* Chapter II.)

Electric and magnetic stresses are passed through the æther with a definite velocity, which has been found to be* **300,000 kilometres** (*i.e.,* 3×10^8 **metres**), or **186,000 miles per second.**

All movements of the æther consist of electric and magnetic forces, alternating in direction ; they produce a disturbance, spreading outwards, which is called an " electro-magnetic wave," or simply an " æther wave."

ÆTHER WAVES.

14. According to their frequencies, æther waves produce different effects, and require different methods of generation and detection. All these waves convey energy, which can be converted to heat energy by means of a suitable detector.

The range of frequencies so far discovered is shown in Table VI.

Æther waves are of a totally different nature from sound waves, and even at audible frequencies they do not affect the ear directly and cannot be heard.

They are classified in groups or bands according to the way in which they are generated. It will be seen that certain bands on the chart overlap, *e.g.,* the ultra-violet and X-ray bands, and the infra-red and wireless bands. This merely means that the same wave can be generated by two different methods. The properties of the wave are unaffected by its mode of generation.

---

* This figure is an approximation. The figure which is generally accepted as being accurate is $2 \cdot 9982 \times 10^8$ metres per second.

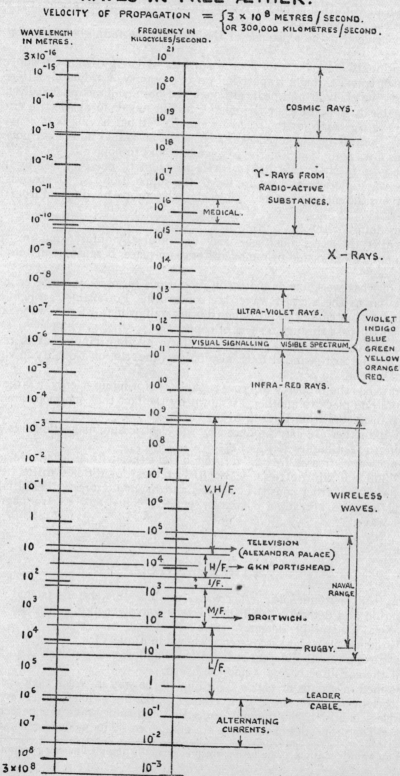

TABLE VI
WAVES IN FREE ÆTHER.

VELOCITY OF PROPAGATION $= \begin{cases} 3 \times 10^8 \text{ METRES / SECOND.} \\ \text{OR } 300,000 \text{ KILOMETRES / SECOND.} \end{cases}$

WAVELENGTH IN METRES.

FREQUENCY IN KILOCYCLES/SECOND.

WAVELENGTH IN METRES	FREQUENCY IN KILOCYCLES/SECOND
3×10^{-16}	10^{21}
10^{-15}	10^{20}
10^{-14}	10^{19}
10^{-13}	10^{18}
10^{-12}	10^{17}
10^{-11}	10^{16}
10^{-10}	10^{15}
10^{-9}	10^{14}
10^{-8}	10^{13}
10^{-7}	10^{12}
10^{-6}	10^{11}
10^{-5}	10^{10}
10^{-4}	10^{9}
10^{-3}	10^{8}
10^{-2}	10^{7}
10^{-1}	10^{6}
1	10^{5}
10	10^{4}
10^{2}	10^{3}
10^{3}	10^{2}
10^{4}	10^{1}
10^{5}	1
10^{6}	10^{-1}
10^{7}	10^{-2}
10^{8}	10^{-3}
3×10^{8}	

COSMIC RAYS.

Υ - RAYS FROM RADIO-ACTIVE SUBSTANCES.

MEDICAL.

X - RAYS.

ULTRA-VIOLET RAYS.

VISUAL SIGNALLING   VISIBLE SPECTRUM.

$\left. \begin{array}{l} \text{VIOLET} \\ \text{INDIGO} \\ \text{BLUE} \\ \text{GREEN} \\ \text{YELLOW} \\ \text{ORANGE} \\ \text{RED.} \end{array} \right\}$

INFRA-RED RAYS.

V.H/F.

WIRELESS WAVES.

TELEVISION (ALEXANDRA PALACE)

H/F. → GKN PORTISHEAD.

I/F.

NAVAL RANGE

M/F. → DROITWICH.

RUGBY.

L/F.

LEADER CABLE.

ALTERNATING CURRENTS.

The waves of highest frequency so far discovered are the so-called "penetrating radiation" or cosmic rays, which appear to be produced in the depths of space and reach the earth in all directions.

The next range is that of X-rays, which are produced by the sudden stoppage of very fast-moving electrons, and are of value for medical purposes. The higher frequencies of this range are also covered by the Gamma (γ)-rays emitted in the disintegration of radio-active substances, some of which are used in medicine.

At its lower end, the X-ray band overlaps with the ultra-violet rays, which are radiated from very hot bodies and ionised gases. These are the rays which affect a photographic plate, and are also valuable rays in "sun-bathing."

The next range is the visible spectrum—the band of frequencies which can be directly detected by the eye. When all present, as in the case of the sun's radiation, they give the sensation of white light, but the different frequencies present can be made visible by passing the white light through a glass prism.

The rays below the red end of the visible spectrum, or infra-red rays, are radiated from hot bodies, e.g., a poker not heated to redness. Their lowest frequencies overlap with the waves on wires produced by electrical means, i.e., the highest frequencies of the wireless range.

This brings us to the range of wireless waves from about 10 kc/s. to 10^{10} kc/s.

They are of too low a frequency to be perceived directly by the eye, and have to be collected on an aerial, and then made perceptible to the senses in one of a variety of ways—generally by giving rise to sounds in a pair of telephones.

They have the supreme advantages over any other form of signalling that they follow the curvature of the earth, and do not suffer nearly so much from dissipation in the atmosphere, and so are suitable for signalling to the greatest possible distances. It is only a question of the use of suitable power and receiving gear for stations to communicate with half the circumference of the earth between them.

15. Table VI is drawn on a "logarithmic" scale, in which equal distances along the vertical axis represent, not equal differences in magnitudes of numbers, but equal differences in their logarithms.

The frequencies and wavelengths correspond, according to the formula of paragraph 4 :—

$$f \times \lambda = c.$$

In the case of electromagnetic waves this velocity is 3×10^8 metres per second, so that, for instance, a frequency of 10^6 cycles/second corresponds to a wavelength of 300 metres.

The above velocity is, strictly speaking, only correct for æther, but the velocity of electro-magnetic waves in air is practically the same. In other substances it may be very different, a common example being that the velocity of light in glass is different from what it is in air. Light of the same frequency, however, moving through glass or air sets up the same sensation of colour in the eye, so it is the frequency which distinguishes one electromagnetic wave from another, and not the wavelength.

Hence the common practice hitherto of alluding to wireless waves by their wavelengths is not so correct as if we allude to them by their frequencies. It has been assumed that they are propagated in air. For this reason, and others, it has been decided that wireless waves will be quoted in frequencies in future, and, owing to the large quantities that would be involved, using " cycles per second," the unit " kilocycles per second " is used. A **kilocycle** is 1,000 cycles.

The product of wavelength in metres and frequency in kilocycles per second is equal to the velocity in kilometres per second. Hence, to convert a given wavelength into frequency in kilocycles, it is necessary to divide **300,000** by the wavelength in metres, and *vice versa*.

Thus the expression " a wavelength of 300 metres " is more accurately represented by " a frequency of 1,000 kilocycles per second." The recognised abbreviation for " kilocycles per second " is kc/s.

In the case of V.H/F waves, the number which gives the frequency in kc/s. becomes very large, and such frequencies are usually quoted in " megacycles per second " (Mc/s.).

$$1 \text{ megacycle per second} = 1,000,000 \text{ cycles per second.}$$
$$= 1,000 \text{ kilocycles per second.}$$

To express the frequency in Mc/s., **300** should be divided by the wavelength in metres and *vice versa*, *e.g.*, a wavelength of 20 metres corresponds to a frequency of $\frac{300}{20} = 15$ Mc/s.

16. For a proper understanding of W/T, the main essential is a thorough grasp of the principles of electricity and of the laws governing alternating and direct currents. Once these are mastered, W/T in itself will be found to be easy of comprehension, provided the student has some imagination, since one is dealing with a wave motion which is invisible, inaudible and intangible.

The problem in W/T is to maintain an electrical oscillation in an aerial circuit. The nature and appearance of an aerial may be assumed to be familiar to everyone nowadays. An aerial circuit is a natural electrical oscillator.

In virtue of certain properties termed " inductance " and " capacity," which are associated with it, it is just as ready to be set in electrical oscillation as is the balance wheel of a watch to be set in mechanical oscillation.

17. The balance wheel of a watch is such a very useful and accurate analogy all through the study of W/T that we may well stop for a moment to consider it (K.39).

The wheel is carefully balanced and mounted in perfect bearings. To its centre is attached one end of a fine spring—the " hair spring." The tension of this hair spring is adjustable by means of the " regulator." The balance wheel oscillates at a rate depending on its weight and the tension on the hair spring. In its oscillation it operates the escapement, which controls the rate at which the main spring is allowed to uncoil and move the hands of the watch ; conversely, the main spring supplies the energy requisite for maintaining the oscillation of the balance wheel.

Now, the weight or inertia of the wheel and the elasticity of the hair spring are two mechanical properties which correspond respectively to the electrical properties of the aerial referred to above— **inductance and capacity.**

The aerial circuit may be thought of as the balance wheel, and the various systems of energising such a circuit, described in this book, as the hair spring and escapement.

18. The four methods employed for the transmission of W/T are : (*a*) the spark system ; (*b*) the arc system ; (*c*) the valve system ; and (*d*) the high frequency alternator system.

Method (*a*) generates damped waves, but it should be noted that the use of these is obsolescent. (*Cf.* A.1.)

Methods (*b*) and (*d*) generate undamped or continuous waves ; method (*c*) generates damped or undamped waves at will.

In the Naval service we are not concerned with the high frequency alternator system, and the arc system is rapidly becoming obsolete.

19. The relative merits of these four systems may be classified as follows. (The full significance of the points dealt with below may not be appreciated until the chapters dealing with the respective systems have been read. They are inserted here for convenience.)

(*a*) The Spark System.

Advantages.

(1) Robust and durable.
(2) Faults easily cleared.
(3) Emits a wave which forces its way well through interference.

Disadvantages.

(1) Wasteful of power.
(2) Short range as compared with continuous wave generators.
(3) Interferes badly.
(4) Requires high insulation on account of initial peak voltages.

(b) The Arc System.

Advantages.	Disadvantages.

(1) Robust and durable.
(2) Faults easily cleared.
(3) Can be easily constructed to handle large powers.

(1) Slow in starting up.
(2) Presents certain " keying " difficulties.
(3) High-power sets radiate harmonics badly.
(4) Unsuitable for use in a fleet, as it is not possible to " listen through " for Admiral's signals, messages of distress, etc.
(5) High frequencies cannot be produced, the limiting value being 250 kc/s.

(c) The Valve System.

(1) Radiates a very pure wave.
(2) Easy to key.
(3) Very suitable for radio-telephony.
(4) Transmits damped or undamped waves at will.
(5) Quick in starting up.

(1) Valves are fragile and require frequent replacement.
(2) If faults develop, they are not so easy to trace as in other sets.

(d) The High Frequency Alternator System.

(1) Radiates a wave which is very pure and free from harmonics.
(2) Easy to key.
(3) Very suitable for radio-telephony.
(4) Suitable for high power working.

(1) Requires very expert supervision and maintenance.
(2) Its frequency cannot be varied so readily as in other systems.
(3) Its first cost is high.
(4) Only suitable for low frequencies.

The spark and valve systems are described fully in subsequent chapters.

20. When the aerial circuit is set in oscillation by one of the above methods, a succession waves is set up in the æther. These waves spread out in all directions over the surface of the earth, in circles of ever-increasing radius. Whenever they encounter any other aerial they endeavour to set it in electrical oscillation, as the wind sets trees shaking.

The currents in the receiving aerial are passed through a " detector," which renders them suitable for energising a device—a pair of telephones, a loudspeaker, a tape machine, &c.—which renders them perceptible to one of the senses.

21. Notice the sequence—the transmitter—the intervening medium—the receiver.

In the same way, in speaking, the transmitter is the human throat and mouth, the medium which carries the sound waves is the air, the receiver is the drum of the ear.

In signalling with a flashing lamp, the transmitter is the lamp, the medium is the æther which carries the light waves, the receiver is the eye.

22. Further, wireless may be used for **telephony.** The only difference is that the human voice is passed through a microphone in order to vary or modulate the aerial current, instead of using a morse key. The wave is carried to the receiver and detected in the same manner as above.

The direction from which a wireless wave is coming may be determined by the use of " direction-finding " apparatus. This is of very great benefit in navigation and is dealt with in a subsequent chapter.

We must now proceed to discuss electricity in general, direct and alternating currents, and the machinery required for producing them, before passing to the details of the various transmitting and receiving circuits used in wireless telegraphy.

CHAPTER II.

ELECTRICITY AND MAGNETISM.

23. In this chapter the elementary principles of electricity and magnetism are explained, in so far as they affect wireless telegraphy and the circuits used in wireless telegraphy.

CONSTITUTION OF MATTER.

24. **Matter.**—It is difficult, if not impossible, to define rigorously what is meant by matter. It may be taken loosely to mean anything which occupies space and is attracted to the earth's surface when in the neighbourhood of the earth, *i.e.*, has weight.

Matter may exist in three states—solid, liquid and gaseous.

Solid matter tends to preserve its shape almost indefinitely, *e.g.*, jewels and ornaments found in the excavated remains of ancient civilisations still retain as sharp outlines as on the day they left the hand of the craftsman.

Liquid matter has no shape of its own and takes the shape of any vessel in which it may be contained.

Gaseous matter also has no shape of its own, but in addition, unlike liquids, it will adapt its volume to that of its containing vessel and fill it completely.

Matter may assume all three states according to the temperature and pressure to which it is subjected. Thus at normal atmospheric pressure, water (liquid between temperatures of 0° C. and 100° C.) can become ice (solid below a temperature of 0° C.) or steam (gaseous above 100° C.).

Air (gaseous at ordinary temperature and pressure) can become liquid at a very low temperature and high pressure, and solid at an even lower temperature.

25. **Molecules.**—It is not possible to take a piece of matter and go on dividing it indefinitely into smaller pieces. A stage is reached at which any further division alters completely the properties of the original matter.

The smallest portion of any substance which cannot be subdivided without its properties being altered is called a " molecule " of the substance. It exhibits the same chemical and physical properties as the substance in bulk.

There are as many different kinds of molecules in the universe as there are different kinds of substances—an almost limitless number.

The distinction between the different states of matter may be examined in the light of this molecular theory.

26. In all states of matter molecules are in continuous rapid motion.

In a **solid** the molecules are crowded very closely together so that, although their motion is rapid, it is an oscillation about an average position. It may be likened to that of a man in a crowd where it is almost or quite impossible for him to leave the space he occupies between his neighbours ; yet he may turn round and have some motion from side to side. It is the attractive force between molecules, very great because of their proximity to each other, which makes it difficult to alter the shape of solids.

In a **liquid** the molecules are usually less closely packed and there is less cohesive force between them. They are sufficiently free to move from one point to another of the liquid. Their motion may be likened to that of a man moving in a crowded thoroughfare. The case of ice, however, which contracts when it is turned into water, shows that the distance between molecules in a liquid may be less than in a solid. It is the difference in the type of motion, *i.e.*, a change in position of the whole molecule as compared with a vibration about a mean position which gives the essential difference in nature between the liquid and the solid states.

In a gas the movement of the molecules is still freer. They are relatively far apart compared with their dimensions. Because of their great speeds, however, they are still continually colliding with other molecules. The cohesive force is practically absent—in other words, gases expand or contract easily.

27. The effect of heat is normally to increase both the amplitude and the speed of the molecular agitation so that the number of collisions increases. The spaces between the neighbouring molecules increase in size and this is observable as an increase in size of the body which is being heated. In the case of a gas heated in an enclosed vessel, the volume cannot increase and so only the speed of the molecules increases. This is observable as an increase in pressure on the walls of the vessel.

As was mentioned above, such changes of temperature may be sufficient to alter the matter from one state to another. The molecules under such conditions are themselves unaltered, it is merely their organisation which has been changed.

28. **The Atom.**—Molecules are capable of further sub-division but the resulting particles are no longer molecules. They are called " atoms " and have different properties from the molecules of which they formed a part. They are, for example, incapable of independent existence for any length of time except in the special case when the molecule contains only one atom, *i.e.*, when the molecule and the atom are the same.

An atom is the smallest portion of matter that can enter into chemical combination, or the smallest portion of matter obtainable by chemical separation.

A molecule may consist of one, two or more atoms of the same kind or it may consist of two or more atoms of different kinds. In chemistry the term " element " is applied to a substance which is composed entirely of atoms of the same kind : thus, two atoms of hydrogen (H) will combine to form a molecule of hydrogen (H_2). Hydrogen is therefore an element. Two atoms of hydrogen and one atom of oxygen will combine to form a molecule of water (H_2O). Water is not an element but a " chemical compound." The number of atoms in the molecule depends on the substance. In a molecule of salt there are two atoms ; in a molecule of alum about 100 atoms. Examples of molecules which consist of only one atom are furnished by the rare gases of the atmosphere such as helium and neon.

The number of different atoms is limited ; it is believed to be 92 and the enormous number of different substances, and therefore different molecules, in the world is given by varying combinations of this limited number.

29. The extremely small dimensions of these divisions of matter are shown by the following figures.

The mass of the hydrogen atom is $1 \cdot 63 \times 10^{-24}$ gram.

The diameter of the atom, regarding it as a sphere, is from about $2 \cdot 4 \times 10^{-8}$ cms. to $5 \cdot 0 \times 10^{-8}$ cms.

There are about 3×10^{23} molecules of hydrogen in a gram of the substance.

The average velocity of the hydrogen molecule at 15° C. is 1,694 metres per second.

30. Atoms vary in mass and size, the hydrogen atom being the lightest.

The **atomic weight** of a substance is the ratio of the weight of an atom of the substance to the weight of an atom of hydrogen.

The atomic weight of oxygen is 16*, of sodium 23, of molybdenum 96, and so on.

---

* In practice atomic weights are referred to that of oxygen, taken as 16. On this basis the atomic weight of hydrogen is $1 \cdot 008$, and not exactly unity as would appear from the text.

ATOMIC STRUCTURE.

31. Atoms may be further sub-divided into their constituents, viz., **Protons** and **Electrons**, but these are quite different in their nature from matter as we normally conceive it.

An **electron** is a minute particle of negative electricity which, when dissociated from the atom, of which it is a part, shows none of the properties of ordinary matter. All electrons are similar, no matter what type of atom they are associated with. It is important to realise that the electron is **nothing but electricity** and is the smallest possible quantity of negative electricity.

The charge of electricity we have called an electron is equal to $1 \cdot 59 \times 10^{-19}$ coulombs, so that there are $6 \cdot 29 \times 10^{18}$ electrons in a coulomb (paragraph 47).

The radius of an electron is of the order of 10^{-13} cm.

A **proton** is electrically the exact opposite of an electron. It also is supposed to be purely electrical in nature, but it consists of positive electricity. The proton and the electron are thus equal electrical charges, but of opposite sign. Due to some difference as yet unexplained, this has the effect of making the mass of the proton very much greater than that of the electron, so that the mass of an atom is, for all practical purposes, the mass of the protons it contains.

The mass of the proton is $1 \cdot 63 \times 10^{-24}$ grams.

32. The structural arrangement of these constituents in an atom appears to take the form of a central positive nucleus around which circulate a number of electrons in various orbits like the planets round the sun, except that these orbits are described in different planes.

Fig. 3 is a conventional representation of this idea for the case of the copper atom, the orbits of the various planetary electrons being projected on to the plane of the paper. For clearness in the figure, only the outer parts of the outer electron orbits have been drawn. They are continued, of course, round the nucleus.

33. The hydrogen atom will be considered first, as it is the simplest.

The nucleus of the hydrogen atom consists of a single proton, round which rotates a single electron in a planetary orbit. The atom is electrically neutral, the charge of negative electricity, which is the electron, being neutralised by the charge of positive electricity which is the proton. The mass of the atom is almost entirely concentrated in the proton.

The distance of the planetary electron from the proton is about 100,000 times the dimensions of the latter, and in more complex atoms the distances are of a like order, so that Fig. 3 must be understood to be a purely conventional drawing and not in any way drawn to scale.

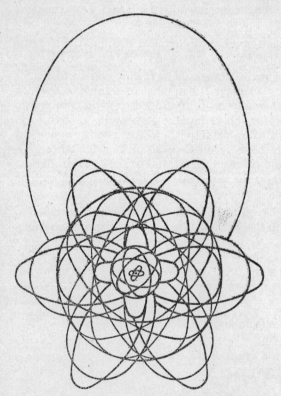

Copper Atom. (29 *Planetary Electrons.*)

FIG. 3.

34. The more complex atoms are made up in the same way of central nuclei and surrounding electrons. The nucleus itself, in these cases, is not composed simply of protons, but of a combination of protons and electrons. For instance, in the case of helium, the central nucleus is made up of four protons and two electrons, while two other electrons revolve round it. In every case the atom is electrically neutral, e.g., in the case of helium the charges on the four protons neutralise the four electrons.

All atoms, and hence all molecules, all elements, all chemical compounds, and in fact the whole of matter, are merely different combinations of positive protons and negative electrons.

The **atomic weight** is practically equal to the number of protons in the atom.

The **atomic number** of an element is the number of surplus positive charges in the inner structure, or nucleus, and it is this quantity which determines the nature of the atom : it is also the number of planetary electrons.

The largest known atomic number is that of uranium, which has 92 revolving electrons. Consequently, as was mentioned before, there are at least 92 different kinds of atoms.

We shall take the more complicated example shown in Fig. 3 to illustrate this theory further. Copper has an atomic weight of about 64 and its atomic number is 29.

That means that the nucleus of the copper atom contains 64 protons, while there are 29 outer electrons associated with it. As the atom is electrically neutral, there must be $64 - 29 = 35$ electrons in the nucleus, so the total composition of the central nucleus is 64 protons + 35 electrons, and it has an excess positive charge of 29 protons.

The nucleus may conveniently be thought of as a charge of positive electricity concentrated at a point.

The atomic number is generally about half the atomic weight.

35. The planetary electrons revolve at inconceivably great speeds round the positive nucleus Thus it is apparent that energy is associated with, and locked up in, every atom.

Electrons from the outer revolving structures of some atoms can, as will be shown later, be caused to move from an orbit in one atom to an orbit in another atom, thus producing electrical phenomena.

The statement that electricity is " generated " by a battery simply means that electricity, already in existence, is given a motion in a particular direction. A battery or dynamo does not generate electricity in the wires connected to it any more than a pump which is impelling a stream of water in a pipe generates the water.

THE ELECTRON THEORY OF ELECTRICITY.

36. **Ions and Ionisation.**—Under ordinary conditions the electrons of any atom are firmly held in the atom and the positive and negative charges neutralise each other as far as effects external to the atom are concerned.

In certain substances some of the constituent electrons describing outer orbits can be removed from the atom if sufficient energy is applied. The removal of such an electron **does not alter the nature of the atom**, but it alters its state of electrification and generally its chemical properties.

An atom which has either a deficit or a surplus of electrons beyond its natural complement is called an " **ion** " and is said to be **ionised.**

If a neutral atom loses an electron, the atom becomes a **positive ion** because it is left with more positive than negative charges.

If an electron is added to a neutral atom, the atom becomes a **negative ion** because it now contains an excess of negative over positive charges.

A positive ion will attract electrons and so will have a strong tendency to become a neutral atom again, while a negative ion will repel electrons and will readily part with the excess electron it has acquired.

The process by which a neutral atom becomes ionised is called " **ionisation** " and can be achieved in various ways.

37. **Positive and Negative Electrification.**—A **positively charged** body is one whose atoms have a deficit of electrons.

A **negatively charged** body is one whose atoms have an excess of electrons.

The amount of electrification depends upon the number of ionised atoms. Normally no single atom gains or loses more than one mobile electron.

It will be seen from the above that, when the poles of a battery are joined by a metallic conductor, the " electric current " which flows " from **positive to negative,**" in accordance with the ideas of the earlier experimenters, is really an electron current flowing from negative to positive, *i.e.*, a surplus of electrons flowing to where there is a deficit so as to equalise the distribution.

When a " negative charge " is spoken of, a surplus of electrons is meant ; when a " positive charge " is spoken of, a deficit of electrons is meant.

It is convenient to use the old method of treatment because of its greater familiarity, but in the explanation of certain facts, especially in the theory of the thermionic valve, the electron theory and the resultant direction of flow of the electron current is important and will be specially pointed out.

Charged bodies exercise forces of attraction and repulsion upon charges and upon each other. If a positively charged body is placed in a gas in an ionised condition, in which both positive and negative ions and electrons may be present, it will attract the electrons and negative ions and repel the positive ions.

38. Conductors and Insulators.—One of the earliest discoveries in the study of electricity was that certain substances, such as amber and glass, when rubbed with silk or flannel, acquired the property of attracting small light objects such as bits of paper or fluff. The experiment may be readily tried, for instance, with a fountain pen rubbed on the hair. Other substances, mostly metals, did not exhibit this property. The name " electricity " is derived from the Greek word for amber.

In terms of the electron theory, this is due to the transfer of electrons from the glass to the silk because of the friction created between them. The glass thus acquires a positive charge and the silk a negative charge. This transfer of electrons takes place in nearly every case where two substances are rubbed together. The distinguishing feature between silk and metals is that the silk possesses the ability to retain the extra electrons it receives, but if the metal is held in the hand, for instance, while performing the experiment, the electrons readily escape from it via the hand to earth, *i.e.*, an electron current flows to earth. This gives a general division of all substances into two kinds when their electrical properties are under consideration. **Conductors** are substances which readily permit a flow of electrons to take place under the influence of electrical forces, and **insulators** are substances in which, under the same circumstances, there is no flow of electrons.

No rigid line can be drawn between conducting and insulating substances. In practice the term " insulator " is applied to substances in which the flow of electrons is so minute compared with that in a good conductor that it may be considered as negligible.

Examples of good insulators are dry air, ebonite, sulphur, mica, indiarubber, shellac, silk and oil ; on the other hand, most metals are good conductors.

39. Types of Electric Current.—The explanation on the electron theory of the processes by which electric currents can flow in different substances makes it possible to classify such currents into three well-defined types :—

(a) Conduction currents.
(b) Displacement currents.
(c) Convection currents.

40. Conduction Current.—This is the type of current which flows in a metallic conductor such as a copper wire when it is connected to the terminals of a battery.

If the representation of the copper atom in Fig. 3 is studied, it will be seen that one of the planetary electrons describes a much larger orbit than any of the others. In a piece of copper, the molecules are closely crowded and each preserves its average position. Its motion consists of a rapid vibration about this position. Under these conditions the outer electron of the copper atom is likely often to come under as great an attraction from the nuclei of neighbouring atoms as that which keeps it attached to its own nucleus. The result is that the outer electrons of various neighbouring copper atoms possess, as it were, a divided allegiance, and readily interchange the nuclei to which they are normally attached. While these changes are occurring, such electrons may be looked upon as free from the sway of any particular nucleus. They are therefore referred to as **free** or **mobile** electrons.

If there are no external electric forces, this transference of electrons will not lead to anything which we can recognise as an electric current. The electrons are just as liable to transfer themselves from atom to atom in one direction as in another. This state of affairs is shown diagrammatically in Fig. 4 (*a*). The net transference of electricity in any particular direction is nil, and no electric current would be observed.

Suppose now that by some means the free electrons, when transferring from atom to atom, were given a tendency to make their transfer in one particular direction. This is essentially what happens when a copper wire is joined between the terminals of a battery. On the average, more electrons will transfer in this direction (towards the positive terminal) than in any other. This is very roughly illustrated by the arrows in Fig. 4 (*b*). The tendencies that can be given in this way produce only small effects compared with the normal haphazard motion of the free electrons. It is unlikely that any one electron ever moves more than the distance between two neighbouring atoms, but the consequence on the large scale is to produce a slow drift of electrons in the direction of the positive terminal. It is this which we recognise as an electric current in the wire.

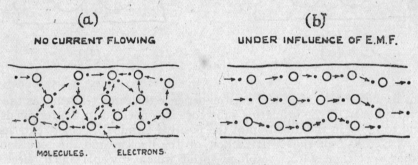

(a)

NO CURRENT FLOWING

(b)

UNDER INFLUENCE OF E.M.F.

MOLECULES.   ELECTRONS.

A Conducting Substance.

FIG. 4.

Conduction currents are thus due to the motion of free electrons. The atoms of the conductor do not alter their mean positions, as may easily be recognised. When a current is flowing along a copper conductor, copper is not transferred from one part of the conductor to another. The more free electrons a substance possesses and the " freer " they are, the better are its conducting properties.

41. Flow of Alternating Current Through a Condenser.—In alternating current work, conduction currents may be made to flow in parts of circuits in which there are certain quite obvious *breaks* from the point of view of direct current electrical engineering. Fig. 5 represents an ordinary electric lamp joined to a source of alternating voltage through two **condensers**, AB and CD. If the alternating voltage is high enough, an alternating displacement of electrons will take place throughout the circuit, the lamp will be lit, and in every way it will appear that current is flowing " through " the condensers, or across the breaks in the circuit which they represent. The explanation of the lighting of the lamp is comparatively simple. During the positive half cycles of alternating current, electrons rush from (say) the alternator towards A and away from D, charging A negatively and D positively ; by electric *induction* across the gap,

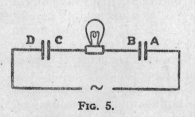

FIG. 5.

the excess of electrons on A produces a similar displacement of electrons away from B, flowing through the lamp towards C. Alternatively, instead of considering the electrons to be repelled from A they may be considered to be attracted by the positive charge on D ; in either case the result is the same. During the negative half cycles the process is reversed, and electrons rush through the lamp from C towards B. Effectively, the lamp is lit by an ordinary conduction current, which alters in direction according to the motive force moving the mobile electrons. The matter only becomes complicated if one attempts to consider precisely what happens in the dielectric between the plates of the condenser.

42. Insulators. Dielectric Displacement Currents.—In insulators, the number of free electrons is negligibly small compared with the number present in a good conductor. The planetary electrons in each atom at every point in their orbits come under a greater attraction from their own nucleus than from the nucleus of any neighbouring atom, and there is no interchange of planetary electrons between adjacent atoms. Thus, under the action of steady electrical forces no current flows in an insulating substance.

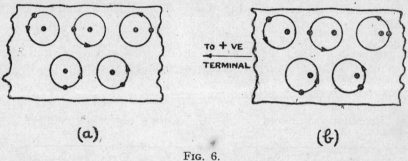

(a)   (b)

FIG. 6.

The electrons in their orbits, however, must experience the same tendency as the free electrons discussed in paragraph 40. If the insulating substance is connected to the terminals of a battery, the electrons tend to move in the direction of the positive terminal. This " external " attractive force, together with the " internal " attraction of the nucleus and the repulsion of the other planetary electrons, determines the resultant orbit which any particular electron describes. Compared with the orbit described by the electron under the atomic forces alone, this new orbit is displaced to some slight extent in the direction of the positive terminal. This is illustrated roughly in Fig. 6. Fig. 6 (a) shows the orbits of some planetary electrons, represented as circles whose centres are the nuclei of their respective atoms, when no E.M.F. is applied to the insulator. (The meaning of E.M.F. is explained in paragraph 49 ; for a moment it may be understood as a method of imposing motion in a particular direction on free electrons, such as is supplied by a battery.) Fig. 6 (b) shows the orbits displaced as the result of an applied E.M.F. The amount by which the orbits are displaced from their normal positions obviously depends on the E.M.F. applied. The greater the E.M.F., the greater the displacement.

As long as the E.M.F. is steady, the electrons will continue to revolve in the orbits to which they have adjusted themselves and there will be no continuous movement of electricity in any particular direction, i.e., no current. When the E.M.F. is altered, however, the electrons have to adjust themselves to a new orbit before settling down under the different conditions. This adjustment will be in the same direction for all the electrons and so will be observed as a momentary current during the time the E.M.F. is changing. Whenever, for instance, an E.M.F. is applied to an insulator, i.e., when the E.M.F. changes from zero to a certain value, a momentary current of this kind will flow. If an alternating E.M.F. (i.e., an E.M.F. whose value is always changing) is applied across an insulator, the electrons are never able to settle down, but are continually re-adjusting their orbits to agree with the variation in E.M.F. In other words, there is always a displacement of electrons in the insulator. These currents are called **dielectric displacement currents,** and are to be distinguished from **free space displacement currents** which are not dependent on the presence of moving electrons or other charged particles ; free space displacement currents can exist between the plates of a condenser having a perfect vacuum as dielectric.

Electric displacement has the same meaning as " **Flux density** " (paragraph 99), or the density of the lines of force in the medium. In paragraph 41 it was shown that a conduction current only flowed in certain parts of the circuit containing two condensers ; the action of the force displacing the electrons apparently ceased at the plates of the condenser but produced an effect across them.

Maxwell went into this matter somewhat deeply and, wishing to write equations for the current in a complete circuit containing capacity, he was led to the idea that the **rate of change of flux density,** which must be associated with the action of an alternating voltage across the space between the plates of the condenser, must really be equivalent to a current which he called a **displacement current.** In his equations, he therefore considered that the term representing the rate of change of flux density had the nature of a current ; in this way, he arrived at the idea that a change of electric flux *through* an area produces a magnetic flux *around* that area, quite independently of the presence of moving electrons. This was one of his philosophical " starting points " which led him further to the conception of the E.M. theory of the radiation of energy.

Charged particles, if any are present, increase the displacement by increasing the flux by virtue of the flux they emit themselves and, in general, increase the rate of change of flux density at a point. Displacement currents absorb energy, some of it being **radiated** away through space, and some dissipated in dielectric losses. In general, the total current in any material medium is the sum of the free space displacement current and the displacement current due to the dielectric ; mathematically, the A.C. circuit of paragraph 41 is continuous, the conduction current flowing in the wire, and the displacement current in the medium between the plates of the condenser. Here the matter must be left, for a full discussion on it is much beyond the scope of this book.

In connection with dielectric displacement currents, if the applied E.M.F. increases to such an extent that the nucleus cannot hold all its electrons against the powerful external attraction, an electron is pulled from the atom and a current of the type of paragraph 40 is established. By cumulative action a large current may be set up, and this effect is called " rupture of the dielectric," or its insulation is said to " break down."

43. Convection Current.—This kind of current is due to the movement of electricity— electrons or positive and negative ions—through a liquid or a gas, or in a perfect vacuum. Common examples are the currents that flow through the chemical solution in a cell, across a spark gap and a Poulsen arc, and between the filament and grid or anode of a thermionic valve. In each case the action is accompanied by ionisation, except in the case of the perfectly exhausted valve, where the convection current is nothing but electrons proceeding from filament to grid or anode. Each of these types of convection current is fully dealt with in the chapters on these subjects.

UNITS.

44. The derivation and definition of the units used in studying electrical phenomena will now be given. They are built up to a large extent from ideas developed in the study of mechanics.

The other primary consideration in developing electrical units is based on the observed effects of electric currents, and these will now be dealt with.

45. Effects of Electric Current.—The more important effects observed when an electric current is flowing are :—

> (*a*) **The heating effect.**—A wire carrying a current becomes heated. This property is made use of in electric radiators and lamps.

> (*b*) **The magnetic effect.**—A wire carrying a current is surrounded by a magnetic field. This property is of very great importance, and its various effects are dealt with in due course.

> (*c*) **The chemical effect.**—This occurs in chemical solutions. Electroplating is a commercial example of its use. It finds a practical application to wireless work in connection with primary and secondary batteries.

The heating effect is not suitable for standardising purposes because of the difficulty of measuring quantities of heat accurately.

The magnetic effect is that on which the absolute electromagnetic unit of current is based. **The chemical effect** gives the practical standard for measuring current.

An account of the flow of electric current in chemical solutions is given below (paragraph 108). The passage of such currents is accompanied by the deposition of the substances composing the chemical in solution, and the amounts deposited are proportional to the current and to the time during which the current is flowing. Measurements of weight and time can both be performed with great accuracy, and so the chemical effect is very suitable for defining a standard current. The chemical used is silver nitrate dissolved in water, and the unit of current defined from it is called the **International Ampere.**

46. The International Ampere is the unvarying electric current which, when passed through a solution of nitrate of silver in water, deposits silver at the rate of 0·00111800 gram per second. For measuring very small currents we use two other units :—

$$\text{The milliampere (symbol mA)} = \frac{1}{1000} \text{ ampere.}$$

$$\text{The microampere (symbol } \mu\text{A)} = \frac{1}{10^6} \text{ ampere.}$$

Current is denoted by the letter I.

47. The Coulomb.—The idea of a current or rate of flow implies the idea of quantity. Quantity of electricity is therefore defined as the amount passing when a certain rate of flow is maintained for a certain time. The quantity of electricity passing through any cross-section of a wire when current is flowing is, of course, merely the sum of the charges of all the free electrons crossing that section.

Quantity is denoted by the letter Q.

The **coulomb** is the quantity of electricity passing per second when the current strength is one ampere.

Hence if a current of I amperes is flowing for t seconds, the quantity of electricity, Q, is given in coulombs by $Q = It$ coulombs.

Conversely, of course, an ampere is a rate of flow of 1 coulomb per second, and $I = \dfrac{Q}{t}$.

A coulomb is $6·29 \times 10^{18}$ electrons.

An ampere is a rate of flow of $6·29 \times 10^{18}$ electrons past a given point in an electric circuit per second.

Example 1.

If a current of 10 amperes flows for 5 seconds, then the quantity of electricity that passes a point in the circuit will be $Q = I \times t = 10 \times 5 = 50$ coulombs.

A larger unit of **quantity,** used in connection with capacities of accumulators, for example, is the **ampere-hour.** This is equivalent to 1 coulomb per second (*i.e.*, 1 ampere) for 3,600 seconds, *i.e.*, 3,600 coulombs.

48. Energy.—The derivation of the idea of energy is explained in any text book on Mechanics. The meaning of the principle of conservation of energy is important and also the transformation of energy from one kind to another in natural processes. Here we are concerned with the transformations that accompany electrical phenomena.

When an electric current flows in a conductor the conductor becomes heated (paragraph 45). Heat is a form of energy, being due to the vibrations of the molecules of the conductor (paragraph 27). It follows that the passage of current is associated with the transformation into heat energy of some other form of energy. We may give this form the name of " electrical energy," as it is connected with an electric current. This electrical energy is linked with the directed motion imposed on the free electrons when a current is flowing (paragraph 40). The electrons acquire energy of motion during their journey from molecule to molecule under the action of the electric forces. When recaptured, part of this energy may help to set free another electron ; the rest is transferred to the molecule and serves to increase the violence of molecular vibration, *i.e.*, the electron's kinetic energy is converted to heat energy of the conductor.

Some other form of energy must have been converted into this electrical energy or extra kinetic energy of the electrons. The two commonest forms are chemical and mechanical. Chemical energy is converted to electrical energy when a primary cell or accumulator sustains an electric current. The chemical reaction between the substances of the cell sets free a certain amount of energy (paragraph 109). Mechanical energy is the source of electrical energy from a dynamo, the dynamo armature being rotated by some mechanical arrangement.

49. Electromotive Force and Potential Difference.—Suppose we consider a simple closed electric circuit, such as a conductor connnected between the terminals of a battery. There are two energy transformations going on concurrently. Chemical energy is being converted to electrical energy by the battery, electrical energy is being converted to heat energy in the conductor. (There will also be a conversion of electrical energy to heat, due to the flow of ions in the battery itself, but we may ignore it for the moment.) These two processes provide the basis of two important ideas in the description of electrical phenomena.

Wherever there is introduced in any part of an electrical circuit another form of energy capable of being converted into electrical energy, we say that an electromotive force (E.M.F.) is acting in the circuit.

If between any two points in a circuit electrical energy may be converted into any other form of energy, we say that a potential difference (P.D.) is established between the two points. Thus, in the simple circuit above, the battery is said to supply an E.M.F. as chemical energy is there being converted to electrical energy. Between any two points on the conductor electrical energy is being converted to heat energy ; there is therefore a P.D. between any two points on the conductor.

50. Electromotive Force (E.M.F.) is produced in four different ways :—

(1) **Chemical.** By two dissimilar metals or other substances being immersed in certain chemical solutions known as electrolytes—such as the acids in primary and secondary cells. Chemical energy is transformed into electrical energy.

This subject is treated further in paragraphs 107 to 127.

(2) **Thermo-electric.** By two dissimilar conductors being placed in contact and their junction heated. Heat energy is transformed to electrical energy. A practical case is the thermal junction of steel and eureka wire used in some wavemeters.

This subject is treated further in the section on wavemeters (Section W).

(3) **Electromagnetic.** By interaction in certain circumstances between a conductor and 'lines of magnetic flux," *e.g.*, in the dynamo, alternator, transformer. Mechanical and " magnetic " energy are converted to electrical energy.

This is treated further in Chapters III, IV and VI.

(4) **Electrostatic.** Various frictional machines produce the result required by converting mechanical energy to electrical energy. From our point of view this method is of no importance.

51. Units of E.M.F. and P.D.—The energy transformations discussed above are used to derive units of E.M.F. and P.D. We shall first consider the unit of P.D.

It has been seen that electrical energy is converted to heat energy between two points in a conductor carrying a current. Each free electron has approximately the same extra energy of motion when recaptured by a molecule, and so the more electrons there are travelling round the circuit the greater will be the heat developed. We might thus take the amount of electrical energy converted per electron between any two points as a measure of the P.D. between the two points. Actually, we consider the energy conversion per coulomb, as the coulomb and not the electron is the practical unit of quantity. The C.G.S. unit of energy is the " erg," the work which can be done by a force of one dyne acting through a distance of one centimetre. This unit is inconveniently small and for electrical measurements a practical unit called a " joule " is used. One joule is equal to ten million (10^7) ergs.

The symbol used for energy is W (Work).

The two units, the coulomb and the joule, are used to derive a unit of P.D., which is called the " volt."

If the amount of electrical energy converted to other forms of energy when one coulomb passes between two points of a conductor is equal to one joule, then the **potential difference** between the two points is said to be one **volt**.

The symbol generally used for P.D. is V.

Thus, if two coulombs are carried from one point to another and the conversion of electrical energy is 5 joules, then the P.D. in volts between the two points is

$$V = \frac{5 \text{ joules}}{2 \text{ coulombs}} = 2 \cdot 5 \text{ volts}.$$

More generally, if Q coulombs are carried from one point to another and the conversion of electrical energy is W joules, then the P.D. in volts between the two points is

$$V = W \div Q.$$
$$\text{Volts} = \text{joules} \div \text{coulombs}.$$

It is not necessary for the coulombs actually to pass in order to find the P.D. If the electrical energy conversion which would occur if one coulomb were allowed to pass, can be calculated, then the P.D. can be found from the formula above. This is the method employed in electrostatic calculations of P.D. (paragraph 102).

52. The idea of electromotive force is also derived from the conversion of energy, and so the **volt** may also be used as the **unit of E.M.F.**

If the amount of other forms of energy converted to electrical energy at any point of a circuit is one joule per coulomb of electricity which passes the point, then the **E.M.F.** developed at that point is said to be one **volt**.

Thus, if a 2-volt accumulator is being used as a source of E.M.F. in a circuit, for every coulomb of electricity that flows round the circuit (including the accumulator itself), 2 joules of chemical energy are converted to electrical energy.

It will be seen that the term electromotive " force " for this concept is rather unfortunate. The concept in electricity which corresponds most closely to that of force in mechanics is " electric field strength," which is discussed under Electrostatics (paragraph 97). The concept in mechanics with which E.M.F. and P.D. are best compared is that of potential energy per unit mass (head or level).

As the volt is the unit of both E.M.F. and P.D., they are often both indiscriminately referred to as " voltage," but the identity of the unit must not be allowed to cause confusion between the two ideas.

53. The above discussion brings out the ideas underlying the definition of the volt, but their application does not provide a very convenient method of measurement. The definition of the International Volt is thus derived from a development of these ideas and will be given when that nevelopment has been explained (paragraph 60).

Other units used are :—

$$\text{The millivolt (symbol } mV) = \frac{1}{1,000} \text{ volt.}$$

$$\text{The microvolt (symbol } \mu V) = \frac{1}{10^6} \text{ volt.}$$

$$\text{The kilovolt (symbol } kV) = 1,000 \text{ volts.}$$

54. **Potential.**—When the height of a mountain is referred to it is generally assumed to mean the vertical distance between the top of the mountain and mean sea-level. If it were given by different observers as the vertical distance from their own position, like the heights referred to bench marks by architects, the numbers quoted by these observers would merely give the **difference**

in height between the observer and the mountain top. This may be compared with P.D. in electricity. If we fix on one point in a circuit, then the P.D. between it and any other point depends on the position of the other point.

It is found convenient in electricity to have an idea corresponding to mean sea level. Just as the difference in height between the top of a mountain and mean sea level is called the height of the mountain, so the difference in potential between a point in an electrical circuit and any point on the earth's surface is called the "potential" of the point, the word "difference" being dropped. This is possible because there is no potential difference between any two points on the earth's surface. If such a P.D. developed momentarily a current would flow until the P.D. had disappeared.

In other words, the earth's surface is taken as being at zero potential, just as mean sea level is taken as being at zero height.

Many parts of the earth's surface are below sea level, e.g., the ocean bottom. If heights above sea-level are taken as positive, then depths below it might be considered negative. A similar state of affairs occurs with regard to electrical potential. It may be positive or negative.

A point has a positive potential if in the passage of a quantity of positive electricity **from the point to earth** electrical energy is converted to other forms of energy.

A point has a negative potential if in the passage of a quantity of positive electricity **from earth to the point** electrical energy is converted to other forms of energy.

These definitions would be reversed if we considered what actually happens, viz., the passage of a number of electrons (negative electricity) between the point and earth.

The distinction between potential and P.D. should be carefully observed. Thus, if a lamp has 110 volts applied across it from the mains, the correct expression is that there is a P.D. of 110 volts across the lamp. If the negative main is earthed, it is permissible to say that the positive main is at a potential of 110 volts, for 110 volts is then the potential difference between the positive main and earth.

55. Earth Return Circuits.—Advantage is often taken of the fact mentioned above that the earth's surface is a good conductor, to utilise an "earth return" as part of a circuit. The hull of a ship may also be used for this purpose.

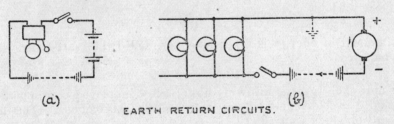

EARTH RETURN CIRCUITS.

FIG. 7.

For example, in Fig. 7 (a) the battery shown is being used to ring a bell. The positive terminal of the battery is joined to the bell through a switch, but connection from the negative battery terminal is made by using an earth return between it and the bell.

Similarly, in Fig. 7 (b) the dynamo is connected to a number of lamps in parallel through a single-line wire, but the return connection is made by earthing the negative dynamo brush and one side of the switch.

This method of economising wire can only be used in cases when the insulation of the single conductor can be relied upon.

If any earth were to develop on the line wire, as shown dotted, the dynamo would be short-circuited, an excessive current would flow, and the machine would be burnt out.

The earth has such a large cross-section that its resistance can be neglected. If the earth return is found to have an unduly high resistance, the fault probably lies in the method in which connection is made to earth.

Frequent use is made in W/T of earth connections.

If a point in a circuit which contains a source of E.M.F. is earthed, electrons may have either to flow out of, or into, the earth. For example, if in Fig. 7 (*b*) the dynamo is developing a P.D. of 100 volts between its brushes, its positive brush will be at 100 volts potential above earth (or zero) potential.

A positive electrification denotes a deficiency of electrons, so that in this case electrons will flow from earth through the lamps, in at the positive brush, through the dynamo and back to earth at the negative brush. If the brush connections are reversed, the brush connected to the line wire will be at 100 volts potential negative to earth, and the electron current is reversed in direction.

56. Power.—We have dealt with the total conversion of energy taking place between different points in a circuit without reference to the time involved, *e.g.*, the time taken for a coulomb to pass from one point to another. The consideration of the time taken leads to the idea of power— the rate of working, or rate at which energy is being transformed.

The unit of power derived from the erg, the C.G.S. unit of energy, is a transformation of energy at the rate of one erg per second.

The practical unit of power is the **watt**, the rate of working when one joule of energy is transformed per second.

The work done when a charge Q is moved through a P.D. of V is given by (paragraph 51)

$$W = QV \ldots \text{(where W will be in Joules if Q is in coulombs and V in volts).}$$

Now $Q = IT \ldots$ (a current I flowing for a time T).

$$\therefore \quad W = VIT \text{ or } \frac{W}{T} = VI.$$

Now $\frac{W}{T}$ is the power (P), or rate at which work is done, and may be expressed in watts, or joules per second. Hence we have

$$\text{Watts} = \text{volts} \times \text{amps.}$$

57. A power of one watt developed over a period of one hour will correspond to the transformation of

$$\frac{1 \text{ joule}}{\text{sec.}} \times 3,600 \text{ secs.} = 3,600 \text{ joules.}$$

of energy. This amount of **energy** is taken as a unit called the **watt-hour** when a larger unit than the joule is required.

$$1 \text{ watt-hour} = 3,600 \text{ joules.}$$

A still larger unit of energy, the **kilowatt-hour**, is also employed, corresponding to a power of 1,000 watts developed over a period of one hour, *i.e.*, 3,600,000 joules. This unit of energy is known as the Board of Trade Unit (B.O.T.U.).

58. Ohm's Law.—If any given conductor is kept at constant temperature and the P.D. between its ends is compared with the current flowing in it, there is found to be a constant relationship between the two, *e.g.*, if the current is doubled, the P.D. is doubled, and so on.

We might anticipate some such relation on the electron theory of metallic conduction. Increasing the current means that the free electrons have to travel faster from molecule to molecule and so have a greater amount of kinetic energy to transfer to the molecules when recaptured, *i.e.*, the conversion of energy per free electron and therefore the P.D. is increased.

This relationship is called Ohm's Law and may be stated symbolically as

$$\frac{V}{I} = \text{constant, or } V = \text{constant} \times I.$$

The constant is a measure of the difficulty the electrons find in escaping recapture by molecules; the greater the constant, the greater is V for a given I, *i.e.*, the greater is the energy transferred to the molecules by the free electrons. It is a criterion of the opposition the conductor offers to the passage of current. It is called the **resistance** of the conductor and denoted by the letter R.

As we should expect, the constant is much smaller in conductors than in insulators. In other words, conductors have low resistance ; insulators have high resistance.

Ohm's Law may therefore be stated as :—

$$\frac{V}{I} = R \text{ or } V = RI.$$

It is true only for conduction currents and the particular type of convection current which flows in chemical solutions. It does not hold for gaseous convection currents. Further, it on y applies in the above form when the current is steady and cannot be used when the current is changing.

59. If $V = 1$ when $I = 1$ in the formula $V = RI$, then R must also be equal to 1 if the formula is to be satisfied.

This enables us to define a **unit** of resistance called the **ohm**.

A conductor has resistance of one ohm if the P.D. between its ends is one volt, when the current flowing in it is one ampere. The symbol Ω (omega) is used as a contraction for ohm.

Owing to the practical difficulty of measuring the volt from the amount of energy transformed, this definition is not convenient for the standardisation of resistances. Consequently, the logical procedure has been reversed, and the ohm has been defined for standardising purposes as the resistance of a certain conductor of dimensions adjusted to give it a value as nearly equal as possible to that of the ohm derived as above.

60. **The International Ohm.** (*i.e.*, the standard value fixed by international agreement) is " the resistance offered to an unvarying electric current by a column of mercury at the temperature of melting ice, $14\cdot4521$ grammes in mass, of constant cross-sectional area, 1 sq. mm., and of length $106\cdot300$ cms.

The following multiples of the ohm are frequently used :—

1 megohm (symbol M Ω) = 10^6 ohms} = a million ohms.

1 microhm (symbol $\mu\,\Omega$ (mu—omega)) = $\frac{1}{10^6}$ or 10^{-6} ohm

= a millionth of an ohm.

By using Ohm's Law a practical way of defining the volt for measuring purposes can now be derived.

The **International Volt** is the P.D. between the ends of a conductor whose resistance is one International Ohm when the current flowing in the conductor is one International Ampere.

These definitions allow accurate comparisons to be made of different resistances and potential differences.

61. **Resistance Formula.**—The resistance of a conductor depends on its dimensions, its material and its temperature.

We should expect this on the electron theory. The material determines the number of free electrons and its temperature gives a measure of the vibratory motion of its molecules, which is bound to affect the chance of recapture by the molecules of the free electrons. The greater the area of cross-section of a conductor, the more electrons will there be crossing any cross-section at a time. The longer the conductor, the greater the number of recaptures by molecules. Hence we find that the resistance of a conductor varies directly as its length and inversely as its cross-section.

At constant temperature the resistance of a conductor may thus be written as

$$R = \rho l/A,$$

where l is its length and A its cross-sectional area. ρ (rho) is the factor which takes account of the material of the conductor. It is called the **specific resistance** or resistivity of the material. If $l = 1$ and $A = 1$ in the formula, then $R = \rho$. The specific resistance may thus be defined as follows :—

62. The **specific resistance** of a material is the resistance of a piece of the material one centimetre in length and having a cross-section of one square centimetre, usually called a centimetre

cube of the material. Since resistance alters with change of temperature, the specific resistance is usually quoted for 20° C.

Some specific resistances are, approximately :—

Copper	..	..	..	..	..	1·7 microhms per cm. cube.
Platinum	..	..	..	..	..	11 ,, ,,
Mercury	..	..	..·	..	..	94 ,, ,,
Manganin	..	..	..	..	..	44·5 ,, ,,

Insulators have enormously high specific resistances compared with the above. As was pointed out before, the difference between conductors and insulators (in the practical sense of the word) is merely one of degree. There are no perfect insulators in the sense of substances that allow absolutely no conduction current to flow, but the current is very small indeed for substances usually termed insulators.

A column of air, one inch long, offers as much resistance to an electric current as a copper cable thirty thousand million million miles long, of the same cross-section, *i.e.*, a cable long enough to reach from the earth to Arcturus and back twenty times.

When testing insulation resistance, for example, by the bridge megger (paragraph 190), it is the passage of a very minute current through the insulating substance that allows the instrument to operate.

Some specific resistances for insulators are :—

Distilled water—7×10^{10} ohms per cm. cube.
Silica—over 5×10^{18} ,,   ,,
Mica—5×10^{16} ,,   ,,

63. Temperature Coefficients.—In all cases the specific resistance depends to some extent on the temperature.

For most materials it increases uniformly with the temperature, and the **temperature coefficient** is defined to be the fractional increase of resistance per degree increase of temperature above a definite temperature, usually taken as 20° C.

Thus if α is the temperature coefficient for 20° C., and ρ is the specific resistance at 20° C., the specific resistance at θ° C. is given by

$$\rho' \text{ (at } \theta° \text{ C.)} = \rho \{1 + \alpha (\theta° - 20°)\}.$$

The temperature coefficient of copper is 0·00393.

The temperature coefficient of iron and steel is 0·006.

Alloys have in general very much smaller temperature coefficients than pure metals, and so are used in the construction of standard resistances which are required to vary as little as possible. The temperature coefficient of German silver, for intance, is about 0·0004 ; of manganin 0·000006.

The temperature coefficients of carbon, glass and electrolytes are negative, *i.e.*, their resistances decrease as their temperatures increase.

In the formula $R = \rho l/A$, the various quantities must always be expressed in the appropriate units, l in centimetres and A in square centimetres.

If ρ is expressed in microhms per cm. cube, then R will be found in microhms.

If ρ is expressed in ohms per cm. cube, then R will be found in ohms.

64. Conductance is defined as the reciprocal of resistance, provided direct currents only are being considered. Its meaning is generalised when applied to the effects of alternating current.

It is a measure of the ease with which current may flow through a conductor, as opposed to resistance which is a measure of the difficulty experienced by a current in flowing.

The symbol for conductance is G, *i.e.*, $G = \dfrac{1}{R}$ for any conductor through which direct **current** is flowing.

The unit of conductance is the " reciprocal ohm " or **mho** and is defined as the reciprocal of the International Ohm.

The reciprocal of the specific resistance of a material is called its **conductivity** and given the symbol γ (gamma).

Example 2.

Find (a) the resistance and (b) the conductance of a copper conductor 5 miles long and $0 \cdot 08$ inch in diameter.

It is first necessary to reduce the various lengths and areas to the units for which the specific resistance is quoted, i.e., centimetres and square centimetres.

$$5 \text{ miles} = 5 \times 1 \cdot 61 \text{ kilometres} = 8 \cdot 05 \times 10^5 \text{ cms.}$$

$$\text{Cross-sectional area} = \pi \times 0 \cdot 04^2 \text{ sq. inches} = 0 \cdot 005026 \text{ sq. inches.}$$
$$= 0 \cdot 005026 \times 6 \cdot 45 \text{ sq. cms.} = 0 \cdot 03242 \text{ sq. cms.}$$

$$\rho = 1 \cdot 7 \times 10^{-6} \text{ ohms per cm. cube.}$$

$$\therefore R = \frac{1 \cdot 7 \times 10^{-6} \times 8 \cdot 05 \times 10^5}{0 \cdot 03242} = \frac{1 \cdot 37}{0 \cdot 03242} = 42 \ \Omega \text{ approx.}$$

$$\text{Conductance } G = \frac{1}{R} = \frac{1}{42} = 0 \cdot 024 \text{ mho.}$$

65. Resistances in Series.—Resistances are said to be in series when they are connected end to end as shown in Fig. 8. We wish to derive an expression for the total resistance (R) of a number of resistances in series in terms of the individual resistances (R_1, R_2 and R_3).

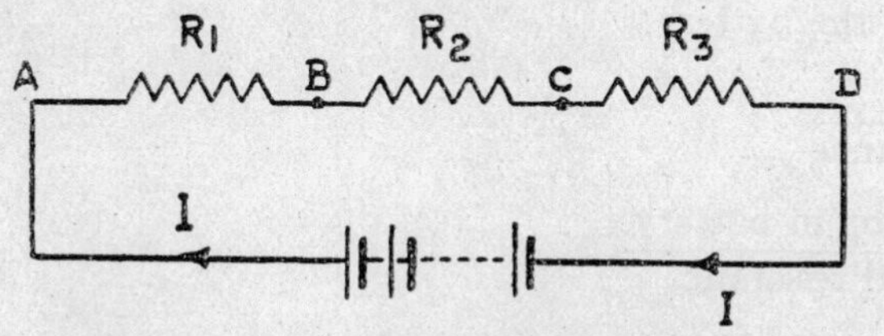

E.M.F. = E.   Internal resistance = r.

FIG. 8.

In a closed circuit in which current is flowing it is not possible for electricity to pile up at any point. Thus in Fig. 8 the same current must flow through each of the three resistances. Suppose this current is I amps and that the total P.D. from A to D is V volts; in other words, when one coulomb passes from A to D the work done (heat energy produced) is V joules. The total resistance R is then given by

$$R = \frac{V}{I}$$

according to Ohm's Law.

The work done by one coulomb in passing from A to D can be divided into three parts, viz., from A to B, B to C, and C to D. If these three quantities of work are V_1, V_2 and V_3 joules respectively, then $V = V_1 + V_2 + V_3$.

But by definition V_1, V_2 and V_3 are the P.D.s in volts from A to B, B to C, and C to D.

Therefore by Ohm's Law $V_1 = IR_1$, $V_2 = IR_2$, and $V_3 = IR_3$.

$$\therefore V = V_1 + V_2 + V_3 = IR_1 + IR_2 + IR_3 = I (R_1 + R_2 + R_2).$$

$$\therefore R = \frac{V}{I} = R_1 + R_2 + R_3$$

i.e., the equivalent resistance of a number of resistances in series is equal to the sum of their individual resistances.

Example 3.

Fig. 9 indicates a battery, whose internal resistance is 2 ohms and E.M.F. 10 volts, connected to a resistance of 3 ohms.   (We may give a definite value to the internal resistance of the battery, *i.e.*, the resistance of the chemical solution between its plates, because Ohm's Law applies to such solutions.)   Find the strength of the current.

The total fall of potential round the circuit (including the battery itself) must be the same as the E.M.F., for all the energy converted to electrical energy from chemical energy finally appears as heat in the battery and external resistance.

The internal resistance of 2 ohms and the 3-ohm resistance are in series, and so the total resistance is $2 + 3 = 5$ ohms.

$$\therefore \text{ by Ohm's Law, } I = \frac{V}{R} = \frac{10}{5} = 2 \text{ amps.}$$

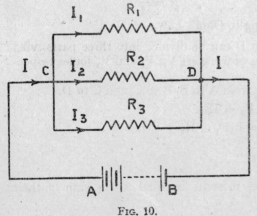

E.M.F. 10 *volts*.
Internal resistance 2 ohms.

3 OHMS.

FIG. 9.

This current, as mentioned above, must be the same at all points in the circuit.

There is a P.D. (also called a " voltage drop " or " IR drop ") between any two points in the circuit.   From B to A in the external circuit a current of 2 amps. flows through a resistance of 3 ohms, and so from B to A there is a voltage drop of 6 volts.

A voltmeter connected across A and B will read 6 volts.

This is called the terminal P.D. of the battery.   It obviously depends on the current flowing. The larger the current, the smaller the terminal P.D. because the IR drop in the battery is greater.

More generally, if we have a battery of internal resistance r ohms and E.M.F. E volts sending current through an external resistance of R ohms, then by the above argument

$$I = \frac{E}{R + r}$$

Similarly, if V in this case is the terminal P.D. of the battery,

$$I = \frac{V}{R} = \frac{\text{Terminal P.D.}}{\text{External resistance}}$$

$$\text{and also } I = \frac{E - V}{r} = \frac{\text{Voltage drop in battery.}}{\text{Internal resistance}}$$

In other words, V is less than E, or some fraction of the energy supplied to the electrons is lost within the source of E.M.F. because of its internal resistance.

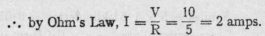

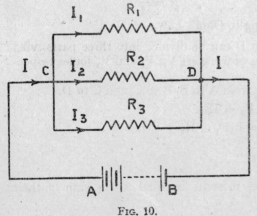

FIG. 10.

66. Resistances in Parallel.—Resistances are said to be in parallel when arranged as shown in Fig. 10. At each end they are connected to a common point. The equivalent resistance of such an arrangement may be found as follows.

Referring to Fig. 10, let the current flowing from the battery be I amps. The P.D. across each resistance must be the same, as it is the P.D. between the points C and D in the circuit. Let it be V volts. As electrons cannot accumulate at the point C, but must move on round the circuit, the sum of the currents I_1, I_2 and I_3, flowing in the three resistances R_1, R_2 and R_3, must be equal to I, *i.e.*, $I = I_1 + I_2 + I_3$.

But, by Ohm's Law,

$$I_1 = \frac{V}{R_1}, I_2 = \frac{V}{R_2}, I_3 = \frac{V}{R_3}.$$

$$\therefore I = I_1 + I_2 + I_3 = \frac{V}{R_1} + \frac{V}{R_2} + \frac{V}{R} = V\left[\frac{1}{R_1} + \frac{1}{R_2} + \frac{1}{R_3}\right]$$

If R is the equivalent resistance of the whole arrangement, then

$$I = \frac{V}{R}.$$

$$\therefore \frac{V}{R} = V\left[\frac{1}{R_1} + \frac{1}{R_2} + \frac{1}{R_3}\right]. \qquad \therefore \frac{1}{R} = \frac{1}{R_1} + \frac{1}{R_2} + \frac{1}{R_3},$$

from which R may be determined.

This result may also be put in the form

$$G = G_1 + G_2 + G_3$$

where G is the equivalent conductance $\left(= \frac{1}{R}\right)$ and G_1, G_2 and G_3 are the conductances of R_1, R_2 and R_3.

In other words, the equivalent conductance of a number of resistances in parallel is equal to the sum of their individual conductances.

The equivalent conductance is thus greater than any of the individual conductances, and so its reciprocal, the equivalent resistance, is less than any of the individual resistances.

The equivalent resistance of n equal resistances of value R arranged in parallel is given by $\frac{R}{n}$.

With only two resistances R_1 and R_2 in parallel, a simple formula for the equivalent resistance can be obtained.

$$\frac{1}{R} = \frac{1}{R_1} + \frac{1}{R_2} = \frac{R_1 + R_2}{R_1 R_2}$$

$$\therefore R = \frac{R_1 R_2}{R_1 + R_2} = \frac{\text{product of individual resistances.}}{\text{sum of individual resistances.}}$$

67. Use of Shunting Resistance.—When only a small proportion of a given current is required in a particular path an alternative path of much lower resistance is connected in parallel. The total current then splits up between the two paths, and the latter takes the major part. This principle is frequently met with in measuring instruments, *e.g.*, ammeters, where the current required to flow through the instrument is very small.

Let R_m be the resistance of the instrument and R_s that of the shunt, and I_m and I_s the currents through each.

I is the total current to be measured.

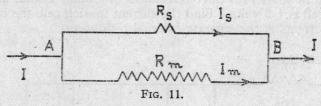

FIG. 11.

The voltage drop between A and B (Fig. 11) is $I_s R_s = I_m R_m$

$$= I \times \text{equivalent resistance} = I \frac{R_m R_s}{R_s + R_m}.$$

$$\therefore I_m = I \frac{R_s}{R_s + R_m}.$$

If R_s is small compared with R_m, this current I_m is a small fraction of I.

For example, to measure a current up to 10 amperes with an ammeter reading up to 1 ampere, we should want only 1/10th of the total current to pass through the instrument, 9/10ths going through the shunt.

$$I_m = \frac{1}{10} I = I \frac{R_s}{R_s + R_m}$$

$$\therefore \frac{R_s}{R_s + R_m} = \frac{1}{10}, \text{ or } R_s = 1/9\text{th of } R_m$$

With this shunt resistance across the ammeter, any reading on the ammeter scale would indicate that 10 times that amount of current was flowing in the circuit.

68. Examples on Resistances in Series and Parallel.

Example 4.

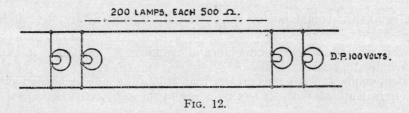

200 LAMPS, EACH 500 Ω.

D.P. 100 VOLTS.

FIG. 12.

Let 200 lamps, each of hot resistance 500 Ω, be connected across 100-volt mains, as in Fig. 12.

Current in each lamp $= \dfrac{E}{R} = \dfrac{100}{500} = 0 \cdot 2$ ampere.

Total current (200 paths in parallel).

$$= 200 \times 0 \cdot 2 \text{ amperes} = 40 \text{ amperes.}$$

Alternatively, the effective resistance of 200 resistances in parallel, each 500 Ω, is $\dfrac{500}{200} = 2 \cdot 5$ ohms.

$$\therefore \text{ Total current} = \frac{100}{2 \cdot 5} = 40 \text{ amperes.}$$

Example 5.

Five cells in parallel, each with a resistance of $0 \cdot 25$ ohm, are connected to an external resistance made up of $0 \cdot 55$ ohm in series with three resistances of 1 ohm, 4 ohms and $0 \cdot 8$ ohm in parallel. The E.M.F. of each cell is $1 \cdot 5$ volts. Find the current in each cell, the current in the $0 \cdot 55$ ohm resistance, and the currents in the separate external resistances.

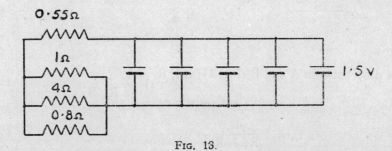

0·55 Ω

1 Ω

4 Ω

0·8 Ω

1·5 V

FIG. 13.

Total resistance of circuit $= \dfrac{0 \cdot 25}{5} + 0 \cdot 55 + R,$

where R is given by

$$\frac{1}{R} = \frac{1}{1} + \frac{1}{4} + \frac{1}{0 \cdot 8} = 2 \cdot 5.$$

$\therefore$ R $= 0 \cdot 4$ ohm.

$\therefore$ Total resistance $= 0 \cdot 05 + 0 \cdot 55 + 0 \cdot 4 = 1$ ohm.

E.M.F. is the same as that of one cell $= 1 \cdot 5$ volts.

$\therefore$ Total current in the circuit is $1 \cdot 5$ amperes.

It follows that

(1) Current through the $0 \cdot 55$ ohm resistance is $1 \cdot 5$ amps.

(2) The current through each cell is $\dfrac{1 \cdot 5}{5} = 0 \cdot 3$ amp.

The current through the separate parallel resistances is given by the P.D. across them divided by their values in ohms.

P.D. across them is $1 \cdot 5 \times 0 \cdot 4$ ohms (their effective resistance)

$$= 0 \cdot 6 \text{ volt.}$$

$\therefore$ Separate currents are $\dfrac{0 \cdot 6}{1}, \dfrac{0 \cdot 6}{4}, \dfrac{0 \cdot 6}{0 \cdot 8}$ amps.

i.e., $0 \cdot 6$, $0 \cdot 15$, $0 \cdot 75$ amp., and the sum of these is $1 \cdot 5$ amps., the total current.

69. Power.—It was shown in paragraph 56 that the power developed in any part of an electrical circuit is the product of the current flowing in it and the P.D. across it.

$$P = IV,$$

or watts $=$ amps. $\times$ volts.

By the application of Ohm's Law, expressions for the power may be obtained either in terms of current and resistance or of P.D. and resistance.

(a) V $=$ IR.

$\therefore$ P $=$ IV $=$ I $\times$ IR $=$ I^{2}R.

(b) I $= \dfrac{V}{R}$ $\therefore$ P $=$ IV $= \dfrac{V}{R} \times V = \dfrac{V^2}{R}.$

Thus, referring back to Example 3 (paragraph 65), the power developed in the $3\,\Omega$ resistance may be calculated in any of the following three ways :—

(1) Current (I) in $3\,\Omega$ resistance $=2$ amps.

P.D. (V) across $3\,\Omega$ resistance $= 6$ volts.

$\therefore$ Power $=$ IV $= 2$ amps. $\times$ 6 volts $= 12$ watts.

(2) Current (I) in $3\,\Omega$ resistance (R) $= 2$ amps.

$\therefore$ Power $=$ I^{2}R $= 4 \times 3 = 12$ watts.

(3) P.D. (V) across $3\,\Omega$ resistance (R) $= 6$ volts.

$\therefore$ Power $= \dfrac{V^2}{R} = \dfrac{36}{3} = 12$ watts.

The power loss in the internal resistance of the battery ($2\ \Omega$) is

$$2^2 \times 2 = 8 \text{ watts,}$$

so that the total power which must be supplied to the circuit is $12 + 8 = 20$ watts when 2 amps. is flowing

It is easily verified that this is the rate of working of the battery.

$$= 10 \times 2 = 20 \text{ watts.}$$

70. The meaning of such expressions as a " 10 kW. 100-volt " dynamo or a " 40-watt 220-volt " lamp should be clearly understood.

The first expression denotes a dynamo which will supply a current of $\frac{10,000}{100} = 100$ amperes at 100 volts pressure without being overloaded when rotated at its designed speed.

The second denotes a lamp which requires a current of $\frac{40}{220} = 0 \cdot 18$ amp. at 220 volts to keep it burning at its designed brilliancy.

71. The idea that I²R represents heat, energy, or even force, is very prevalent. This is quite wrong. I²R represents the **rate** at which light and heat energy are produced in the lamp, or the **rate** at which mechanical energy is turned out by the motor, or the **rate** at which a load is raised.

A cyclist travels at 10 miles per hour. This does not tell us the distance he covers, but simply the **rate** at which he covers it. To know the distance traversed we must know the length of time for which he rides.

$$\text{Distance} = \text{rate} \times \text{time} = \frac{10 \text{ miles}}{1 \text{ hour}} \times 2 \text{ hours (say)} = 20 \text{ miles.}$$

Similarly, when a certain power is employed for a certain length of time, an amount of energy —in various forms—is available.

$$\text{Energy} = \text{Power} \times \text{Time} = \text{EI (or I²R) watts} \times t \text{ seconds} = \text{EI}t \text{ (or I²R}t) \text{ joules.}$$

Example 6.

A 100-volt lamp of 500 ohms hot resistance is connected across 100-volt mains. Find the energy taken from the mains in one minute and the heat developed by the lamp.

$$\text{Energy} = \text{power} \times \text{time} = \frac{E^2}{R} \text{ joules per sec.} \times 60 \text{ secs.}$$

$$= \frac{100^2}{500} \times 60 = 1,200 \text{ joules.}$$

$$\text{or } I = \frac{100}{500} = 0 \cdot 2 \text{ amp.}$$

$$\text{Energy} = \text{EI}t = 100 \times 0 \cdot 2 \times 60 = 1,200 \text{ joules,}$$

$$\text{or } \quad \text{Energy} = \text{I²R}t = 0 \cdot 2^2 \times 500 \times 60 = 1,200 \text{ joules.}$$

This amount of energy is converted into heat. The unit of heat is the " calorie " and
$$1 \text{ calorie} = 4 \cdot 2 \text{ joules.}$$

Thus, $1,200 \text{ joules} = \frac{1,200}{4 \cdot 2} = 286 \text{ calories.}$

Example 7.

Ten accumulators, each having an E.M.F. of 2 volts and a resistance of $0 \cdot 05$ ohm, are to be charged with a current of 8 amps.

Find the amount of energy stored in them in 15 minutes (assuming that their E.M.Fs. remain at 2 volts) and the amount of heat energy wasted.

E.M.F. of battery opposing applied E.M.F. = 20 volts.
Resistance of battery = $0 \cdot 05 \times 10 = 0 \cdot 5$ ohm.
Voltage to drive 8 amps. through battery resistance = $8 \times 0 \cdot 5 = 4$ volts.
Voltage to overcome back E.M.F. of battery = 20 volts.
Hence required charging voltage = 24 volts.

Energy stored up in 15 minutes in the form of chemical energy

$$= E \times I \times t$$
$$= 20 \times 8 \times (15 \times 60) = 144,000 \text{ joules,}$$
$$\text{or } 20 \times 8 \text{ watts} \times \tfrac{1}{4} \text{ hour} = 40 \text{ watt-hours.}$$

Heat energy $= E \times I \times t$
$$= 4 \times 8 \times \tfrac{1}{4} = 8 \text{ watt-hours,}$$
$$\text{or } 4 \times 8 \times 15 \times 60 \text{ joules} = 28,800 \text{ joules}$$
$$= \frac{28,800}{4 \cdot 2} = 6,860 \text{ calories.}$$

72. Kirchhoff's Laws.—These are generalisations of the ideas developed above which facilitate the calculation of the currents in a complicated arrangement of resistances. They are two in number.

(1) **Kirchhoff's First Law.**—At any junction of resistances, the sum of the currents flowing towards the junction is equal to the sum of the currents flowing away from it.

This merely expresses the fact mentioned above that electricity cannot accumulate at any point of a circuit (paragraph 65).

(2) **Kirchhoff's Second Law** is a generalisation of Ohm's Law. It states that in any closed circuit the sum of the E.M.Fs., reckoned positive in the direction of the current and negative in the opposite direction, is equal to the sum of the products of current and resistance in every part of the closed circuit.

If the term " vector sum " is used, these laws become applicable to A.C. circuits.

73. Wheatstone's Bridge.—This is a network of resistances which is in common use for the measurement of resistance, *e.g.*, in the Bridge Megger (paragraph 190). Its theory will be considered here as an example of the application of Kirchhoff's Laws.

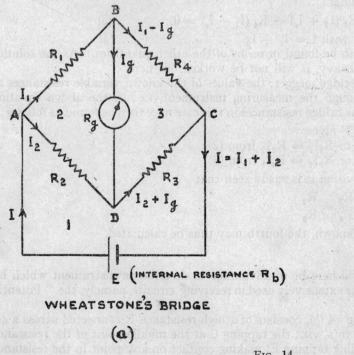

WHEATSTONE'S BRIDGE

(a)

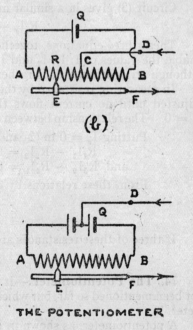

(b)

THE POTENTIOMETER

(c)

FIG. 14.

Fig. 14 (*a*) shows the arrangement. R_1, R_2, R_3 and R_4 are four resistances, one of which is unknown and whose value is to be determined. A current-measuring instrument G, whose resistance is R_g, is connected as indicated and current is sent through the arrangement by the battery E of internal resistance R_b.

We shall first obtain the equations for finding the current in any part of the circuit in terms of the resistances and E.M.F., *i.e.*, the various currents labelled I_1, I_2, I_g, etc.

The current flowing through the battery is taken to be I. At A this divides into two parts, I_1 and I_2. Kirchhoff's First Law states that $I = I_1 + I_2$. According to the values of I_1 and I_2, current will flow through G either from B to D or D to B. It is assumed to flow from B to D in this case and to be of value I_g. If it actually flows from D to B, I_g will turn out to be negative in the solution, *i.e.*, in the other direction to that assumed for it.

Kirchhoff's First Law then enables us to derive the currents in the other branches as labelled in the figure.

The next step is to apply the Second Law to each closed circuit in the arrangement. These are labelled (1), (2) and (3). [EABC and ABCD are also closed circuits, but it will be found that no information is derived from them which is not contained in that given by the application of the law to (1), (2) and (3).]

Circuit (1). The sum of the products of current and resistance, taking account of direction, is

$$R_b I + R_2 I_2 + R_3 (I_2 + I_g).$$

The E.M.F. is E and acts in the direction of I.

$$\therefore R_b I + R_2 I_2 + R_3 (I_2 + I_g) = E. \quad \ldots \quad \ldots (1)$$

Circuit (2). There is no E.M.F. acting and so the sum of the IR drops is zero,

$$i.e., R_1 I_1 + R_g I_g - R_2 I_2 = 0. \quad \ldots \quad \ldots \quad \ldots (2)$$

Note that I_2 acts in the opposite direction round circuit (2) to that of I_1 and I_g and so must be reckoned as negative if they are taken to be positive.

Circuit (3) gives in a similar manner

$$R_g I_g + R_3 (I_2 + I_g) - R_4 (I_1 - I_g) = 0. \ldots \quad \ldots (3)$$

These three equations, together with $I = I_1 + I_2$, $\ldots \quad \ldots \quad \ldots \quad \ldots (4)$ enable the values of I, I_1, I_2 and I_g to be found in terms of the other quantities. As the solution, although straightforward, is rather heavy, it will not be worked out here.

In measuring resistance by the bridge megger, the values of the known variable resistances are adjusted until no current flows through the measuring instrument, *i.e.*, in the above equations $I_g = 0$. The relationship between the bridge resistances in this case may then be found as follows :—

Putting $I_g = 0$ in (2) and (3) gives
$R_1 I_1 - R_2 I_2 = 0$, or $R_1 I_1 = R_2 I_2$ from (2)
and $R_3 I_2 - R_4 I_1 = 0$, or $R_3 I_2 = R_4 I_1$ from (3)

From these relations by division it is easily seen that

$$\frac{R_1}{R_4} = \frac{R_2}{R_3}.$$

If three of these resistances are known, the fourth may thus be calculated.

74. The Potentiometer.—It will here be of advantage to describe an instrument which has not been mentioned so far, but which is extensively used in receiving circuits, namely, the " Potentiometer."

A potentiometer, as shown in Fig 14 (*b*), consists of a high resistance R connected across a cell Q, and provided with two tapping points, viz., the tapping C at the middle point of the resistance, connected to terminal D, and the sliding tapping E, making contact on any point in the resistance, connected to terminal F.

The resistance R should be large enough to prevent the current passing through it from discharging the cell rapidly. In practice a resistance of 200-300 ohms is suitable, and will allow a 2-volt cell to maintain its voltage for many weeks with continuous working.

If the voltage of the cell Q is 2 volts, then the P.D. between A and B will be 2 volts, and there will be a steady fall of potential along the whole resistance.

The P.D. between A and C, and between C and B, will be 1 volt in each case.

The P.D. between terminals F and D will depend on the relative position of the slider E to the point C.

(a) If E is opposite C, there will be no difference of potential between F and D.

(b) If E is opposite A, there will be a P.D. of 1 volt between F and D, and F will be positive to D.

(c) If E is opposite B, there will again be a P.D. of 1 volt between F and D, but D will be positive to F.

Hence, as E is slowly moved from A to B, the P.D. across any circuit joined between F and D will vary from a maximum in the direction F to D, down to zero, and up to a maximum in the direction D to F.

In short, a potentiometer is an arrangement for varying the strength and direction of voltage applied to any circuit joined across it.

It should be noted that the resistance of the external circuit is in parallel with the resistance of the potentiometer between C and E.. This will modify the actual values of the P.Ds. quoted above, but the principle remains the same. The higher the resistance of the external circuit, the more nearly do the above values represent the true state of affairs.

An alternative arrangement for wiring a potentiometer, if the resistance has no centre tapping point, is shown in Fig. 14 (c).

The terminal D is now joined to the centre point of the battery Q. The left-hand cell is trying to force a current through the resistance between A and E, and through the outside circuit in the direction of F to D.

The right-hand cell is trying to force a current through the outside circuit in the direction D to F, through the resistance E to B.

The resultant current will be the difference between the two, i.e., if the resistance A to E is less than the resistance E to B, current in the outside circuit will be from F to D and vice versa.

As there is a resultant current in the outside circuit, a steady voltage will be applied across this circuit, equal to its resistance multiplied by the resultant current flowing.

LAMPS.

75. Incandescent lamps are rated by their voltage, power and candle power. There are three types in common use—carbon filament, metallic filament, and " gas-filled." The bulb of the ordinary metallic filament lamp is evacuated ; the gas-filled lamp has its bulb filled with an inert gas such as argon. The filaments of both are usually made of tungsten. These two kinds are of more modern introduction and, though perhaps more costly, are more efficient (as regards consumption of electrical energy) and do not blacken as do carbon lamps, owing to deposition of carbon.

Each type is referred to as consuming so many " watts per candle power." Carbon lamps take, roughly, 3·5 to 4 watts per c.p., whereas metallic filament lamps vary, roughly, from 1 to 2 watts per c.p., and gas-filled lamps take $\frac{1}{2}$ watt per c.p.

The two latter consume less power to give the same amount of light, and hence are more efficient.

Example 8.

A 220-volt 32-c.p. metallic filament lamp of efficiency 1·7 watts per p.c. is burned from 220-volt mains ; find what current it takes.

Watts supplied $= 32 \times 1·7 = 54·4 = EI.$

$$I = \frac{EI}{E} = \frac{54·4}{220} = 0·247 \text{ amps.}$$

For general lighting purposes metallic filament lamps are preferable, but for accumulator charging on a small scale, where lamps in parallel are used to regulate the charging current, carbon lamps are preferable, as they pass more current, and fewer are required.

MAGNETISM AND MAGNETIC FIELDS.

76. Permanent Magnets.—Pieces of a certain natural iron ore, called lodestone, are found to exercise on each other forces of attraction or repulsion, which vary according to definite laws. These are called permanent magnets. When freely suspended by a piece of silk fibre, any such permanent magnet sets itself in a definite direction with regard to the North and South Magnetic Poles of the Earth. That end which tends to point towards the North Magnetic Pole is termed the " North-seeking " or " North " (N) pole of the magnet, and that end which tends to point towards the South Magnetic Pole of the Earth is termed the " South-seeking " or " South " (S) pole of the magnet.

The magnetism inherent in the magnet is found to be more concentrated towards the ends, so that for purposes of investigation each end can be considered as a magnetic pole of a certain polarity ; the longer and thinner the permanent magnet, the more is this assumption justified.

This concentration of magnetism at the ends or poles gives them the property of attracting small pieces of iron. Either end of a small piece of iron is attracted by either pole of a permanent magnet, and we shall see that this is explained by the fact that the iron, supposed unmagnetised at the start, is made into a temporary magnet under the influence of the permanent magnet, and the resultant attraction is simply an example of the general forces of attraction and repulsion which exist between magnetic poles.

Permanent magnets can be artificially produced by bringing a bar of steel under the influence of magnetising forces. A common example of a permanent magnet is a compass needle.

77. Laws Governing Magnetic Action.—The forces of attraction and repulsion can be studied by suspending two magnets by pieces of silk fibre and bringing them close to each other.

It is found that :—

   (1) Like poles repel, unlike poles attract, each other.

   (2) The force exerted between two poles is inversely proportional to the square of the distance between them.

The magnitude of the force exerted gives rise to the idea of pole strength. Two poles are said to have equal pole strengths if the forces they exert on another pole at the same distance in the same medium are equal. By the use of the C.G.S. units of force and distance, the dyne and the centimetre, a definition of **unit pole strength** is then obtained. If two poles of equal strength, when placed 1 cm. apart in a vacuum, exert on each other a force of one dyne, they are said to possess **unit pole strength** or to be **unit poles.** A unit North pole is taken as the positive unit, and so a unit South pole has a pole strength of — 1.

   (3) With this definition of the strength of a unit pole, it is found that the force between two poles is proportional to the product of the strengths of the poles.

Combining these results, it may be stated that if two poles have strengths m_1 and m_2, i.e., they are m_1 and m_2 times a unit pole, respectively, and they are placed d centimetres apart *in vacuo*, the force between them will be

$$\frac{m_1 m_2}{d^2} \text{ dynes.}$$

   (4) The two poles of the same magnet have the same strength.

The results of (2) and (3) above are modified if the medium between the poles is other than a vacuum, according to a property of the medium called its " permeability."

Permeability is denoted by the letter μ. and will be investigated further in the following paragraphs.

The formula of section (3) becomes, for an intervening medium with permeability, μ,

$$F = \frac{m_1 m_2}{\mu d^2} \text{ dynes.}$$

It will now be seen that the unit magnetic pole defined above is derived on the basis that the permeability of a vacuum is unity ($\mu = 1$). We can only compare the relative permeabilities of various media, and so this has been adopted as the simplest assumption for investigating magnetic phenomena, but it introduces an arbitrary element into the system of units developed from the unit magnetic pole. This system is called the **electromagnetic system of units.** The unit pole defined above, for instance, is called the **electromagnetic unit (E.M.U.)** of pole strength.

78. The Magnetic Field.—The magnetic field is the space in the neighbourhood of a magnet or magnets in which the forces of attraction and repulsion mentioned above can be observed. If a small magnetised compass needle is introduced into such a field and freely suspended, the various forces of attraction and repulsion acting on its two poles will have some resultant effect, so that it will settle in some position of equilibrium and its N. (or S.) pole will point in some definite direction. The direction in which its **North pole** points is by convention taken as the **direction of the field.**

As the compass needle is moved from one position to another in the field, the direction in which it points varies, so that the magnetic field has a varying direction. If the magnetic field we are considering is produced by one bar magnet, and the small compass needle we are to use as our indicating device is brought very near to the N. pole of the bar magnet, the N. pole of the needle will point directly away from the magnet. If the compass needle is then moved carefully along the direction in which its North pole is pointing, that direction will continuously vary, and the path traced out by the compass needle will come round to the South pole of the bar magnet. The tangent to this path at any point is the direction of the magnetic field there. By starting at different points, a series of different paths can be obtained, with the result shown in Fig. 15.

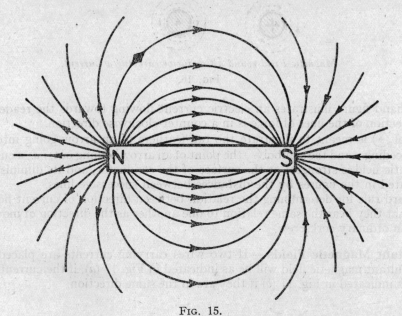

FIG. 15.

The curved paths above are known as **Lines of Magnetic Force,** and they denote the **direction** of the field.

79. Magnetic Fields Produced by Electric Currents.—So far we have only considered so-called permanent magnets, which are either natural magnetic ores or, for example, bars of steel which have been artificially " magnetised." An explanation of the latter process is bound up with the investigation of the effect of an **electric current in setting up a magnetic field,** which we now go on to consider.

It was mentioned in paragraph 45, as one of the effects of electric currents, that a wire carrying a current, *i.e.*, electricity in motion, sets up a magnetic field around it. This field is composed of lines of force which are in the form of concentric circles round the wire carrying the current, both inside and outside the conductor. (*See* Fig. 16.)

In other words, a small compass needle in the vicinity of a current-carrying conductor is acted on by exactly the same type of forces of magnetic attraction and repulsion as if it were brought near to a bar magnet.

The direction of the magnetic field is shown by the two figures 16 (*c*), below, which are end-on views of the conductor. The left-hand figure illustrates an electric current flowing away from the reader, in which case the positive direction of the lines of force is in a clockwise direction.

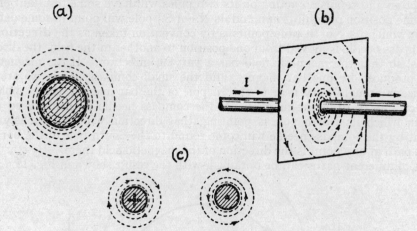

Magnetic Field round a Conductor carrying a Current.

FIG. 16.

The right-hand figure illustrates an electric current flowing towards the reader, in which case the positive direction of the lines of force is in a counter-clockwise direction.

The symbol ⊕ is meant to illustrate the tail-feathers of an arrow going into the conductor, *i.e.*, a current receding ; and the symbol ⊙ the point of an arrow coming out, *i.e.*, a current advancing.

The magnetic field is strongest at the surface of the conductor, and its diminishing intensity is roughly illustrated in the figures by the distances between successive lines.

The standard rule for determining the relation between direction of current flow and direction of the field is that they bear the same relation to one another as the direction of movement and that of rotation of an ordinary corkscrew.

80. Resultant Magnetic Fields.—If two wires carrying currents are placed parallel to one another the resultant magnetic field will be as indicated in Fig. 17 (*a*), if the currents are in opposite directions, or as indicated in Fig. 17 (*b*) if they are in the same direction.

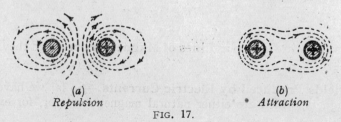

(a)   *(b)*
Repulsion   *Attraction*

FIG. 17.

In the first case the wires tend to be pushed apart, and in the second case to come together.

If the wire carrying the current is wound in a loop, the lines of force all pass through the loop in the same direction, as shown in Fig. 18.

A coil of wire is simply a number of continuous loops and a current sent through such a coil produces lines of force in a lengthwise direction through the coil, emerging at the ends, and completing the magnetic circuit through the surrounding medium. The diagram, Fig. 19, shows how the concentric lines of force merge together to give the resulting field.

Every line of force is closed on itself, and in our original investigation of a bar magnet this statement is justified by assuming the lines of force, which experimentally can only be plotted outside the magnet, to continue from the S. pole of the magnet to the N. pole inside the magnet itself.

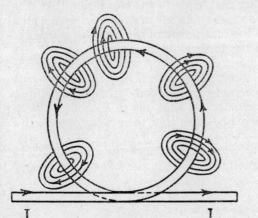

FIG. 18.

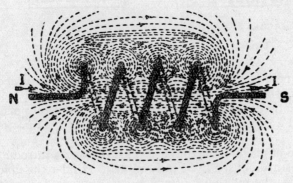 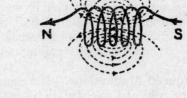

Field round Solenoid.

FIG. 19.

81. A coil of wire carrying a current and so having a magnetic field as shown is called a **solenoid** (from the Greek, meaning " a pipe-like " coil). The end of the coil from which the lines of force emerge is termed its NORTH POLE and the end at which they enter is termed its SOUTH POLE, just as in the case of the bar magnet.

The " end rule " or " clock rule " for determining the polarity of a coil is :—" Look at one end of the coil ; if the current flows in a clockwise direction (either towards or away from you) then that end will have south polarity ; if anti-clockwise, north polarity."

This is illustrated in Fig. 20, the arrows on the letters S and N being, as shown, indicative of the current being clockwise or not.

Another useful rule is the right-hand " gripping rule " :—" Grip the coil or solenoid with the right hand, wrapping the fingers round it in the direction in which the current is flowing ; extension of the thumb in the direction of the axis of the coil indicates the end having north polarity."

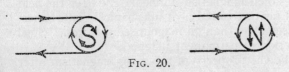

FIG. 20.

It should be obvious that the solenoid produces exactly the same distribution of magnetic field as the bar magnet—in other words, as long as the solenoid is carrying current, it is an electromagnet.

82. Molecular Theory of Magnetism.—This similarity between the magnetism produced by an electric current and that produced by a permanent magnet leads to the conclusion that it is the same fundamental cause that is operative in the two cases. An electric current is nothing but a movement of electrons in some definite direction, and the magnetism of the permanent magnet is due to the fact that the electrons which revolve round the nucleus of the atom do so in a less haphazard way than in a non-magnetic substance. The electrons rotating round the nucleus of any atom set up magnetic effects, because they constitute a current of electricity. Each molecule is thus effectively a small magnet, or equivalent to a small current-carrying coil. In non-magnetised substances the molecules lie " anyhow," so that the minute magnetic field due to any one of them is neutralised by the field of some other one, which is in such a position that their fields oppose and annul each other.

In a magnetised substance, however, it appears that a large proportion of the molecules have their axes pointing in the same direction, so that their magnetic fields are in the same direction and therefore additive.

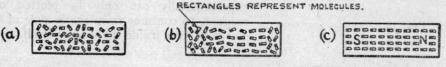

RECTANGLES REPRESENT MOLECULES.

Illustrating Magnetisation.

Fig. 21.

When a substance is completely magnetised, all the molecules have their axes turned in the same direction and the resultant effect is strongest. These conditions are illustrated in Fig. 21, the three diagrams representing non-magnetised, partially magnetised, and completely magnetised substances. When completely magnetised a substance is said to have attained " saturation."

83. Induced Magnetism.—If a piece of magnetic material, say, soft iron, is introduced into the magnetic field of a solenoid, it becomes magnetised by " **induction.**" Under the influence of the magnetic field, the elementary magnets, the molecules of which it is composed, tend to come into the definite arrangement referred to in the last paragraph, and so the soft iron itself is a **temporary magnet,** as long as the current which produces the effect is kept flowing.

As a result the following effects are noticed :—

(1) The strength of the original magnetic field is increased, due to the fact that the magnetic effects of the constituent molecules of the soft iron now act in conjunction with the magnetic effect of the current in the coil.

(2) Forces of attraction and repulsion are operative between the solenoid, which is, as we saw, a magnet, and the soft iron, which is now a temporary magnet.

(3) The iron tends to move from weaker to stronger parts of the field.

When the piece of soft iron is removed from the magnetic field, or the current is cut off, it loses most of the temporary magnetisation it has acquired.

Similar effects are observed if steel is substituted for soft iron ; but, for the same inducing field, the induction in steel is less than in soft iron, and the residual magnetism immediately after the field is removed is also smaller. It is found, however, that heating to red heat, mechanical disturbance, or the mere passage of time has less effect on magnetised steel than on magnetised soft iron. Steel is therefore a more suitable material for the construction of permanent magnets.

The term " retentivity " has been used to describe the property of retaining magnetism after the magnetising field has been removed.

All materials do not give the results quoted in this paragraph. The substances, such as iron, steel and nickel, which show magnetic properties strongly when subjected to a magnetising force, are called **ferro-magnetic.**

Substances which show magnetic properties to a very slight degree are called **para-magnetic,** and those which act in the opposite way—that is, diminish the strength of a magnetic field when placed in it, are termed **dia-magnetic.**

The latter two characteristics are of little practical importance in our study of electro-magnetism.

84. Field Strength.—So far we have dealt very little with the quantitative aspect of magnetism, and in paragraph 78 only considered the direction of the magnetic field without reference to its intensity. The intervening paragraphs have been concerned with a descriptive account of phenomena which must now be investigated more strictly.

The **Intensity** of the magnetic field at any point is the force in dynes acting on a unit pole placed at that point.

This is also referred to as the **Magnetic Field Strength** at the point, and is denoted by the letter H. It is measured in dynes per unit pole, sometimes called " gauss."

Unit field strength exists at a point where the force on a unit pole equals one dyne, and therefore unit field exists at a distance of one centimetre *in vacuo* from a unit pole. **This is the electromagnetic unit.** The field strength at a distance of one centimetre from a unit pole in a medium of permeability μ is $\frac{1}{\mu}$ gauss or dynes per unit pole.

85. Lines of Magnetic Flux.—It has been seen that the direction of the magnetic field strength at any point in the field is quite definite, being given by the tangent to the " line of magnetic force " passing through the point. In other words, the force of attraction or repulsion on a magnetic pole is fixed, both in magnitude and direction, at any point of the field.

To provide some picture of how such " action at a distance " may take place, it has been found convenient to look upon the " lines of magnetic force " as if they had a physical existence, and to regard them as if they were in the nature of tentacles which a magnetised body shoots out into the space around it, and which act directly on other magnetised bodies in the neighbourhood and pull and push them about It has further been found possible to give a quantitative significance to the number of these tentacles in any part of the field. They are then called " lines of magnetic flux."

86. Magnetic Flux.—The two quantities with which we might relate a number of " lines of magnetic flux " for quantitative purposes are :—

    (1) The strength of the magnetic pole producing them.
    (2) The mechanical forces which are exerted on poles at various parts of the field, *i.e.,* the magnetic field intensity.

The latter suffers from the disadvantage that it changes abruptly in value when the medium changes, so that if, for instance, a piece of iron were in a magnetic field mostly consisting of air as medium, and if we identified a number of lines with field strength, we should be forced to assume that many of the " tentacles " vanished at one edge of the iron and only reappeared at the other edge. Their existence in the iron would have to be denied, as the field strength in the iron is very much less than in the surrounding air.

It has been found more convenient to assume that these lines of magnetic flux are continuous and their number independent of the medium, and for this reason the number of lines is derived from the strength of the magnetic pole from which they set out. Their direction, of course, at any point is the direction of the magnetic field at that point, *i.e.,* the direction of the " lines of magnetic force."

87. The Unit of Flux.—In the field round a unit pole concentrated at a point, the field strength is the same at all points the same distance away from the pole (H $=\frac{1}{\mu r^2}$ at a distance r). All such points lie on a sphere whose centre is the unit pole, and the direction of the field is radially outwards. The lines of magnetic flux thus are straight, and diverge radially from the pole like the spokes of a wheel (in three dimensions). The surface area of a sphere of radius r is $4\pi r^2$, and so the surface area of a sphere of 1 cm. radius is 4π sq. cms.

The number of lines of magnetic flux emanating from a unit pole is taken to be such that one line goes through each sq. cm. of the surface of a sphere of radius 1 cm. described about the pole as centre.

Thus, for a pole strength of three units, three lines would go through every sq. cm. on the surface of such a sphere.

In the case of a unit pole, the total number of lines crossing this sphere is 4π, i.e., 4π lines of magnetic flux emanate from a unit pole.

Lines of magnetic flux used as quantitative units in this way are usually called "**lines.**" The name "Maxwell" for this unit has also been suggested. It is an E.M.U.

The total number of lines of magnetic flux passing through any area is called the "**flux**" through that area and denoted by the letter Φ (phi).

The "**flux density**" or "**magnetic induction**" at any point in a magnetic field is the flux passing through an area of 1 sq. cm. at right angles to the direction of the field at that point. It is denoted by B. B is thus measured in lines per sq. cm. or Maxwells per sq. cm. $\Phi = BA$ for an area A, which the flux Φ (of uniform density B) crosses at right angles.

88. Relation between Flux Density and Field Strength.

—From the derivation of the "line" it will be seen that the flux density at a distance of 1 cm. from a unit pole is B = 1 line per sq. cm. The field strength *in vacuo* at this distance is H = 1 gauss. Thus, *in vacuo*, B = H numerically.

In any other medium the field strength at a distance of 1 cm. from a unit pole is $H = \dfrac{1}{\mu}$ gauss, where μ is the permeability of the medium. B is unaffected by the medium and depends only on the pole strength, *i.e.*, B is still 1 line per sq. cm., and so $B = \mu H$ in a medium of permeability μ, *i.e.*, the permeability μ now appears as the numerical ratio of the flux density to the magnetic field strength at any point in the field.

$$\mu = \frac{B}{H}$$

This ratio of flux density to field strength, or permeability, μ, differs widely for different substances, and it is variable in value for the same substance. In the case of iron it may vary with the quality of the iron, the value of B, and the temperature of the iron.

The distinction between materials drawn at the end of paragraph 83 can now be explained more accurately :—

Ferro-magnetic materials, such as iron, steel, nickel, cobalt and their alloys, have a high and variable value of μ. It may vary between, say, 200 and 1,000, for some specimen, but these numbers are simply indicative of its order of magnitude.

Para-magnetic materials, such as the ordinary non-magnetic metals, copper, aluminium, etc., have values of μ which are constant and very little greater than unity.

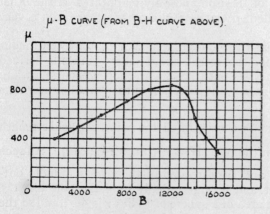

μ-B curve (from B-H curve above).

FIG. 22.

Dia-magnetic materials, such as bismuth, have μ constant and very little less than unity.

In practice, we may neglect the deviation of μ from unity in all substances except the ferro-magnetic ones. In other words, for all substances, except ferro-magnetic substances, it may be taken that B = H, numerically. The units of B and H are, of course, quite different (the line per sq. cm. and the gauss respectively) as they represent different properties of the field.

A curve of B against H for a ferro-magnetic material is shown in Fig. 22, and also a permeability curve, showing variation of μ with B.

89. Hysteresis.—The property of steel already referred to as *retentivity* is a special case of a more general property exhibited by ferro-magnetic materials and known as **hysteresis.** This property may be studied by winding a coil of wire round an anchor ring of some ferro-magnetic metal, say, cast steel, and sending a current through the coil. It will be seen in the next paragraph

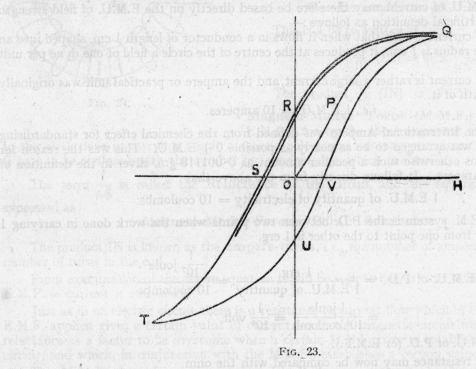

FIG. 23.

that the field strength in the ring is proportional to the current. Instruments for measuring flux directly are also available. Thus, corresponding values of flux and magnetising current may be measured, and the equivalent values of B and H obtained from them. The curve OPQ in Fig. 23 is obtained in this way by gradually increasing the current from zero to a certain value and measuring the amount of flux produced by various currents.

If now the current is gradually reduced from its maximum value, the flux density does not diminish along the same curve as it increased, but along QR. When the current is reduced to zero, there is a residual magnetisation, shown in Fig. 23 by OR, and if the current is then increased in the opposite direction and a complete cycle of current changes completed, the flux density curve assumes the shape of the loop QRSTUVQ.

The magnetisation may be said to lag continually behind the magnetising force, and the word **Hysteresis,** meaning " lagging behind," is used to describe this effect. It can be proved that the area of the **Hysteresis Loop** is indicative of energy loss, and is a definite factor to be considered in all apparatus where changing currents set up changing states of magnetisation. The energy is expended in heating the iron. This property is common, in varying degrees, to all ferro-magnetic substances.

It should, however, be noted that the resemblance is purely formal. As far as we know, there is nothing flowing round a magnetic circuit and composing the flux in the way that electrons flow round an electric circuit and compose the current.

93. If the magnetic circuit is not uniform, the separate parts are treated individually, as in an electric circuit, and their reluctances added.

If the circuit is composed of materials whose dimensions and permeabilities are varying, and, in the same notation as used above, are given by l_1 A_1, μ_1, l_2 A_2 μ_2, etc., the total M.M.F. required to establish a certain flux Φ through the combined circuit is given by :—

$$\text{M.M.F.} = \Phi \left(\frac{l_1}{\mu_1 A_1} + \frac{l_2}{\mu_2 A_2} + \;-\;-\;-\; \right).$$

The equation is often written in the form which gives the **ampere-turns** necessary to produce a given flux in the circuit.

Since

$$\frac{4\pi}{10}(\text{IN}) = \Phi \times \frac{l}{\mu A},$$

$$\text{IN} = \frac{10}{4\pi} \cdot \Phi \cdot \frac{l}{\mu A} = \frac{0 \cdot 8 \, \Phi l}{\mu A} \text{ approximately.}$$

In the general case,

$$\text{IN} = 0 \cdot 8 \, \Phi \left(\frac{l_1}{\mu_1 A_1} + \frac{l_2}{\mu_2 A_2} + \;-\;-\;-\; \right)$$

As μ varies with B for ferro-magnetic materials, the value of μ must be obtained from a permeability curve, or a B-H curve, in the case of a definite numerical example, where the ampere-turns are required to give a certain total flux, or flux density. An example is appended.

Example 9.

(1) Calculate the ampere-turns necessary to produce a flux of 144,000 lines in a closed ring of mild steel made up of two sections, one (a) of length 100 cms. and square cross-section, the side of the square being 3 cms., and the other (b) of length 60 cms. and square cross-section, the side of the square being 4 cms., using the B-H curve of Fig. 22 (or the μ-B curve).

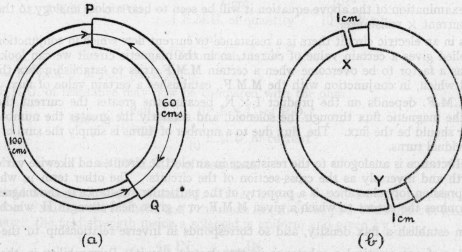

Fig. 25.

The areas of the cross-sections are 9 sq. cms. and 16 sq. cms., respectively.

Flux Φ = 144,000 lines.

∴ Flux density in (a) is given by $B = \dfrac{\Phi}{A} = \dfrac{144,000}{9} = 16,000$ lines per sq. cm.

Flux density in (b) is given by B $= \dfrac{\Phi}{A} = \dfrac{144,000}{16} = 9,000$ lines per sq. cm.

Section (a)	Section (b)
$l = 100$ cms.	$l = 60$ cms.
A $= 9$ sq. cms.	A $= 16$ sq. cms.
B $= 16,000$ lines per sq. cm.	B $= 9,000$ lines per sq. cm.
H (from B–H curve) $= 54$.	H (from B–H curve) $= 12$.
$\mu = \dfrac{16,000}{54} = 296.$	$\mu = \dfrac{9,000}{12} = 750.$

Reluctance $= \dfrac{l}{\mu A} = \dfrac{100}{296 \times 9}$ Reluctance $= \dfrac{l}{\mu A} = \dfrac{60}{750 \times 16}$

Total reluctance $= \dfrac{100}{296 \times 9} + \dfrac{60}{750 \times 16}$

$$IN = 0 \cdot 8 \; \Phi \times \text{Total Reluctance} = (0 \cdot 8)\,(144,000) \left\{ \dfrac{100}{296 \times 9} + \dfrac{60}{750 \times 16} \right\}$$

$$= 115,200 \{0 \cdot 03754 + 0 \cdot 005\} = 115,200 \,(0 \cdot 04254)$$

$$= 4,900.$$

This could be produced by 7 amps. flowing through 700 turns, or 49 amps. through 100 turns, etc.

(2) Suppose now the ring is cut across at the diametrically opposite points X and Y, both in Section (a), and the two halves are separated so as to leave an air gap of 1 cm. at each of these points, as shown in Fig. 25 (b).

The reluctance is found to be greatly increased, because of the small air-gaps. Their total length is small, only 2 cms., but the μ for them is unity.

The additional reluctance is given, as before, by $\dfrac{l}{\mu A}$, where $l = 2$ cms., $\mu = 1$, A $= 9$ sq. cms.

So that $\dfrac{l}{\mu A}$ for the air-gaps in series $= \dfrac{2}{9} = 0 \cdot 222.$

Total reluctance $= 0 \cdot 04254 + 0 \cdot 222 = 0 \cdot 26454.$

Ampere Turns $= 115,200 \,(0 \cdot 26454) = 30,500.$

Thus, with 100 turns, a current of 305 amperes would be necessary instead of 49 amperes.

This effect of the majority of the reluctance of a magnetic circuit being due to an air-gap, where such is included, is very important in machine construction, and air-gaps are designed to be as short as possible in order to minimise their tendency to diminish flux density.

ELECTROSTATICS AND ELECTRIC FIELDS.

94. It has already been stated, in paragraph 37, that like charges repel one another and unlike charges attract one another.

The forces of attraction and repulsion are called **electric forces,** and the space in which they act is called the **electric field.**

Electric fields and magnetic fields, which were treated in the previous section, have many points in common.

95. **Unit Charge.**—It is possible to isolate a " charge " of positive or negative electricity by friction.

If a stick of sealing-wax is rubbed with flannel it acquires the property of attracting small pieces of paper, etc. It has become negatively charged, or, in terms of the electron theory, it has acquired a surplus of electrons. The flannel is left with a deficit of electrons, and is thus positively charged. Two such electrified sticks of sealing-wax will repel one another. A glass rod rubbed with silk will be positively charged, and will attract the sealing-wax. By such simple experiments the mutual action of electrified bodies can be studied, and this is the way in which the first experimenters built up the theory.

It is found that the force between two charged bodies varies inversely as the square of the distance between them.

A system of units based on the mechanical forces acting on electric charges may thus be developed in an exactly similar manner to the system based on the forces between magnetic poles (paragraph 77). This is called the **electrostatic system** of units.

The **electrostatic unit (E.S.U.) of charge or quantity of electricity** is defined as follows :—

Two **unit charges** placed at a distance of one centimetre apart *in vacuo* exert on each other a force of one dyne.

The relation between this unit and the practical unit, the coulomb, is given by :—1 coulomb $= 3 \times 10^9$ E.S.U.

96. The force between two charges is proportional to their product, so combining this with the result above relating to distance between them, two charges, of Q_1 and Q_2 units respectively, at a distance d cms. apart will exert a mutual force of $\dfrac{Q_1 Q_2}{d^2}$ dynes.

If the charges are like, the force is one of repulsion ; if unlike, one of attraction.

The mutual force is dependent on another factor, a property of the material between the charges called its "**dielectric constant,**" or "specific inductive capacity" (S.I.C.), or "Permittivity," and denoted by the letter K.

When modified to take account of this property of the medium, the law of force between charges becomes

$$F = \frac{Q_1 Q_2}{K d^2} \text{ dynes.}$$

Thus the electrostatic system of units is based on the assumption that $K = 1$ *in vacuo*.

97. **Electric Field.**—This has already been defined as the space in the neighbourhood of charges where forces of attraction and repulsion are exerted on other charges.

Its **strength** at any point can be measured by the force which would be exerted on a unit charge placed there, and, using the same units as before, the **field strength** is the **force in dynes per unit charge.** It is denoted by X. The field strength at a distance r *in vacuo* from a point charge Q is

$$X = \frac{Q}{r^2}.$$

In a medium of dielectric constant K, $X = \dfrac{Q}{K r^2}$ under the same conditions.

98. **Lines of Force.**—The direction of the electric field round an isolated electric charge is radial. This can be represented by drawing a series of straight lines outwards from the charge, in which case the direction of the field at any point is along the line passing through that point.

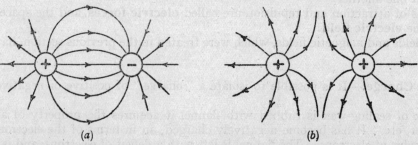

(a) *Electric Field between Two Unlike Charges.*　　　(b) *Electric Field between Two Like Charges.*

Fig. 26.

The direction of the resultant electric field set up by two charges is more complicated. The field between two equal and opposite charges is as shown in Fig. 26 (*a*). The similarity between this field and that existing between two equal and opposite magnetic poles (*see* Fig. 15) should be noted.

99. Lines or Tubes of Electric Flux.—In the quantitative study of magnetic phenomena it was found convenient to develop the idea of the magnetic flux through an area in the magnetic field (paragraph 86). The same type of concept is also found useful in electrostatics and is derived in a very similar manner. Lines or tubes of electric flux are supposed to emanate from electric charges. Each line is assumed to start from a positive charge and end on an equal negative charge, as indicated in Fig. 26 (*a*).

If we assume that these lines or tubes behave like stretched rubber cables, *i.e.*, tend to contract in the direction of their length, a simple explanation of the attraction at a distance between two opposite charges is obtained. The lines, by tending to contract, tend to pull the charges together.

Repulsion effects between like charges may also be explained on this basis if we assume that the tubes of flux in contracting lengthwise expand laterally, *i.e.*, increase in cross-section.

The field in the neighbourhood of two like charges is shown in Fig. 26 (*b*). The tubes of flux from one of these charges cannot end on the other ; and because of their tendency to contract lengthwise, there will be a competition between them to end on the nearest possible negative charges. This brings the tubes from each charge running sideways in the same general direction. Their tendency to expand sideways will then force the two charges apart.

Electric flux is denoted by the symbol ψ (psi). The unit is derived on a slightly different basis from the unit line of magnetic flux, the definition of which led to the result that 4π lines started from a unit pole.

One **line** or **tube of electric flux** is defined as the total flux which starts from a unit positive charge (or ends on a unit negative charge).

It may be considered rather difficult to picture the single tube of flux from a unit point charge, as presumably it must spread out to enclose all the space around the point, and the idea of " tube " rather loses its significance. It should be remembered, however, that if these tubes are more than a convenient way of obtaining results, and if there is anything corresponding to them in reality, there must be at least one tube per electron, *i.e.*, one unit tube, as above defined, must correspond in reality to about two thousand million electron tubes, which makes the flux easier to visualise. It is on account of unitary considerations that the unit tube is defined as above, and it is to be taken merely as the representative of an unknown number.

The **Electric Displacement or Flux Density** at any point in a field is the number of lines of flux passing through an area of 1 sq. cm. at right angles to the direction of the field at the point.

Flux density is given the symbol D. Thus by definition $D = \dfrac{\psi}{A}$, where ψ is the flux through an area A.

100. Relation between Field Strength and Flux Density.—The field strength X at a distance r from a point charge Q in a medium of dielectric constant K is given by

$$X = \frac{Q}{Kr^2} \text{ dynes per unit charge, or } \frac{Q}{r^2} = KX.$$

The total flux through the sphere of radius r described about the charge Q as centre is Q lines. The surface area of this sphere is $4\pi r^2$, and the flux distribution is obviously uniform through its surface, so that the flux density

$$D = \frac{Q}{4\pi r^2} \text{ lines per sq. cm., or } 4\pi D = \frac{Q}{r^2}.$$

$$X = \frac{4\pi D}{K}, \text{ and } D = \frac{KX}{4\pi}.$$

These results should be compared with $H = \dfrac{B}{\mu}$ and $B = \mu H$ respectively. It is seen that they differ by the factor 4π. This is due to the 4π lines of magnetic flux taken to be associated with a unit pole compared with the one line of electric flux attributed to a unit charge.

Though derived from the special case of a point charge, the results above can be shown to be perfectly general and to hold for any distribution of charges.

101. Potential Energy of Electric Field.

—It has been shown that a charged body placed in an electric field has a force acting on it and will generally be set in motion, *i.e.*, it will acquire kinetic energy. The only possible source of this energy is the electric field itself. Thus, whenever an electric field is established, there is a certain amount of energy stored up. By allowing the charges which have produced the field to come together under their mutual attractions, this stored energy will be converted to energy of motion of the charges and eventually to heat or light energy when the motion is stopped. Thus we may consider the electric field to be a storehouse of electrical potential energy.

102. Potential Difference and Potential.

—When a charged body moves under the action of the field, the work done on it is obtained from the field energy.

Just as in the case of a current flowing in a conductor, this transformation of energy leads to the concept of potential differences between different points in the field.

The potential difference between two points in an electric field is defined as the work done when a unit positive charge moves along a line of force from one point to the other. If this movement takes place owing to the field forces themselves, the first point is said to be at a higher potential than the second. If the charge has to be moved from one point to the other against the opposition of the field forces, the first point is at a lower potential than the second. The zero of potential, as before (paragraph 54), is taken as the potential of the earth's surface, thus enabling absolute values (P.Ds. to earth) to be given to the potentials at various points of the field.

The E.S.U. of P.D. is thus the P.D. between two points when the work done in moving one E.S.U. of charge from one point to the other is one erg,

$$\text{\textit{i.e.,} } 1 \text{ E.S.U. of P.D. } = \frac{1 \text{ erg}}{1 \text{ E.S.U. of charge}}.$$

The practical unit of P.D. is the volt, *i.e.*, the P.D. between two points when the work done in moving 1 coulomb from one point to the other is 1 joule.

Since 1 coulomb $= 3 \times 10^9$ E.S.U. of charge,
and 1 joule $= 10^7$ ergs,
we may easily find the connection between the E.S.U. of P.D. and the volt.

$$1 \text{ E.S.U. of P.D. } = \frac{1 \text{ erg}}{1 \text{ E.S.U. of charge}} = \frac{\dfrac{1}{10^7} \text{ joule}}{\dfrac{1}{3 \times 10^9} \text{ coulomb}}$$

$$= \frac{300 \text{ joules}}{\text{coulomb}} = 300 \text{ volts}.$$

The relation between the practical and electrostatic units of other electrical quantities may be similarly obtained.

103. The above ideas will now be illustrated for the case of a uniform electric field, *i.e.*, a field in which the electric field strength has the same value and direction at every point. Such a field is obtained approximately in practice by the arrangement shown in Fig. 27 (a) where two large conducting plates are set up parallel to each other with a layer of some dielectric between them, and connected to the terminals of a battery. The P.D. between the plates is the terminal P.D. of the battery (V). Plate Y has a positive charge, say, $+ Q$, and plate Z has an equal negative charge $-Q$. Owing to their longitudinal contraction and lateral expansion the tubes of flux will be arranged

as shown. They then have the minimum possible length. Tubes at the edges of the plates are bowed outwards because there is no lateral pressure on the outside of them to counterbalance that of the more central tubes. Thus, in practice, the field is not uniform at the edges. For simplicity we shall neglect this and assume the field to be uniform everywhere between the plates.

The flux starting from plate Y is $\psi = Q$.

If Y has an area of A sq. cms., then $D = \dfrac{\psi}{A} = \dfrac{Q}{A}$ is the flux density.

The field strength X is therefore given by $X = \dfrac{4\pi D}{K} = \dfrac{4\pi Q}{KA}$, where K is the S.I.C. of the dielectric. This is the force on a unit charge anywhere in the field.

Suppose a unit charge is allowed to move from Y to Z (a distance of d cms., say) under the action of the field. It will move along a line of force, *i.e.*, it travels d cms. under a force X and so the work done on it is Xd.

By definition this is the P.D. (V_{yz}) between Y and Z.

$$i.e.,\ V_{yz} = Xd,$$

or P.D. between two points = field strength × distance between the two points.

In this case, $V_{yz} = Xd = \dfrac{4\pi Qd}{KA}.$

If Z were at earth potential, V_{yz} would be the absolute potential of Y.

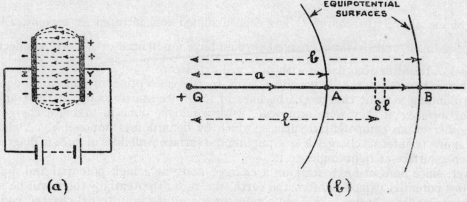

FIG. 27.

104. The relation between field strength and P.D., just derived for a *uniform field*, may also be written $X = V/d$. It is true of *non-uniform fields*, provided we consider two points close enough to each other for us to assume that the field is uniform between them.

With reference to Fig. 27 (*b*), let Q be a positive charge concentrated at a point. The field strength X decreases as one moves outwards from Q to a point an infinite distance away, where the potential is zero, namely the earth. Between points A and B the field is non-uniform, and the P.D. between them can only be found by adding up (integrating) the small increments of work necessary to move a unit charge from B to A by moving between a succession of points so close together that the field X may be assumed uniform over the small distance δl between them.

The force at distance l is given by $X = Q/Kl^2$, and is uniform over the small distance δl. Now X acts from A towards B, hence the force from B to A must be $-X$, and is the force against which the unit charge is carried. The work done (δV) over the small distance δl is given by $\delta V = -X \cdot \delta l$, which gives a general formula $X = -\dfrac{dV}{dl}.$ Since the potential falls, as one moves outwards from Q, the rate of change of potential with distance $\left(\dfrac{dV}{dl}\right)$ is negative, and thereby gives positive values of X, the field strength at any point.   This gives a new idea of **field strength** as **the rate of change of P.D. along a line of flux,** and leads to the practical unit of field strength, the **volt per cm.**, *i.e.,* the field strength is such that the P.D. between two points 1 cm. apart on a line of flux is 1 volt.

Since 1 E.S.U. of P.D. = 300 volts, and the centimetre is the same on both systems,

$$\text{1 E.S.U. of field strength} = 300 \text{ volts per cm.}$$

The electrostatic field strength at a receiving aerial is often quoted in terms of a sub-multiple of the above unit, the **millivolt per metre.**

$$\begin{aligned} \text{1 volt per cm.} &= 100 \text{ volts per metre.} \\ &= 100{,}000 \text{ millivolts per metre.} \end{aligned}$$

At Portsmouth, the field strength due to Droitwich B.B.C. station is of the order of 15 millivolts per metre.

It is of interest to perform the operation of integrating the work done between B and A.   From the foregoing treatment we have

$$\text{P.D.}_{\text{A to B}} = V_{AB} = \int_b^a -X \cdot dl = \int_b^a -\frac{Q}{Kl^2} \cdot dl$$
$$= \left[\frac{Q}{Kl} \right]_b^a = \frac{Q}{Ka} - \frac{Q}{Kb}.$$

If B is at earth potential $b = \infty$ and we get the absolute potential at A,

$$V_A = \frac{Q}{Ka} - \frac{Q}{\infty} = \frac{Q}{Ka}.$$

In all of the above, the charge Q has been assumed concentrated at a point.   A spherical conductor of radius a, and having a charge Q, would have a potential of $\frac{Q}{Ka}$.   If a is decreased, the potential rises, a result in accordance with practical experience.

A further extension of the above ideas leads to the conception of concentric equipotential surfaces surrounding a point charge Q, the lines of force necessarily being at right angles to an equipotential surface ; if they were otherwise, work would be done in taking a charge from one point to another on an equipotential surface, which by definition is impossible.   A charged conductor containing no internal charges is an equipotential surface ; all lines of force in diagrams should intersect such a surface at right angles to it.

Moreover, since lines of force start on a charged body at a high potential and must end on one at a lower potential (which is often the earth, the zero of potential), there will be no lines of force, and hence no force, inside a charged conductor containing no internal charged bodies.   This matter has been the subject of many practical and theoretical proofs.   It is important, since it is the basis of the **electrostatic screening** of wireless apparatus.

105. **Systems of Units.**—In the brief description of electrical phenomena given in the previous paragraphs, three systems of units have been derived :—

(1) The practical system.
(2) The electromagnetic system.
(3) The electrostatic system.

The two latter systems are based on the absolute units of length, mass and time (cm., gm. and sec.).

The electromagnetic system, however, assumes that the permeability of a vacuum is unity, while the electrostatic system assumes that the specific inductive capacity of a vacuum is unity, thus introducing another arbitrary element into both systems.   It can be shown by comparing the values of the same quantity, *e.g.*, a current, on the two systems that these assumptions are not consistent with each other.   It is actually found that for a vacuum

$$\frac{1}{\sqrt{K}} = 3 \times 10^{10} \text{ numerically,}$$

and has the units of centimetres per second, *i.e.*, it is of the nature of a velocity. This velocity of 3×10^{10} cms. per sec. is the measured velocity with which light travels (*cf.* R.3).

It was this fact which led to the idea that light waves were electromagnetic in nature, and gave rise to the attempt to produce similar waves by electrical means which laid the foundations of wireless telegraphy.

106. Following on the description of direct-current phenomena given above, a section on batteries is appended. In the next chapter, the meaning of the electrical quantities which are particularly important in wireless circuits, viz., inductance and capacity, will be developed from the outline of electromagnetism and electrostatics given in this chapter.

PRIMARY CELLS.

107. The existence of an electric current in any circuit means that energy in some form is being liberated at the generating source, and the continuance of the current necessitates the continuous expenditure of energy. In the case where the current is supplied by a dynamo driven by a steam or gas engine, the source of the supply is the coal, and the place where the energy is being liberated is the furnace. Coal contains a large supply of energy, which it readily liberates in the form of heat, and which, after several transformations, may appear in a circuit in the form of electrical energy, and is there used for lighting, running motors, energising W/T sets, etc.

The coal becomes oxidised or burnt in the process, and the quantity of energy that can thus be obtained is clearly limited by the amount of coal consumed or burnt.

In the case of an ordinary voltaic cell the conversion of the energy of supply into electrical energy is a much simpler and less wasteful process, but the material which acts as the source of supply—in other words, the fuel—is far more expensive.

In most cells the fuel consists of zinc and acid, which are consumed, but which, instead of giving out their energy in the form of heat, give it out directly in the form of current.

A cell is in reality nothing more than a little furnace in which zinc instead of coal is used as fuel, and in which the " burning " is not simple oxidation.

108. **Conduction of Electricity through Liquids.**—Pure water is a very good insulator, *i.e.*, if a P.D. is applied across two terminals in pure distilled water, no measurable current will flow. It is found, however, that if certain chemical substances are dissolved in water, the solution is conducting, although its conductivity is much less than that of a metallic conductor.

Such chemical solutions are called " electrolytes " and belong mainly to three types of chemical compound, " acids," *e.g.*, sulphuric acid, " bases," *e.g.*, caustic soda, and " salts," which are formed by the interaction of an acid and a base, *e.g.*, common salt, which is formed by the interaction of hydrochloric acid and caustic soda.

Just as gases are ionised under various conditions (*see* paragraph 36), so it is supposed that the molecules of these chemicals are ionised by the process of solution in water. Sulphuric acid may be taken as an illustration. The molecule of sulphuric acid (H_2SO_4) consists of two atoms of hydrogen, one of sulphur, and four of oxygen. On solution, this molecule splits up into three parts, two atoms of hydrogen, which have each lost an electron, *i.e.*, hydrogen ions, and one complex ion containing an atom of sulphur, four atoms of oxygen, and the two electrons from the hydrogen atoms.

This complex ion therefore has a nett negative charge of two electrons. The process may be represented as

$$H_2SO_4 \rightarrow H^+ + H^+ + SO_4^{--},$$

where the $+$ and $-$ indices represent loss and gain of one electron respectively.

Electrolytic ions differ from gaseous ions in two respects :—

(1) They are stable in solution and do not tend to recombine with each other as gaseous ions do.

(2) Negative ions are never free electrons, but always consist of an atom or group of atoms having more than its normal share of electrons.

If a P.D. is applied across an electrolyte, the negative ions will be attracted to the positive plate and the positive ions to the negative plate.   There is thus a passage of electricity through the electrolyte in consequence of an applied P.D., *i.e.*, the electrolyte is a conductor.   Electrolytic conductors, like metallic conductors, obey Ohm's Law.

109.   If a plate of zinc is dipped into dilute sulphuric acid, chemical action takes place—hydrogen is given off, zinc sulphate is formed in solution and considerable heat is produced, *i.e.*, in addition to the chemical changes there is a conversion of energy from one form to another, the conversion being from chemical energy of constitution to heat energy in this case.

A primary cell is a device by which the energy made available by chemical reactions may be converted to electrical energy instead of heat.   This can be brought about by dipping a copper plate into the dilute sulphuric acid in addition to the zinc plate.   As long as the zinc and copper rods are not connected, no chemical action takes place, but an E.M.F. is set up between the rods. If they are connected by a wire, a current flows from copper to zinc in the wire and from zinc to copper in the electrolyte.   As we are chiefly interested in what happens in the wire or external circuit, the copper is therefore looked on as the **positive " electrode "** or **" anode "** of the cell and the zinc as the **negative electrode** or **" cathode."**   As soon as flow of current is made possible, the zinc starts to dissolve in the acid.   The energy made available by this interaction of zinc and sulphuric acid appears in the form of electrical energy, which maintains a current round the circuit.

110.   **Polarisation.**—The action is accompanied by the liberation of hydrogen at the surface of the copper.   This has two bad effects :—

(1) The conductivity of hydrogen is very much less than that of dilute sulphuric acid, and so the internal resistance of the cell is greatly increased.

(2) If we could construct a cell with zinc and hydrogen electrodes in the same electrolyte, we should find that although a current still flowed from hydrogen to zinc in the external circuit, *i.e.*, zinc was still the cathode of the cell, the current was much smaller than with a copper anode because the E.M.F. developed between the electrodes was smaller.   This is essentially what happens when a hydrogen film collects on the copper plate.   Hydrogen becomes the anode of the cell, and its E.M.F. is greatly diminished.

This effect is called " polarisation," and on the method adopted to avoid it, to " depolarise " the cell, depends very largely the efficiency of all primary cells.

111.   The essentials of a primary cell are thus :—
(*a*) Positive and negative electrodes.
(*b*) Electrolyte.
(*c*) Depolarising device.

The E.M.F. of a cell depends only on the chemical nature of the electrodes and electrolyte and not at all on their size or quantity.   The resistance of the electrolyte, like that of a metallic conductor, varies directly as its length and inversely as its area, and so the larger the surface area of the plates, and the less their distance apart, the smaller is the internal resistance of the cell.   Naturally, also, the larger the cell the longer its life, since a greater quantity of chemicals is available.

The Daniell and Menotti-Daniell cells consist of copper, zinc, dilute sulphuric acid, and copper sulphate solution (depolariser).   Their E.M.Fs. are 1·1 volts each.   Their resistances depend on their size.   They give a steady current when in service.

The Leclanche cell consists of carbon, zinc, salammoniac solution, and manganese peroxide (depolariser).   E.M.F., 1·5 volts.   Resistance varies with size.

When in service the current quickly falls, and so these cells are chiefly used for intermittent work such as bells.   Nearly all dry cells are of this type, the salammoniac being contained in a paste **or** jelly.

The Menotti test battery (Fig. 28) consists of a Menotti-Daniell cell (1 volt and 30 ohm resistance approximately), a key and a 20-ohm galvanometer. The circuit under test is connected between the other terminal of the galvanometer and the positive battery terminal.

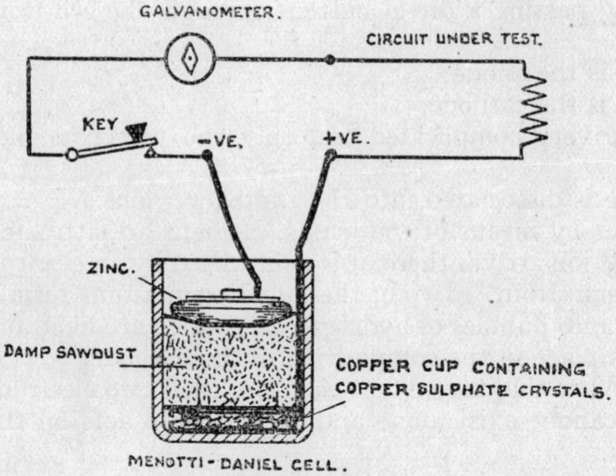

In wireless work it is chiefly used to test for "conductivity." When the key is pressed and a swing of the galvanometer needle is obtained, the circuit is continuous or unbroken. Its high resistance is necessary in testing detonator or gun circuits, so that the current will be small and there will be no risk of firing.

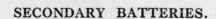

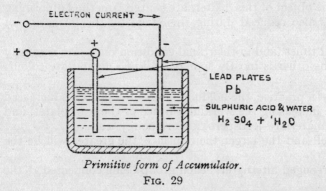

Test Battery.

FIG. 28

112. As a typical example of the action of a primary cell, the action of a Menotti will be described.

The Menotti consists of a copper cup (positive plate) containing $CuSO_4$ crystals (depolariser), a zinc slab (negative plate), and damp sawdust. The sawdust makes the cell portable. The electrolyte is dilute sulphuric acid formed by the interaction of water and the copper sulphate crystals.

The chemical action is roughly as follows. The zinc dissolves in the acid, forming zinc sulphate, and hydrogen ions travel to the copper cup. Here, in the simple cell described above, they each collect an electron which has formed part of the current in the external circuit, and become hydrogen atoms, which combine into molecules, giving the film of gas causing polarisation.

In the Menotti, the hydrogen ions have to pass through the moist copper sulphate crystals before they can reach the copper electrode, and a chemical reaction takes place, sulphuric acid and copper being formed. The copper is deposited on the copper cup and the acid replaces that which has been used up in dissolving zinc. The net result is that copper sulphate and zinc are used up and zinc sulphate and copper are produced. No hydrogen thus appears at the copper cup and polarisation is prevented.

SECONDARY BATTERIES.

113. A secondary battery, or accumulator, is an arrangement from which an electric current may be drawn for a certain time, as from a primary battery ; unlike the primary battery, however, when the accumulator is exhausted it may be recharged by having an electric current passed through it.

An accumulator does not store electricity ; it stores energy.

When it is being charged the electrical energy imparted to it is transformed into chemical energy, which is stored in the cell. Then, when the cell discharges, that is, when an external circuit is completed through which current can be forced by the E.M.F. of the cell, the stored energy is reconverted into electrical energy.

Primitive form of Accumulator.

FIG. 29

The simplest accumulator consists of two lead plates immersed in dilute sulphuric acid, as in Fig. 29. The first operation necessary is to " form " the plates, *i.e.* to bring about that change in the composition of the electrodes which finally gives the cell its ability to produce an E.M.F.

114. Forming the Plates.—This is done by passing a direct current through the cell from the mains.

The plate at which the current enters the cell is the anode.

The plate at which the current leaves the cell is the cathode.

The actual chemical changes which occur are very complicated and only the principal ones can be considered here.

As explained in paragraph 108, the electrolyte is dissociated into H^+ and SO_4^{--} ions.

When a P.D. is established between the plates by means of the mains, H^+ ions are attracted towards the negative plate or cathode. As each H^+ ion arrives there, it is neutralised by an electron (supplied from the mains) and becomes a hydrogen atom. Two of these hydrogen atoms form a hydrogen molecule, and the molecules agglomerate into bubbles of hydrogen gas, which are liberated at the surface of the plate. Thus no change takes place in the composition of the cathode.

The SO_4^{--} ions are attracted to the anode. When they arrive they each lose their two electrons to the positive main. The group of atoms SO_4 cannot exist alone and immediately acts on the water present, giving sulphuric acid and oxygen.

$$SO_4 + H_2O \rightarrow H_2SO_4 + O.$$

The oxygen liberated combines with the lead of the anode to give lead peroxide PbO_2, a chocolate-brown coloured substance.

The results of this process may be summarised as follows :—

(1) Cathode—No change.

(2) Anode—From lead to lead peroxide.

(3) Electrolyte—The hydrogen given off at the cathode, and the oxygen which oxidises the anode, both come from the electrolyte, which therefore loses water (H_2O).

As a result, the concentration of sulphuric acid increases.

The end of this stage may be detected by observing that both plates will then " gas " freely—for the oxygen formed at the anode will then be liberated as oxygen gas.

The next step is to reverse the connections to the mains and pass current through the cell in the opposite direction.

The previous cathode, which is still unchanged lead, is now the anode, and so the SO_4^{--} ions repeat upon it their action on the original lead anode, *i.e.*, it ends with a covering of chocolate-brown lead peroxide.

The previous anode, which is covered with PbO_2, is now the cathode, and the H^+ ions are attracted to it. On arrival, they each collect an electron as before and become neutral atoms, which combine with the oxygen of the lead peroxide to form water. The lead peroxide is thus reduced to metallic lead once more, but the lead thus produced has a porous, spongy texture. This renders it considerably more efficient, and is the object of this " alternate charge " method of forming the plates. The concentration of the acid is also reduced during this stage by the formation of water.

The whole process is now repeated several times, and in their final condition one plate is mostly PbO_2 and chocolate-brown in colour, while the other is mostly spongy lead of a light slate colour.

115. Construction of Accumulators.—In practice, the holding power or capacity is increased by furrowing, grooving, gimping or otherwise increasing the working surface of the lead plates, and the prepared surface is filled with the active material—lead peroxide or spongy lead.

The greater the number of plates in a cell and the larger their surface, the greater will be the capacity and current output.

The positive and negative plates are arranged alternately, each group being connected at the top by lugs to a lead bar.

The negative group contains one plate more than the positive group, except in two-plate cells.

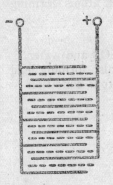

FIG. 30

The plates are placed close together to ensure low resistance, and are kept apart by separators of wood, glass, celluloid, etc. (as indicated in Fig. 30).

116. The Electrolyte.—The sulphuric acid and water must be free from impurities. If distilled water is not available, rain water or melted artificial ice is recommended.

Sulphuric acid, when concentrated, has a " specific gravity " of about $1 \cdot 84$, i.e., it is $1 \cdot 84$ times as heavy as an equal bulk of water.

When the cell is charged the acid strength should be about $1 \cdot 22$ (or, as sometimes written, 1220). Slightly different strengths are stated by different makers. This strength gives approximately the least specific resistance. A stronger acid, in addition to having a higher specific resistance, attacks the plates to an undesirable degree.

To " break down " the acid it is mixed with about four times its bulk of water, and care must be exercised in the mixing. When mixed with water a large amount of heat is developed. The acid should be added gradually to the water, stirred meanwhile, and not used till cool.

On no account must water be added to acid.

The strength or " specific gravity " is tested by a " hydrometer "—an instrument with a weighted bulb and a thin graduated stem ; when in the acid, the reading is taken at the point on its scale at the surface.

As will be explained shortly, the acid becomes weaker as the cell is discharged, and will fall to about 1170 at about $1 \cdot 85$ volts—the point at which discharging should be stopped. Its strength is recovered on recharging.

117. Initial Charge.—The makers issue directions, which must be carefully followed if the battery is to be maintained in a state of efficiency.

The general plan is to give a prolonged first charge immediately after the acid has been poured in. The acid will fall in specific gravity as soon as it is poured into the cells and will continue to do so for the first twelve or eighteen hours. During charge it will gradually rise, and the charge should not be considered complete until the voltage and specific gravity show no rise over a period of, say, five hours, and gas is being given off freely from all plates. At the end of the charge the voltage will have risen to $2 \cdot 5$-$2 \cdot 7$ volts per cell.

After the charging current is cut off the voltage per cell will immediately fall to about $2 \cdot 2$ volts, or slightly less, at which it will remain while the battery is left on open circuit.

The battery should not be left unused for more than a week without recharging.

With large cells, in which a hydrometer can be inserted, the specific gravity of the acid is the most reliable guide. With small cells the acid should be tested occasionally by transferring some acid with a syringe to a narrow tube and using the hydrometer in the latter.

Tests for Completion of Charge.

    (1) Appearance of plates : Positive, chocolate brown ; negative, slate grey ; and no trace of whiteness on either.

    (2) Voltage : $2 \cdot 5$ to $2 \cdot 7$ volts.

    (3) Plates gassing freely.

    (4) Specific gravity of acid : About 1220, according to maker.

In the first week the cell should be given plenty of work, and an hour's extra charging on the first few charges.

118. Discharging.—If the plates of an accumulator are joined by an external resistance, it is found that a current flows from the brown plates to the slate-coloured ones through the resistance, and therefore in the opposite direction through the electrolyte. (Fig. 31).

H$^+$ ions thus go to the brown plate and combine, when neutralised, with the oxygen of the lead peroxide. This action does not go so far as when the plates were being formed, and instead of spongy lead being formed, the peroxide molecule loses only one of its two oxygen atoms, forming lead monoxide (PbO).

$$PbO_2 + 2H \rightarrow H_2O + PbO.$$

Lead oxide readily combines with sulphuric acid, forming lead sulphate (PbSO$_4$) and water.

At the spongy lead plate the SO$_4$ group of atoms combines with the lead, also forming lead sulphate. This is the process which is facilitated by obtaining the lead in a porous condition.

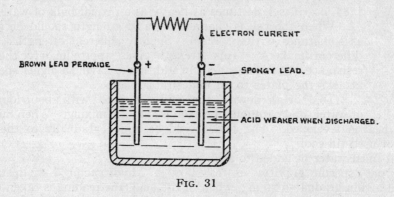

FIG. 31

As a result both plates become partly coated with white lead sulphate and the E.M.F. falls. Some sulphuric acid is used up and water is formed, so that the acid concentration is reduced. This is recognised by a fall in the specific gravity of the electrolyte.

The voltage should not be allowed to fall below about 1·85 volts.

The specific gravity will be about 1170 at this stage. If the discharge is carried persistently beyond this point, more sulphate will form on each plate, and when each plate is totally covered the voltage will be zero.

Caution.—A cell must not be left for any length of time in a discharged state.

119. **Recharging.**—This consists in removing the lead sulphate and restoring the plates to their condition before discharge. It is accomplished by passing current through the cell from the mains.

As before, hydrogen atoms are liberated at the negative plate, and interact with the lead sulphate forming sulphuric acid and reducing the plate to spongy lead.

$$PbSO_4 + 2H_2 \rightarrow H_2SO_4 + Pb$$

At the positive plate the SO$_4$ groups combine with water, forming sulphuric acid and oxygen. The oxygen acts on the lead sulphate, forming brown lead peroxide and sulphuric acid.

$$SO_4 + H_2O \rightarrow H_2SO_4 + O$$
$$PbSO_4 + O + H_2O \rightarrow PbO_2 + H_2SO_4$$

It will be seen that sulphuric acid is formed at both plates during recharging and so the specific gravity of the electrolyte rises.

When the cell is fully recharged, *i.e.*, when the sulphate has been entirely removed from the plates, the hydrogen and oxygen atoms can no longer react with the plates, and so bubbles of gas are given off at each plate. This is allowed to continue until the acid reaches the required specific gravity and the E.M.F. is from 2·5 to 2·7 volts.

When the cell is fully charged and lying idle the plates are less liable to be attacked by the acid.

The charge in ampere-hours should generally be about 10 per cent. more than the discharge in ampere-hours.

120. **Method of Charging.**—The positive plate must be connected to the positive main and the negative plate to the negative main. Passing current through the cell in the wrong direction will ruin it.

To determine which is the positive terminal, connect an ammeter in the circuit, as in Fig. 32.

The ammeter terminals are always marked " $+$ " and " $-$ " If the pointer swings in the correct direction over the scale, the lead connected to the " $+$ " of the ammeter will be that from the positive main.

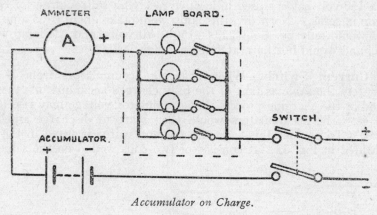

Accumulator on Charge.

FIG. 32.

According to the size of the cell a certain charging rate or current is necessary ; this is stated by the maker. We shall consider how the particular value of the charging current is obtained.

Example 10.

Suppose two small accumulators, each of E.M.F. 1·9 volts and resistance 0·1 ohm, are to be charged by a current of 4 amps. from 220-volt mains through leads of resistance 0·1 ohm.

If they were connected directly across the mains an enormous current would flow.

The voltage of the mains has to overcome the back E.M.F. of the cells in series (3·8 volts) and the resistance of the cells and leads (0·3 ohm altogether). Thus $220 - 3 \cdot 8 = 216 \cdot 2$ volts are available to drive current through 0·3 ohm.

$$\text{Current} = \frac{216 \cdot 2}{0 \cdot 3} = 721 \text{ amperes,}$$

which would burn up the cell.

In order that just the right amount of current shall flow, some form of resistance must be included in the circuit. The most convenient form for small charging currents is a " lamp resistance," consisting of lamps, of the voltage of the mains, arranged in parallel (Fig. 32). The more lamps there are in parallel the greater will be the current that will flow through the circuit, but naturally we wish to use as few lamps as possible, and so we choose high c.p. carbon lamps.

Suppose that the 220-volt lamps available for our use are two 50-c.p., and a number of 16-c.p. carbon lamps.

50 c.p. (4 watts per c.p.) take 200 watts :

$$I = \frac{200}{220} = 0 \cdot 9 \text{ A.}$$

16 c.p. (4 watts per c.p.) take 64 watts :

$$I = \frac{64}{220} = 0 \cdot 3 \text{ A.}$$

Thus two 50-c.p. (1·8 amp.) and **seven 16-c.p.** (2·1 amp.) lamps in parallel will allow a current of $1 \cdot 8 + 2 \cdot 1 = 3 \cdot 9$ amps. to flow.

C

If a number of 50-c.p. lamps were available, four of these (3·6 amp.) and one 16 c.p. (0·3 amp.) would give 3·9 amperes. This would be preferable, as fewer lamps are required.

When only a few cells in series are being charged, their back E.M.F. is negligible in comparison with the voltage of the mains.

The lamps in the circuit are taking practically their " full brilliancy " current.

High potential batteries (50 volts or 100 volts) have naturally a greater back E.M.F., and the lamps used do not get the full voltage of the mains.

For example, a 150-volt battery used in a valve receiving set requires, for charging, a 2½ c.p. 220-volt carbon lamp in series. Normally, this lamp would take about 0·05 amp., but in this case the applied voltage would only be about 220 — 150 = 70 volts, and the lamp would not take as much as 0·05 amp., and would not burn at full brilliancy.

121. Reverse Current Switch.—When charging accumulators from a generator whose voltage is approximately the same as that of the fully charged accumulators, there is a possibility that towards the end of the charging process the accumulator voltage may rise temporarily above the generator voltage. The accumulators would then start to discharge and try to drive the generator as a motor. To prevent this a reverse current switch is fitted in the charging circuit. This switch is illustrated in Fig. 33. It consists of two coils wound on the same bobbin. One of

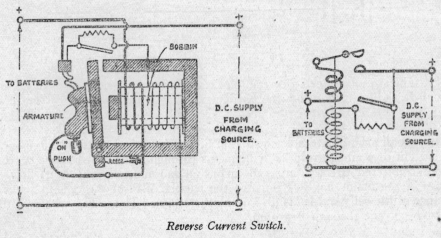

Reverse Current Switch.

FIG. 33.

these, in series with a resistance, which may be short-circuited, is directly across the generator terminals and is called the shunt coil. The other is in series with the batteries to be charged when the " On " push is made, and is called the series coil.

The flux through the bobbin core produced by the shunt coil current is alone sufficient to hold on the soft iron armature and therefore to keep the " On " push made. When the battery circuit is completed current also flows through the series coil. As long as this current is in the correct direction, *i.e.*, the generator voltage is higher than the battery voltage, the flux it produces in the bobbin core assists the shunt coil flux in holding on the armature. If the battery voltage rises above the generator voltage, current flows in the opposite direction through the series coil and so its flux opposes the shunt coil flux.

When the reverse current reaches a specified value the resultant flux is too weak to hold on the armature, the " On " push contact is broken, and the generator is disconnected from the batteries.

The resistance in the shunt coil circuit is short-circuited or not according to the generator voltage and charging current required. The charging current determines the series coil flux. The shunt coil current and flux must be adjusted correspondingly for the contact to fall off at the correct value of reverse current. The resistance allows the P.D. across the shunt coil to be altered to give the correct current through it.

122. **Sediment.**—In time the active material on the plates gradually disintegrates and a sediment forms at the bottom of the cell. Care must be taken that this does not reach the bottom of the plates to cause short-circuiting. Too much sediment may be produced by charging too much or at too high a rate. Its colour indicates whether the cell is receiving normal treatment ; if so, the sediment should be brown.

123. **Sulphating.**—In the discharge action, described above, we saw that lead sulphate forms on the plates in the ordinary discharging process.

This is not what is known as " sulphating." The latter is due to incorrect treatment—such as cell not charged sufficiently, especially if new, over-discharge, acid too strong, and a discharged cell unattended to.

A coating of hard white lead sulphate forms on the plates, and this is difficult to remove. The plates in consequence become light in colour and lose their porosity and holding power. " Buckling " of the plates is also very liable to occur.

The simplest remedy, if the sulphating is not too deep-seated, is prolonged and repeated charging at low rate, say, at half normal charging current, and, when full gassing occurs, at quarter-normal.

124. **Change of Acid Strength.**—The water in the electrolyte gradually evaporates and must be replaced at intervals to the proper level. The solution should be stirred to prevent the water lying on top, or, in small enclosed cells, the water should be introduced well below the surface by a syringe. This is best performed just before the charge, and the gassing will ensure thorough mixing.

Acid may be lost by over-vigorous gassing ; thus a check must be kept on the electrolyte. It is very inadvisable to add strong acid to a cell to bring up the specific gravity. A better plan is to refill the cell with fresh acid of correct specific gravity.

125. **Capacity, Efficiency and Precautions.**—The " capacity," or holding power, is rated in " ampere-hours " and in " watt-hours." Service cells are usually rated on their output over a period of five hours.

The output at other rates will be greater or less than the standard rate according as the time of discharge is more or less than five hours, *e.g.*, a 100 amp.-hour cell discharged in one hour would only give about 60 amp.-hours, but if discharged in ten hours would give 120 amp.-hours.

The efficiency denotes the ratio of the capacity output to the input. The " ampere-hour " efficiency is from 80-90 per cent., and the " watt-hour " efficiency from 60-75 per cent.

Thus, if a cell is charged at 10 amps. for 16 hours, the input is 160 amp.-hours.

The output would be about $160 \times \frac{80}{100} = 128$ amp.-hours, which would give, say, a discharge

current of 9 amps., for about 14 hours, and an efficiency of $\frac{128}{160} \times 100 = 80$ per cent.

Precautions.

Give battery proper initial charge.

Give a new battery plenty of work and liberal charging.

Do not charge too much or too little, or at too high or too low a rate.

Do not run batteries too low in voltage or specific gravity.

Do not allow batteries to stand long completely discharged.

Charge once a week if possible.

Sediment should not reach bottom edges of plates.

Keep plates covered with electrolyte, making up evaporation losses with distilled water.

Test strength of acid periodically.

Keep terminals and top of cell clean and dry, and terminals coated with vaseline.

126. **Cells in Series and Parallel.**—When cells are arranged in series, the total E.M.F. is the sum of their separate E.M.Fs. and the total resistance is the sum of their separate resistances.

When they are connected in parallel (all positives to one terminal and all negatives to another) their total E.M.F. is that of one cell, and their total resistance that of one cell divided by the number of cells (assuming each to have the same E.M.F. and resistance).

127. **The Nickel/Iron (NiFe) Alkaline Cell.**—This is also known as the Edison cell and, with improved construction, it may become a serious rival of the lead accumulator. The electrolyte is a potassium hydroxide (KOH) solution, the positive plate being formed of an oxide or hydroxide of nickel held in a nickel-steel frame, the negative plate consisting of pure iron (Fe), in a container of welded steel.

No acid enters into the working, and the chemical action has been described as

$$Ni(OH)_4 + Fe \rightleftharpoons Ni(OH)_2 + Fe(OH)_2.$$

During discharge the iron is oxidised to ferrous hydroxide $Fe(OH)_2$; during charging the changes are reversed.

The Edison cells may be made of moderate size, and have found considerable application for traction work in small vehicles, since they are much lighter than the ordinary heavy lead accumulators.

The electrolyte is a 21 per cent. solution of potassium hydroxide, of specific gravity 1·21, to which a little lithium hydroxide is added. Water must be added periodically during working, since during charging there is a loss of water due to "gassing." The E.M.F. of such a cell is 1·33 to 1·35 volts, and is only slightly dependent on the strength of the potassium hydroxide.

The efficiency of the cell is low. The advantage of the iron cell is its indifference to violent mechanical treatment, to over charging, and to discharging above the normal rate, and in its freedom from deterioration on standing or after long use—a factor which appears to increase its efficiency and capacity.

As the mutual flux-link
that was used in dealing with
i.e., we may write

where I is the current in ei
relative position of the two

It may be defined as the
is flowing in either circuit.

(*Note.*—Owing to the va

are only correct provided el
142 and 144.)

Since both self and mut
current alters the flux-linkag
linkage of a circuit is alterin

136. Mutual Inductio
circuit similar to that shown
of coil Y were connected to a
tained in coil X, *i.e.*, as lon
galvanometer pointer was ob
pointer was deflected. In ot
was changing, a current flow
in opposite directions accord
opposite directions round t
being made) or decreasing (S

This phenomenon is cal
called an **induced** current.
acting in it. This E.M.F. is

The production of an i
current flows because the E.M
an E.M.F. is produced in it a

Faraday found that the
mutual flux-linkage between
greater was the induced E.M

It has been stated that t
mutual flux-linkage is an incr
a magnetic field of its own, giv
increase or decrease the total
of the current in Y. It is f
decreasing (S being broken) t
linkage ; and conversely, whe
in Y is such that it produces
by saying that the current in
to increase, due to an increase
the fact that it endeavours to
linkage decreases, current flov
open circuit and no current c
same considerations, *i.e.*, it is
current through Y in that di
The direction of the in
could cause a current to fle

Illustrating Reaction
between Current-carrying
Conductor and Magnetic
Field.

Fig. 34.

CHAPTER III.

ELECTROMAGNETISM, INDUCTANCE AND CAPACITY.

128. In the last chapter (paragraphs 79–81) the production of a magnetic field by an electric current was described and some typical fields were discussed. It is now proposed to consider in greater detail the mechanical effects produced by the interaction of these magnetic fields.

These mechanical effects may all be explained by attributing to magnetic lines of flux the same properties as were found to be successful in explaining electrostatic effects in terms of electric lines of flux, viz. :—

    (1) They tend to shorten themselves as far as possible, *i.e.*, to contract in the direction of their length.

    (2) They tend to expand laterally, *i.e.*, to increase in cross-section, and so resist lateral compression.

129. These properties may be applied to the case of two parallel conductors carrying current, as illustrated in Fig. 17. When the current is flowing in opposite directions in the two conductors, it will be seen that where the lines of flux due to the two currents approach each other, their direction is the same. Each current endeavours to extend its flux in the direction of the other so that the lines of flux may be circles, *i.e.*, have their shortest possible length. Where the two sets of flux lines are competing for the same space they will therefore endeavour to push each other back. Their resistance to lateral compression then becomes operative, with the result that the conductors are forced apart.

When the two currents are flowing in the same direction, their lines of flux are in opposite directions when they meet each other. They can thus coalesce. Where they are equal and opposite there will be no magnetic field and so no lines of flux. At other points they take the direction of the resultant magnetic field due to the currents. The result is to produce lines of flux encircling both conductors as shown. These lines then endeavour to contract and in doing so bring the two conductors together, *i.e.*, the conductors appear to be attracted towards each other.

The component magnetic fluxes which interact to give these mechanical forces need not be produced by currents. The deflection of a compass needle in the vicinity of a current-carrying conductor has already been mentioned, and is due to the interaction of the conductor flux and the flux from the needle, which is a permanent magnet.

The mechanical forces produced by the interaction of the flux due to a permanent or electro-magnet and that due to a current flowing in a conductor are of great importance. Some of the measuring instruments described later in this chapter depend on the motion resulting from these forces. The principle of the electric motor, described in Chapter IV, is also based on them. Because of their origin they are often called **electro-dynamic** forces.

The calculation of the magnitude and direction of electrodynamic forces usually presents mathematical difficulties owing to the complicated shape of the circuits involved. A simple case which illustrates the general principles will now be considered.

130. An arrangement which commonly occurs in practice is shown in Fig. 34. A straight conductor carrying a current is placed between two large plane pole faces of a permanent or electro magnet. The component fluxes are as in the figure. The flux due to the magnet is uniform in the

A simple result for t

or two turns and assumi

unit pole, and so the flux

The number of turns

linkages is $N \Phi = \dfrac{4\pi N^2 A I}{10l}$

134. Self-Inductanc
depending on the shape o
so also will be the total fl

F

the constant being differe
self-inductance of the ci

The self-inductance o
the shape and arrangemen
in the magnetic field of the
when unit current is flow

The word " self " is o
the " inductance " of the

Thus, when a current
the circuit is LI.

135. Mutual Inducta
wire. Coil Y is supposed t
by the battery E, and som
that a number of them link

(1) The current flo
(2) The shape and
(3) The shape and
(4) The positions o

The number of flux-lin
mutually by the two circui

If the situation is revers
in coil Y as was previously fl
is exactly the same as bef
flowing

---

been stated that the E.M.F. (E) is to be considered positive when it is due to a decrease of flux-linkage. Thus Faraday's Law is expressed by the formula

$$E = K \times -\frac{d\,(N\,\Phi)}{dt} = -K\frac{d\,(N\,\Phi)}{dt}$$

where K is the factor of proportionality.

Also it has been seen that flux-linkage is equal to inductance multiplied by current,

$$i.e.,\ N\,\Phi = LI,\ \text{(if we consider self-inductance),}$$

and so $\dfrac{d\,(N\,\Phi)}{dt} = \dfrac{d\,(LI)}{dt} = L\dfrac{dI}{dt}$, since L is constant.

$$\therefore\ E = -KL\frac{dI}{dt}.$$

142. The units of E.M.F. and current have already been chosen from direct current considerations, but no unit of inductance has so far been specified, and we are at liberty to choose any unit that simplifies the above formula. The unit of inductance is defined so that $K = 1$ in the expression of Faraday's Law when the E.M.F., current, and inductance are measured in electromagnetic units. The law then becomes

$$E = -L\frac{dI}{dt},$$

and defines the E.M.U. of **self-inductance** as follows :—

The **self-inductance** of a circuit is **one E.M.U.** if the E.M.F. induced in it is one E.M.U. when the current is changing at the rate of one E.M.U. of current per second.

The E.M.U. of **mutual inductance** is obtained in a similar manner.   As $N\,\Phi = MI$ in this case, Faraday's Law becomes

$$E = -M\frac{dI}{dt}$$

if the E.M.U. of mutual inductance is defined to correspond with that of self-inductance.

The **mutual inductance** of two circuits is one E.M.U. if, when the current in one of them is changing at the rate of one E.M.U. of current per second, the induced E.M.F. in the other is one E.M.U.

The E.M.U. of self or mutual inductance is called the centimetre.   The centimetre of inductance has, of course, no relationship to the centimetre of length.

As $\dfrac{d\,(N\,\Phi)}{dt}$ has been taken equal to $L\dfrac{dI}{dt}$ and $M\dfrac{dI}{dt}$ in the derivation of the above units, this is really equivalent to defining what is to be considered one flux-linkage on the electromagnetic system. In a circuit of unit self-inductance, when the current is changing at the rate of one E.M.U. per second, $i.e.,\ L = 1,$ and $\dfrac{dI}{dt} = 1,$

$$L\frac{dI}{dt} = 1,\ \text{and therefore}\ \frac{d\,(N\,\Phi)}{dt} = 1.$$

In other words, the flux-linkage changes by one whenever the current changes by one E.M.U., and so a current of one E.M.U. flowing in a circuit whose inductance is one E.M.U. must produce one flux-linkage on the electromagnetic system, or one E.M.U. of flux-linkage.

Thus $N\,\Phi = LI$, or $N\,\Phi = MI$, provided each quantity is expressed in electromagnetic units. It will be seen in paragraph 144 that this equation is modified by a numerical factor when the quantities are expressed in practical units.

143. **Faraday's Law in Practical Units.**—In this case the constant K is again made equal to unity by a suitable choice of the practical units of inductance, $i.e.,$ the law is again written as

$$E = -L\frac{dI}{dt}\ \text{or}\ E = -M\frac{dI}{dt}$$

The **practical unit of inductance** is called the **Henry** and the above law involves its definition as follows :—

(1) **Self-Inductance.**—A circuit has a self-inductance of one henry if the E.M.F. induced in it is one volt when the current is changing at the rate of one ampere per second.

(2) **Mutual Inductance.**—Two circuits have a mutual inductance of one henry if the E.M.F. induced in one of them is one volt when the current in the other is changing at the rate of one ampere per second.

In the circuits used in wireless telegraphy, the henry is an inconveniently large unit, and inductance is usually given in the following submultiples :—

1 millihenry (mH) = one thousandth (10^{-3}) of a henry ;

1 microhenry (μH) = one millionth (10^{-6}) of a henry.

The microhenry is often abbreviated to the " **mic.** "

144. The relation between the E.M.U. of inductance (the cm.) and the henry is easily obtained from the corresponding relations for current and E.M.F.

$$1 \text{ henry} = \frac{1 \text{ volt}}{1 \text{ amp. per sec.}} = \frac{10^8 \text{ E.M.U. of E.M.F.}}{\frac{1}{10} \text{ E.M.U. of current per sec.}}$$

$$= 10^9 \times \frac{1 \text{ E.M.U. of E.M.F.}}{1 \text{ E.M.U. of current per sec.}} = 10^9 \text{ cms.}$$

Thus 1 mic. = 10^3 cms.

No corresponding practical unit of flux-linkage is used. The E.M.U. of flux-linkage is the only unit employed. One flux-linkage is associated with a circuit of inductance 1 cm. when a current of one E.M.U. is flowing, and so 10^9 flux-linkages are associated for the same current with a circuit whose inductance is one henry. If the current is one amp. (one-tenth of an E.M.U.) the number of flux-linkages is therefore $\frac{10^9}{10} = 10^8$ for a circuit of inductance 1 henry. Thus when L, or M, and I are expressed in practical units, the flux-linkage is given by

$$N \Phi = LI \times 10^8 \text{ and } N \Phi = MI \times 10^8,$$
$$\text{or } LI = N \Phi \times 10^{-8} \text{ and } MI = N \Phi \times 10^{-8}.$$

It follows that the rate of change of flux-linkage with a circuit must be 10^8 flux-linkages per second to induce an E.M.F. of one volt.

Thus Faraday's Law may be written in terms of induced E.M.F. and rate of change of flux-linkage as

$$(1) \ E = -\frac{d (N \Phi)}{dt} \text{ E.M.U. of E.M.F. or } (2) \ E = -\frac{d (N \Phi)}{dt} \times 10^{-8} \text{ volts.}$$

Example 12.

The current is increasing uniformly at the rate of 2 amps. per second in a circuit of inductance 0·5 henry. Find

(1) The induced E.M.F. in volts ; and (2) the rate of change of flux-linkage.

(1) $\frac{dI}{dt} = 2 \frac{\text{amps.}}{\text{sec.}}$; $L = 0 \cdot 5$ henry ; $\therefore E = -L\frac{dI}{dt} = -0 \cdot 5 \times 2 = -1$ volt.

The minus sign indicates that the E.M.F. is acting to oppose the **increase** of current, *i.e.*, it is a back E.M.F.

(2) The flux-linkage produced by a current of 2 amps. flowing in a circuit of inductance 0·5 henry is given by

$$N \Phi = 0 \cdot 5 \times 2 \times 10^8 = 10^8.$$

As the current is increasing by 2 amps. every second, the flux-linkage must therefore be increasing by 10^8 units per second.

The application of Faraday's Law in its flux-linkage expression also shows that this gives rise to a back E.M.F. of one volt.

$$E = - \frac{d (N \Phi)}{dt} \times 10^{-8} = - 10^8 \frac{units}{sec.} \times 10^{-8} = - 1 \text{ volt.}$$

Example 13.

The field in an air-cored coil of 300 turns, axial length 15 cms. and area 50 sq. cms., decreases uniformly from 600 gauss to 400 gauss in 0·005 second. Assuming that the field is uniform everywhere inside the coil, find

(a) The E.M.F. induced ; and (b) The self-inductance of the coil.

(a) When H = 600 gauss ; $N \Phi = 300 \times 600 \times 50 = 9 \times 10^6$ E.M.U.
   When H = 400 gauss ; $N \Phi = 300 \times 400 \times 50 = 6 \times 10^6$ E.M.U.

$$\frac{d (N \Phi)}{dt} = - \frac{3 \times 10^6}{0 \cdot 005} = - 6 \times 10^8 \text{ E.M.U. per sec.}$$

$$\therefore \text{ Induced E.M.F.} = - \frac{d (N \Phi)}{dt} \times 10^{-8} \text{ volts} = 6 \times 10^8 \times 10^{-8} = 6 \text{ volts.}$$

The E.M.F. appears as positive, *i.e.*, it is trying to keep the current and therefore the field up to its initial value.

(b) For a solenoid, $H = \frac{4\pi NI}{10l}$, where I is the current in amps. and $\frac{N}{l} =$ turns per cm. $= \frac{300}{15}$ = 20 in this case.

When H = 600 gauss, $I = \frac{10Hl}{4\pi N} = \frac{6,000}{80\pi}$ amps. and $N \Phi = 9 \times 10^6$. In practical units $LI = N \Phi \times 10^{-8}$,

$$\therefore L = \frac{9 \times 10^6 \times 10^{-8} \times 80\pi}{6,000} \text{ henry} = 3 \cdot 77 \times 10^{-3} \text{ henry} = 3 \cdot 77 \ mH.$$

Alternatively :—

$$H = 600 \text{ gauss, } I = \frac{6,000}{80\pi} \text{amps.} \quad H = 400 \text{ gauss, } I = \frac{4,000}{80\pi} \text{amps.}$$

$$\therefore \frac{dI}{dt} = - \frac{2,000}{80\pi \times 0 \cdot 005} \text{ amps. per sec.}$$

$$E = - L \frac{dI}{dt}$$

$$\textit{i.e.,} \ 6 = - L \times - \frac{2,000}{80\pi \times 0 \cdot 005} \quad \therefore L = \frac{6 \times 80\pi \times 0 \cdot 005}{2,000} \text{ henry} = 3 \cdot 77 \ mH.$$

It should be noted that for an actual coil of these dimensions these results are rather high, as in practice, with an air core, every line of flux does not link with every turn (*cf.* Fig. 19).

145. There are various ways, other than alteration of current, by which the flux-linkage of a circuit may be changed. Thus, in Fig. 36 the coil Y might be moved about in the magnetic field of coil X. Such movements would obviously alter its mutual flux-linkage and an E.M.F. would be

induced in it. Again, the magnetic field need not be directly due to a current. It may be the field of a permanent magnet. The methods for inducing E.M.Fs. may be classified as follows :—

(1) Variable flux and stationary conductor.
(2) Moving flux and stationary conductor.
(3) Stationary flux and moving conductor.
(4) Variable flux and moving conductor.

Case (1) is that which has already been considered. The other cases occur in the production of E.M.Fs. in dynamos and alternators. Case (3) will now be considered. It is illustrated in Fig. 37 (a).

146. It is more convenient in this instance to consider the flux cut by the conductor in its motion. It is at once evident that lines of flux are only cut across by the conductor, provided its motion has some component at right angles to the direction of the field. If the conductor is moved straight from one pole face to the other it is moving parallel to the lines of flux and does not cut them. Thus no E.M.F. is induced in it (paragraph 140). If the conductor is moving in any other direction it must cut flux lines and so have an E.M.F. induced. The simplest case to consider is that in which the motion of the conductor is at right angles both to its own length and to the direction of the field (assumed to be uniform).

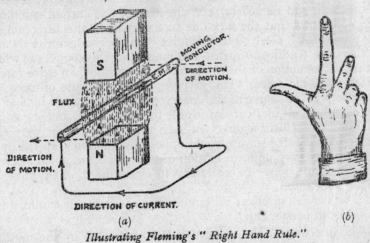

(a)   (b)

Illustrating Fleming's " Right Hand Rule."

FIG. 37.

If the velocity of the conductor is v cms. per second and its length in the field is l cms., then the area it traverses at right angles to the field in one second is lv sq. cms. If the flux density is B lines per sq. cm., the flux Φ through this area is Blv lines. The conductor thus cuts Blv lines per second, and so by Faraday's Law the E.M.F. induced in it is $Blv \times 10^{-8}$ volts.

More generally, if the motion of the conductor makes an angle θ with the direction of the flux, instead of being perpendicular to it, the distance the conductor travels perpendicular to the flux is $v \sin \theta$ cms. per second. It thus sweeps out an area of $lv \sin \theta$ sq. cms. perpendicular to the field every second and so cuts $Blv \sin \theta$ lines per second. Hence the induced E.M.F. is $Blv \sin \theta \times 10^{-8}$ volts.

In the particular case when $\theta = 90°$, *i.e.*, the conductor is moved perpendicular to the field, $\sin \theta = 1$ and the induced E.M.F. is $Blv \times 10^{-8}$ volts, as was directly calculated above for this case.

Example 14.

A conductor 25 cms. long is moved at right angles to its own length across a magnetic field whose flux density is 2,000 lines per square centimetre with a velocity of 50 ft. per second, the direction of motion being such that it makes an angle of 30° with the direction of the field. Find the E.M.F. induced in the conductor.

E.M.F. in volts $= 10^{-8} \times$ rate of change of flux-linkage. The rate of change of flux-linkage is the rate at which the conductor cuts across the lines of flux, *i.e.*, it is given by the formula above,

$$E = Blv \sin \theta \times 10^{-8} \text{ volts.}$$

$B = 2,000$ lines per sq. cm., $l = 25$ cms., $v = 50 \times 30 \cdot 48$ cms. per sec.

$$\sin \theta = \sin 30° = 0 \cdot 5.$$

$$\therefore E = 2,000 \times 25 \times 50 \times 30 \cdot 48 \times 0 \cdot 5 \times 10^{-8} \text{ volts} = 0 \cdot 381 \text{ volt.}$$

147. Fleming's Right Hand Rule.—When the motion of the conductor is at right angles both to its own length and to the magnetic field, this rule provides a convenient method of determining the direction of the induced E.M.F. The thumb, forefinger and middle finger of the **right** hand are extended at right angles to each other as shown in Fig. 37 (*b*). The hand is then arranged so that the thuMb points in the direction of Motion of the conductor, and the ForeFinger in the direction of the Flux. The Middle Finger then gives the direction of the induced E.M.F. It can easily be verified that if either the flux or the motion is reversed in direction, the E.M.F. is also reversed in direction. If both flux and motion are reversed, the direction of the E.M.F. is unaltered.

The principle behind this rule is the same as that which has already been derived in considering E.M.Fs. induced by varying currents, viz., that the circuit opposes any alteration in the electrical conditions, and that the induced E.M.F. is an attempt to preserve the *status quo*. Suppose the ends of the moving conductor are joined by a wire so as to form a closed circuit. A current will flow owing to the induced E.M.F. In Fig. 37 (*a*), the direction of this current is indicated by arrows.

Reference to Fig. 35 shows that the flux due to a current in this direction interacts with the flux of the magnet to produce an " electrodynamic force " on the conductor in the **opposite** direction to its motion, and therefore tending to arrest the motion of the conductor which is causing the induced E.M.F. Thus, if the motion of the conductor is to continue, an extra force must be applied to overcome the electrodynamic force. This involves the expenditure of more work on the conductor, and this extra work is the source of the energy which is converted to heat when the induced E.M.F. is acting in a closed circuit and current is able to flow. If the moving conductor is on open circuit, the induced E.M.F. is still in a direction such that if the circuit were closed and current could flow, the electrodynamic force set up would oppose the motion. In the open circuit case no extra work is necessary to preserve uniform motion of the conductor, as no conversion of energy is taking place. A force will, of course, be necessary to overcome mechanical resistance to motion such as friction and air resistance.

These " inertial " tendencies of electrical circuits are conveniently summed up, for conductors moving in magnetic fields, in Lenz's Law.

Lenz's Law.—The direction of the induced E.M.F. produced by the motion of a conductor in a magnetic field is such that if induced current could flow, it would produce a force opposing the motion.

148. We are now in a position to discuss the solution of the problem indicated in paragraph 131, viz., when placed in a magnetic field, a conductor carrying current is acted on by an electrodynamic force proportional to the current, and is therefore accelerated with consequent increase in kinetic energy. What is the source of the energy, and will the velocity of the conductor increase indefinitely ?

We shall assume the same arrangement as in Fig. 35, and suppose that the source of current in the conductor is a cell connected across its ends by means of long extensible leads whose resistance we may neglect. Thus, when placed between the poles of the magnet, the current-carrying conductor has an acceleration to the right. But, as soon as it starts in motion, it cuts lines of flux and so has an E.M.F. induced in it. The application of Fleming's Right Hand Rule to Fig. 35 shows at once that the E.M.F. is in a direction opposing the flow of current in the conductor. The current falls, and the electrodynamic force, being proportional to the current, is correspondingly decreased. As the current is now less than its original value (battery E.M.F. $\div$ resistance), this indicates that the energy taken from the battery is no longer being completely converted into heat energy in the conductor. If at any moment I is the current flowing, E the E.M.F. of the battery, and R the resistance of the conductor circuit, then the resultant E.M.F. is

$$E - \text{induced E.M.F.,}$$

and by Kirchhoff's Law this is equal to the fall of potential RI round the circuit,

i.e., E — induced E.M.F. = RI.   ∴   EI — induced E.M.F. × I = RI².

EI is the energy taken from the battery per second, and RI² is the heat energy produced in the circuit per second.

There is thus an amount of energy, equal to induced E.M.F. × I per second, which is being used up in some other way. It is this energy which supplies the kinetic energy acquired by the conductor.

As the electrodynamic force decreases, so the acceleration of the conductor decreases, *i.e.*, the amount of kinetic energy it acquires per second decreases, but as long as any current flows there will be a force and therefore an acceleration. As the velocity of the conductor increases, however, the induced E.M.F., which is proportional to the velocity (paragraph 146), also increases, so that eventually a time will come when it is equal to the battery E.M.F. The current in the conductor then falls to zero, and the latter experiences no further acceleration, but goes on with constant velocity. No energy is then being taken from the battery (I = 0), as we should expect, for there is no heat produced in the conductor, nor is its kinetic energy increasing.

In a practical case, of course, this limiting condition is not reached, as sufficient current must flow to give a force overcoming friction and air resistance. The velocity of the conductor thus becomes constant before the current in it falls to zero and the induced E.M.F. never quite becomes equal to the battery E.M.F.

The above argument gives the essential theory of the electric motor (Chapter IV). We shall now return to the discussion of self and mutual inductance.

149. Inductances in Series.—Three inductances, L_1, L_2 and L_3, are shown in series in Fig. 38 (*a*). In this arrangement the same current (I) flows through each of them, by Kirchhoff's First Law. If the inductances are in henries and the current in amps., the flux-linkages associated with the three coils are $L_1 I \times 10^8$, $L_2 I \times 10^8$, and $L_3 I \times 10^8$ respectively (paragraph 144).

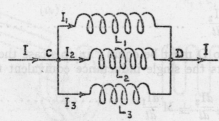

INDUCTANCES IN SERIES.

(*a*)

INDUCTANCES IN PARALLEL.

(*b*)

FIG. 38.

Thus the total flux-linkage is $(L_1 + L_2 + L_3) I \times 10^8$ and so the equivalent inductance L producing the same number of flux-linkages ($LI \times 10^8$) is given by

$$L = L_1 + L_2 + L_3.$$

It will be seen that the procedure for finding the equivalent inductance of a number of inductances in series is the same as in the corresponding arrangement for resistances.

It should be noted that the above result depends on the assumption that none of the flux produced in one of the inductances links with either of the others. If this occurred, the equivalent inductance of the three coils would be less or greater than the sum of their individual inductances, according to the amount of such mutual flux linkage and its direction.

150. Inductances in Parallel.—The arrangement is shown in Fig. 38 (*b*). The equivalent inductance is found most simply in this case by a consideration of the back E.M.Fs. induced when the current is increasing. With a steady current (I) flowing, the currents flowing in the three parallel paths are taken as I_1, I_2 and I_3.

By Kirchhoff's First Law

$$I = I_1 + I_2 + I_3 \quad \therefore \quad \frac{dI}{dt} = \frac{dI_1}{dt} + \frac{dI_2}{dt} + \frac{dI_3}{dt}$$

These two results have several important applications, since they apply equally when L_1 and L_2 each represent coils of several turns, with a mutual inductance M between them, as shown in Fig. 39 (b).

The practical measurement of M in the laboratory consists in measuring the total inductance of the combination resulting when the primary and secondary are joined in " series aiding " and, " series opposing " respectively. In Fig. 39 (b), the primary may be joined, as shown, to the point A, or the connection may be made to point B ; the difference between the two measured inductances is then 4M.

Fig. 39 (c) also illustrates the principle of **the variometer** (paragraph 154). The latter consists of two coils in series, arrangements being made so that one coil may be rotated through 180° inside the other. Fig. 39 (f) is the symbolical representation of a variometer.

If the coupling between two loops, arranged as in Fig. 39 (c), is sufficiently tight, the whole of the flux will link with both loops and the mutual flux will equal the individual flux. In the ideal case, complete cancellation of the flux results, and the arrangement is completely **non-inductive**. A non-inductive coil may be arranged by winding it on the " bight," as shown in Fig. 39 (d), or it may be arranged in the form of a grid, Fig. 39 (e).

152. The self-inductance of a solenoid is easily deduced from the result obtained in paragraph 133, viz.,

$$\text{Flux-linkage} = \frac{4\pi N^2 AI}{10l}. \quad \text{But flux-linkage} = LI \times 10^8$$

$$\therefore L = \frac{4\pi N^2 A}{l} \times 10^{-9} \text{ henry.}$$

It will be recalled that this result was based on the assumption that every line of flux produced linked with every turn. This is hardly justifiable for air-cored solenoids, as reference to Fig. 18 will show. It is much more nearly the case if the solenoid has an iron core, for the lines of flux find a much easier path in iron and do not tend to " leak " to the outside of the solenoid and complete themselves after linking with only a few turns, as happens with the air-cored solenoid. In addition, when a current flows in the coil, the iron becomes magnetised and adds its own flux lines to those produced directly by the current. The total flux-linkage is thus much greater in an iron-cored solenoid than in an air-cored solenoid of the same dimensions. The self-inductance of such a solenoid may be calculated as follows :—

$$H = \frac{4\pi NI}{10l} \text{ dynes per unit pole.} \quad \therefore \Phi = \mu HA = \frac{4\pi N\mu AI}{10l} \text{ lines}$$

$$\therefore \text{Total flux-linkages} = \frac{4\pi N\mu AI}{10l} \times N = \frac{4\pi N^2 \mu AI}{10l} = LI \times 10^8$$

$$\therefore L = \frac{4\pi N^2 \mu A}{l} \times 10^{-9} \text{ henry.}$$

Since μ is variable and depends on the current flowing in the coil (paragraph 88), the inductance of an iron-cored coil is likewise variable, a point which is of considerable importance in the design of such coils for wireless telegraphy circuits (cf. paragraph 154 and F.20).

153. Another representation of non-inductive winding is given in Fig. 40 (a). The wire is doubled back on itself, before winding, or in a bight as shown. Thus the current flows in opposite directions in adjacent turns and no resultant field and flux can be set up. Such a coil is said to be " non-inductively wound."

The coils in Fig. 40 are shown in order of increasing inductance from left to right, to illustrate the above remarks. In Fig. 40 (f), a complete path in iron for the lines of flux is provided ; there is thus practically no leakage, and every line links with every turn.

In a dynamo or motor the flux lines produced by the current flowing in the field coils are established in material that is nearly all ferromagnetic, the only air they traverse being in the narrow gaps between the poles and the armature. The field coils, which may have many turns and carry large currents, are thus highly inductive, and very large induced E.M.Fs. are developed when the current is altering. The effect of this is not important on making the field circuit, the current merely taking longer to rise to its final value, but undesirable results may follow on breaking the

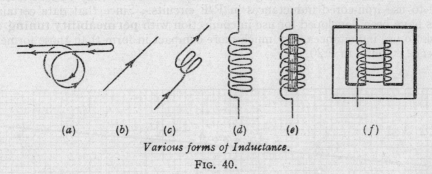

(a)　　(b)　　(c)　　(d)　　(e)　　(f)

Various forms of Inductance.

FIG. 40.

circuit. The induced E.M.F. may be large enough to produce a spark or arc at the break or across the insulation of various turns and so damage the machine. Provision must be made in the design for the current to die away slowly enough to limit the induced E.M.F. to a reasonable amount.

154. Inductances met with in Wireless Telegraphy Circuits.—These may be classified as:—

(a) Inductances having a maximum of inductance (of the order of henries) in a minimum of space, and large current-carrying capacity. These will have iron cores. Such are armatures and field coils of motors, dynamos and alternators, transformers, induction coils, etc.

(b) Receiving Inductances.

Inductances used in receiving circuits usually consist of a number of insulated turns of wire, closely wound on a cylinder of insulating material. Owing to the fact that voltages and currents are small in receiving circuits, the insulation need not be excessive, and such inductances can be very compact. Ohmic resistance must be kept small, and this is secured by using wire made of interwoven insulated strands. Either single layer or mutliple layer coils can be used. Variations in the value of the inductance can be ensured in two ways, either by having a sliding contact which only brings in a certain number of turns into the circuit, or by employing a **variometer**—Fig.39 (f).

A variometer inductance is composed of two coils in series, so arranged that their fields can be made to assist or to oppose each other. In one limiting position, the direction of the windings of the two coils is such that the field produced by one annuls nearly all the field due to the other, and the inductance of the two coils is a minimum. When the moving coil is rotated through 180° the fields are additive, and the inductance is a maximum. In intermediate positions the combined inductance can be made to vary continuously between one extreme and the other according to the angle between the axes of the coils.

Thus a variometer affords a very delicate variation of inductance.

The maximum values of inductances used in receiving circuits may be of the order of hundreds or thousands of mics.

(c) Transmitting Inductances.

In general the difference between receiving and transmitting inductances may be summed up in the statement that the latter are

(1) of far larger dimensions,
(2) not always capable of continuous variation.

They have to carry much greater currents and have much greater voltages induced across them. Thus they are generally constructed of copper tubing or multi-stranded wire, with well-spaced turns and high insulation. Inductances used in the primaries of spark oscillators are of small value, of the order of mics., while those used in the aerial coils of spark and continuous wave sets are considerably larger value, though still of the same order.

(d) Iron-cored Inductances.

Up to about 1933 the tuning of circuits was carried out principally by means of variable condensers and fixed inductances. Owing to large hysteresis and eddy current losses, it had not been possible to use iron-cored inductances in R/F circuits. Since that date certain special low loss iron cores have been developed for use in connection with **permeability tuning** (F.20), and it is now possible to use inductances very much more compact in form than those formerly available. A fuller reference is found in F.20.

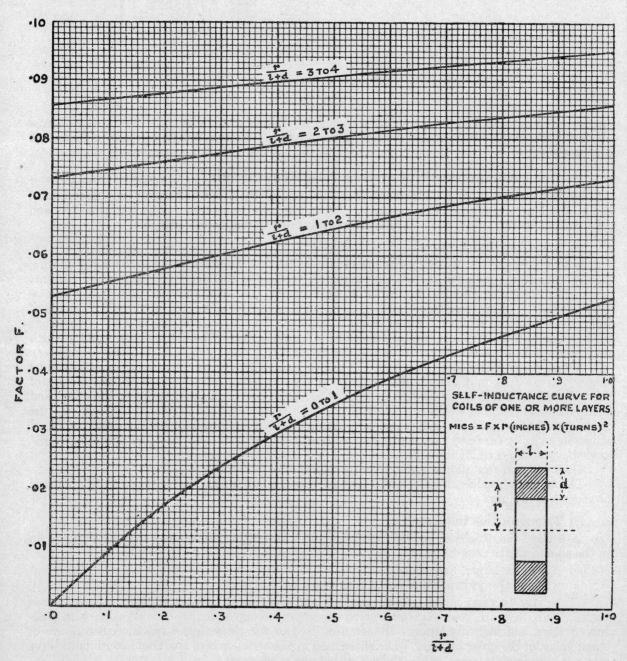

FIG 41

155. Practical Calculation of Self-Inductance.—The limitations of the formulæ obtained for the self-inductance of air and iron-cored solenoids have already been mentioned. For a toroidal coil, *i.e.*, a coil wound on an iron anchor ring, the formula for an iron-cored solenoid, viz.,

$$L = \frac{4\pi N^2 \mu A}{l} \times 10^{-9} \text{ henry}$$

is very nearly correct, if the cross-section of the ring is circular, and small in dimensions compared with the length of the ring.

Large corrections may have to be made to fit the formula for practical calculation in other cases, but the practical formula which will now be developed for air-cored coils is based on the theoretical result found for such a coil in paragraph 152,

$$\text{viz., } L = \frac{4\pi N^2 A}{l} \times 10^{-9} \text{ henry.}$$

N is the number of turns. Also, in a circular coil $A = \pi r^2$, where r is the radius of the coil.

Hence we may write $L = \dfrac{4\pi^2 N^2 r^2}{l} \times 10^{-9}$ henry.

In the practical formula the factor N^2 is retained and one of the "r"'s in r^2. The remaining factors are assimilated into a "form factor" F, which depends on the dimensions of the coil, and which is determined from the curve in Fig. 41 in a way to be described. The formula then becomes

$$L = r \times N^2 \times F \text{ mics.,}$$
$$\text{where } r = \text{mean radius of coil in inches,}$$
$$N = \text{number of turns in coil,}$$
$$F = \text{form factor of coil.}$$

To obtain F, the ratio $\dfrac{r}{l+d}$ is first determined

where $l =$ winding length in inches,
 $d =$ depth of the winding in inches, or thickness of the wire used if the coil is single layer.

The corresponding value of F is then read off from the graph of F against $\dfrac{r}{l+d}$ in Fig. 41.
The above data can be obtained in the following manner :—

(1) Measure the radius of the former and add half the depth of the winding (Fig. 42), or half the diameter of the wire used ; or, measure the circumference of the former, divide by 2π and add half the depth of the winding. This gives "r."

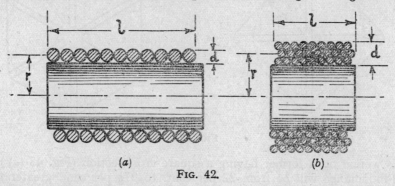

(a)   (b)

FIG. 42.

(2) Measure the total winding length of the coil in inches. This gives "l."

(3) Count the total number of turns in the coil ; or, if there are a great many turns, count the number in, say, one inch of winding length and multiply by l. This gives "N."

(4) Determine " d," the depth of the winding. In a single-layer coil this will be the diameter of the wire used.

(5) Work out the ratio $\dfrac{r}{l+d}$

(6) Find the value of F from the curve corresponding to the ratio $\dfrac{r}{l+d}$, being careful to work on the right part of the curve, and to read the scale very accurately.

For values of $\dfrac{r}{l+d}$ which are between 4 and 8, the value of F can be found

thus : divide $\dfrac{r}{l+d}$ by 2 ; look up the value of F corresponding to this, add 0·0220

to this value, and the answer will be the correct value of F.

(7) Work out the formula

$$L = r \times N^2 \times F \text{ mics.}$$

Example 15.

It is required to determine the inductance of a single layer coil of 64 turns of wire 0·08 in. in diameter, wound on a former of 2·65 in. radius, for a winding length of 16·2 in.

(1) Radius of former   = 2·65 in.
     Half diameter of wire   = 0·04 in.

     Mean radius of coil   = 2·69 in.

(2) l = 16·2 inches.
(3) N = 64 turns.
(4) d = 0·08 inches.
(5) $\dfrac{r}{l+d} = \dfrac{2·69}{16·2+0·08} = \dfrac{2·69}{16·28} = 0·1652.$
(6) F = 0·0145 (from the lowest curve).
(7) L = 2·69 × 64² × 0·0145 = 160 mics.

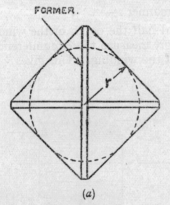
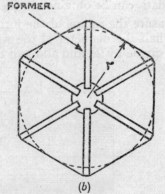

(a)   (b)

FIG. 43.

If the coil is wound on a former having a square cross-section (Fig. 43 (a)) instead of on a cylinder, its self-inductance will be from 22 per cent. to 27½ per cent. greater than that of the corresponding cylindrical coil which would be bounded by the circle inscribed in the square that forms the boundary of the coil.

If the coil is wound on a hexagonal (six-sided) former (Fig. 43 (b)) its self-inductance will be about 10 per cent. greater than that of the corresponding cylindrical coil which would be bounded by the circle inscribed in the hexagon bounding the coil.

$$\therefore \quad \log_e \left(1 - \frac{Ri}{E} \right) = - \frac{Rt}{L}$$

$$\therefore \quad 1 - \frac{Ri}{E} = e^{-\frac{Rt}{L}}$$

$$\therefore \quad i = \frac{E}{R} \left(1 - e^{-\frac{Rt}{L}} \right).$$

$\frac{E}{R}$ is the steady value I which the current eventually takes according to Ohm's Law. Hence the relation between the instantaneous value i of the current at any time t and its final value I is given by

$$i = I \left(1 - e^{-\frac{Rt}{L}} \right).$$

In theory $e^{-\frac{Rt}{L}}$ does not become zero, *i.e.*, the current does not reach its final value I until t is infinite, but, practically speaking, $e^{-\frac{Rt}{L}}$ becomes small enough to be negligible in a very short time.

Example 17.

Find the percentage of the final value of current reached in $0 \cdot 01$ second, when a circuit for which $L = 1$ henry and $R = 600$ ohms is made.

It is only necessary to find the value of the term

$$\left(1 - e^{-\frac{Rt}{L}} \right).$$

In this case the value is $(1 - e^{-6}) = 1 - 0 \cdot 00248 = 0 \cdot 99752$.
So that, in this short space of time, the current rises to $99 \cdot 75$ per cent. of its maximum value.

In a time $t = \frac{L}{R}$, the current rises to $(1 - e^{-1}) = 1 - 0 \cdot 368 = 0 \cdot 632$, or $63 \cdot 2$ per cent., ot its final value.

This time $t = \frac{L}{R}$ is known as the **Time Constant** of the circuit, and is a measure of the rapidity of growth of current in different circuits.

★159. **Decay of Current in a Circuit containing Inductance and Resistance.**—When steady conditions have been reached in the circuit of Fig. 45, *i.e.*, a current $I = \frac{E}{R}$ is flowing, let the switch S be made to X. This removes the battery from the circuit, and if there were no inductance the current would fall instantaneously to zero. In the inductive circuit the magnetic energy in the field has to be converted to heat energy and so a current continues to flow while this is occurring. Let i be this current in amps, t seconds after the switch is put over, *i.e.*, $t = 0$, $i = I$. The induced E.M.F. at this time is $- L \frac{di}{dt}$, and the P.D. across the resistance is iR. By Kirchhoff's Law these must be equal, *i.e.*,

$$- L \frac{di}{dt} = Ri \qquad \therefore \quad \frac{di}{i} = - \frac{R}{L} . d$$

Integrating both sides $\log_e i = - \frac{Rt}{L} + \text{constant}$

$$\therefore i = C e^{-\frac{Rt}{L}}.$$

At $t = 0$, $i = I$, $\therefore$ $I = C$,

and finally $i = I e^{-\frac{Rt}{L}}.$

The graph of i against t is shown in Fig. 44. It is the growth curve inverted. Theoretically, the current should take an infinite time to decay, but in practice it dies away in a very short time. Thus, in Fig. 44, which might correspond to a circuit of inductance 2,000 mics. and resistance 1 ohm $\left(\frac{L}{R} = 0 \cdot 002 \right)$, the current has fallen to about 1 per cent. of its original value in $0 \cdot 009$ second.

After a time equal to the time constant, $\frac{L}{R}$, of the circuit, the percentage of the initial current still flowing is

$$e^{-1} \times 100 \text{ per cent.} = 36 \cdot 8 \text{ per cent.}$$

160. The **time constant** $\dfrac{L}{R}$ is a measure of the rate at which current either grows or decays in an inductive circuit. From its form the following general deductions may be made :—

(1) In a circuit of given resistance the rate of growth or decay is directly proportional to the inductance of the circuit. This is to be expected on general grounds.

(2) The current may be made to grow or decay more quickly in a circuit of given inductance by **increasing the resistance** of the circuit. This is of practical importance in the design of brushes for electrical machines (paragraph 220).

161. The Sign of M.—It has already been seen that the total self-inductance of a simple circuit, such as a coil, depends very largely on the mutual inductance between its component parts, *e.g.*, the individual turns of the coil. When all the turns are wound in the same way, the mutual inductance is such that it increases the total self-inductance. The non-inductively wound coil gives an example of the opposite effect.

In some problems on valve oscillator circuits and networks, we are interested in the direction (or rather phase) of the induced electromotive forces and currents, and it becomes necessary to adopt some convention as to positive and negative directions of currents in coils, and positive and negative directions of induced electromotive forces.

To make the problem concrete, assume that there are two right-hand spirals wound on a common former, as shown in Fig. 46 (*a*), and that a current i_1 is flowing into spiral AB, *in* at A and *out* at B. We shall define this as a **positive current**. Magnetic flux will be produced by this spiral and, since the end B will act like the north pole of a magnet, the flux will thread the solenoid in the direction shown by the arrow. We shall define this as **positive flux**. It will thus be seen that the positive current direction and the positive flux direction are related by a right-hand corkscrew rule.

Some of the flux from coil AB will pass through coil CD in the positive direction from C to D. If now by some external means we increase the current i_1, we shall also increase the flux through CD. This will give rise to an induced electromotive force of magnitude $M\dfrac{di_1}{dt}$ in the coil CD. The E.M.F. in the turns of the coil (the " space " E.M.F.) will be directed as shown by the dotted arrows, and since we have defined positive rotation relative to the flux as right-hand rotation, we say that the induced E.M.F. is $-M\dfrac{di_1}{dt}$. Since the E.M.F. in the turns is acting from D to C, it would tend to drive a current through an external circuit joining C and D from C to D ; if we put a voltmeter between C and D we would find that C was positive relative to D.

Now consider the position which results if we join B and C, as in Fig 46 (*b*), and have a common current i flowing in at A and out at D. It will be clear that the flux from both coils is in the same direction, *i.e.*, the positive direction. If we increase the current i, just as before, the increase of flux through CD due to current in AB, induces an E.M.F. in CD., as shown by the dotted arrows. At the same time the increase in current i through CD increases the flux through AB and induces an E.M.F. in AB, as shown by the dotted arrows. On the convention stated above, the effect of the mutual inductance is to introduce an E.M.F. $-2M\dfrac{di}{dt}$ into the whole coil, an E.M.F. acting in the direction D to C. Now we already know that the effect of self-inductance is to induce E.M.Fs. $-L_1\dfrac{di}{dt}$ and $-L_2\dfrac{di}{dt}$, *i.e.*, E.M.Fs. acting in the coils in the directions D to C and B to A. Thus the total effect of the inductive action is to introduce into the circuit an E.M.F.

$$\left(L_1\frac{di}{dt} + L_2\frac{di}{dt} + 2M\frac{di}{dt}\right)$$

acting in the direction D to A. If now we consider the coil as a whole, if L is its total inductance, the effect of this inductance would be to introduce an E.M.F. $- L\frac{di}{dt}$ into the circuit, *i.e.*, an E.M.F. $L\frac{di}{dt}$ acting in the direction D to A.   Thus we obtain the result

$$- L\frac{di}{dt} = - L_1\frac{di}{dt} - L_2\frac{di}{dt} - 2M\frac{di}{dt}$$

or

$$L = L_1 + L_2 + 2M.$$

As we know from experiment that L is greater than $L_1 + L_2$, we see that on this convention **M is to be regarded as a positive quantity in this case.**

Next consider the case where B is joined to D, and a current is flowing round the circuit in the direction A, B, D, C, as shown in Fig. 46 (*c*).

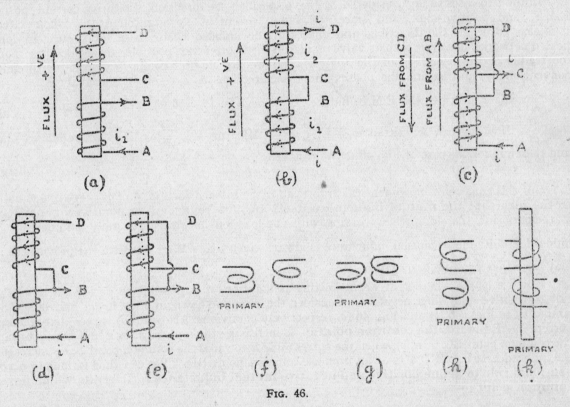

FIG. 46.

In this case the end B of coil AB would act like the north pole of a magnet and the end C of coil CD would also act like a north pole, and hence the fluxes from the two coils are in opposition, as shown by the arrows at the side.   Part of the flux from AB passes through CD and *vice versa*.   Now consider what happens in coil AB when we increase current *i*.   First, due to the increase in its own flux we get an E.M.F. of magnitude $L_1\frac{di}{dt}$ acting in the direction B to A, or, on the convention, $- L_1\frac{di}{dt}$ in the circuit.   Secondly, due to the increase in the current in coil CD, we get an E.M.F. induced in coil AB, due to the increase in flux from CD.   But this flux is in the opposite direction to that from AB itself and therefore induces an E.M.F. of magnitude $M\frac{di}{dt}$, but acting in the direction

A to B, as shown by the dotted arrows. Thus the total E.M.F. induced in AB is $-L_1\dfrac{di}{dt} + M\dfrac{di}{dt}$ in the direction A to B. Similar reasoning for coil CD shows that the total E.M.F. induced is $-L_2\dfrac{di}{dt} + M\dfrac{di}{dt}$ acting in the direction D to C. Thus for the whole circuit from A to C, the total E.M.F. induced is

$$-L_1\frac{di}{dt} - L_2\frac{di}{dt} + 2M\frac{di}{dt}.$$

But considering the circuit as a whole it also equals $-L\dfrac{di}{dt}$.

$$\therefore \quad L = L_1 + L_2 - 2M,$$

and M is again a positive quantity.

In the two cases so far considered, we have specified the direction of positive current, positive E.M.F. and positive flux, and since the same current is flowing round the whole circuit, it is easy to decide the directions and phases of the induced E.M.Fs., currents, etc. In complicated networks, however, such as valve oscillators, it is often not possible, to decide these points too readily at the beginning of the analysis, and we are led to assume (say) positive directions conventionally, and to find the phases and true directions as a result of the analysis.

Now if we return to the E.M.F. induced in coil AB in Fig. 46 (c), we see that it was $-L_1\dfrac{di}{dt} + M\dfrac{di}{dt}$. Now this can be written as $-L_1\dfrac{di}{dt} - (-M)\dfrac{di}{dt}$ or $-L_1\dfrac{di}{dt} - M'\dfrac{di}{dt}$, where $M' = (-M)$; and therefore for the case of Fig. 46 (c) we can write

$$L = L_1 + L_2 + 2M'.$$

But this equation is now identical in form to that obtained for Fig. 46 (b). We are thus led **to the idea that the mutual inductance itself may be regarded as positive or negative.** Mathematicians, therefore, when working with complicated networks, generally assume that the induced E.M.F. due to mutual inductance is always given by $-M\dfrac{di}{dt}$, but with the proviso that M may be either positive or negative.

Now let us see whether, if we make this assumption, it is possible to decide when we shall call M positive and when negative. Consider the circuits shown in Fig. 46 (d) and (e). Their similarity to Figs. 46 (b) and Fig. 46 (c) respectively is obvious. Now in (d) we see that when the current in AB towards **the common point** BC is increasing the induced E.M.F. in CD acts towards the common point BC. In (e), when the current in AB towards the common point BD is increasing, the induced E.M.F. in CD acts away from the common point BD. We can thus formulate a conventional rule to define positive and negative mutual inductance for circuits which have a common point :—

> If when the current in the primary circuit flowing towards the common point is increasing, the induced E.M.F. in the secondary acts towards the common point (*i.e.*, the common point tends to become positive relative to the free point of the secondary), the mutual inductance is regarded as positive.

> If when the current in the primary circuit flowing towards the common point is increasing, the induced E.M.F. in the secondary acts away from the common point (*i.e.*, the common point tends to become negative relative to the free point of the secondary), the mutual inductance is regarded as negative.

162. Calculation of Mutual Inductance.—It will readily be realised that the calculation of the mutual inductance of two circuits is an even more complicated problem than the calculation of self-inductance, except in very simple cases.

One case which lends itself to calculation is that of two coils wound on the same former. If we make the assumption that when a current flows in either coil, all the flux lines associated with the current link with both coils, a simple result may be obtained. The limitations of this assumption in practice have already been mentioned (paragraph 152). An air core will also be assumed.

Let one coil have N_1 turns. Its self-inductance L_1 is given by $L_1 = \dfrac{4\pi A N_1^2}{l} \times 10^{-9}$ henry, where A is the area of the former.

If the corresponding quantities for the other coil are N_2 and L_2,

$$L_2 = \frac{4\pi A N_2^2}{l} \times 10^{-9} \text{ henry.}$$

If a current of I amps. is established in coil L_1, the flux is

$$\Phi = HA = \frac{4\pi A N_1 I}{10 l}.$$

This links with N_2 turns of the coil L_2.

Therefore mutual flux-linkage $(N\,\Phi) = \dfrac{4\pi A N_1 N_2 I.}{10 l}$

But

$$MI = N\,\Phi \times 10^{-8},$$

where M is the mutual inductance of the two coils,

$$\therefore \quad M = \frac{4\pi A N_1 N_2}{l} \times 10^{-9} \text{ henry.}$$

163. Coupling and Coupling Factor.—When two circuits are arranged so that some of the flux lines due to one circuit link with the other they are said to be coupled to each other. There are several ways of coupling circuits (Chapter V), and this particular method is called " mutual magnetic," " mutual inductive," or simply " mutual " coupling. According to the proportion of the total flux produced by the first circuit which links with the second, the coupling is said to be " tight " (or " close "), or " loose." Thus, on the assumptions made in the last paragraph, the coupling between the two coils L_1 and L_2 is as tight as it possibly can be, for all the flux produced by one coil links with the other. This case is made the basis of a criterion of the tightness of coupling between any two circuits. It was found that

$$M = \frac{4\pi A N_1 N_2}{l} \times 10^{-9} \text{ henry.}$$

$$\therefore \quad M^2 = \frac{16\pi^2 A^2 N_1^2 N_2^2}{l^2} \times 10^{-18} = \frac{(4\pi A N_1^2 \times 10^{-9})}{l} \times \frac{(4\pi A N_2^2 \times 10^{-9})}{l}$$

$$= L_1 L_2,$$
$$\text{and } M = \sqrt{L_1 L_2}.$$

This is the maximum possible mutual inductance between the circuits, and so M can never be greater than $\sqrt{L_1 L_2}$. In any practical case, M is less than $\sqrt{L_1 L_2}$, for it is impossible to arrange that all the flux produced by one circuit links with another ; there is always some " leakage " of flux, i.e., some lines complete themselves without passing through every turn.

The ratio $\dfrac{M}{\sqrt{L_1 L_2}}$ is taken as a criterion of the closeness of the coupling between two circuits. It is called the " coupling factor," and is denoted by K.

Thus $K = \dfrac{M}{\sqrt{L_1 L_2}}$, or $M = K \sqrt{L_1 L_2}$.

It is obvious that K is a pure number and has no units. Its maximum value is unity, which corresponds to the ideal case discussed above $(M = \sqrt{L_1 L_2})$. Its value in any given case is a measure of how many lines of flux from one circuit are linking with the other compared with the case when all the flux-linkages are mutual.

Another term used is " **percentage coupling,**" which is 100K. The ideal case above has 100 per cent. coupling between the coils.

Fig. 46 (f), (g), (h) and (k) is a diagrammatic representation of two coils in which the mutual coupling becomes progressively tighter from left to right ; the two coils wound on the iron core have tightest coupling because the core minimises flux-leakage.

Mutual coupling is further discussed in Chapter V.

CAPACITY.

164. An account of the simpler electrostatic effects was given in Chapter II. It was there seen that the behaviour of charged bodies could be rendered intelligible by the idea of lines of electric flux, which tended to longitudinal contraction and lateral expansion ; the meaning of field strength and P.D. was explained, and the electric field was seen to be a storehouse of potential energy.

The existence of an electric field depends, of course, on the presence of electric charges. Remove the charges and the field disappears. The nature of the field and the direction of the lines of electric flux depend on the value of the charges and their distribution. For instance, the field due to an isolated point charge is different from that between two parallel plates with equal and opposite charges.

When a charge moves in an electric field its motion involves the transformation of energy. Work must be done on the charge if it is moved against the field forces ; work is done by the field forces if the charge moves under their influence. This led to the ideas of the P.D. between two points in the field, and the absolute potential at a point in the field. The charged body producing the field is, of course, in the field and so has a potential, viz., the work necessary to bring a unit positive charge up to it from earth (or from a point where there is no electric field due to the charge).

It is found that in all cases the potential of a charged body is proportional to its charge. Thus, in the case of two parallel plates, if the negatively-charged plate is earthed, the potential of the positive plate is $\frac{4\pi dQ}{KA}$ (paragraph 103), and so is directly proportional to Q, the charge on the plate.

In general, for any charged body we may write $Q \propto V$, or $Q = CV$, where C is the constant of proportion.

This relation is of great importance and the constant C is given a special name. It is called the **capacity** of the charged body.

Hence capacity $= \dfrac{\text{charge}}{\text{potential}}.$

165. **Condensers.**—Every charged body has a certain capacity, but, unless special arrangements are made, it will not be of large amount. In other words, an electric charge given to the body will raise it to a high potential, sufficient perhaps to break down the insulation of the material surrounding it. The charge which a body can hold for a given potential may be increased by concentrating the region over which its field extends. Devices in which this takes place are called **condensers.** The electric field is confined to a small space and so can be made much more intense without raising the body to too high a potential. The condenser may also be regarded as a device for concentrating electrostatic field energy. Increase of field strength means that there is a greater density of electric flux, i.e., the flux lines are packed more closely together. They resist this packing because of their tendency to lateral expansion, which forces them apart. The extra work necessary to accomplish the packing appears as an increase of energy in the field.

166. **Parallel-Plate Condenser.**—One of the commonest forms of condenser consists of two parallel metal plates with some dielectric between them. The lines of flux from one of these plates would normally end on any convenient points, e.g., the walls of the room. If the other plate

is earthed and brought near the first one, the lines of flux can shorten themselves considerably, and most of them will now end on the earthed plate, thus concentrating the field.

The operation of charging such a condenser may be considered from the electron standpoint. Fig. 47 shows a simple charging arrangement. The two plates A and B are connected to a battery and galvanometer (G) through the switch S.

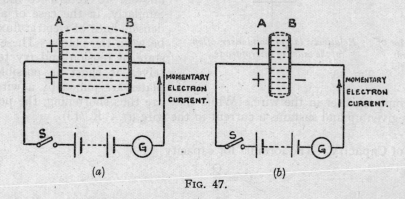

FIG. 47.

(a) When the plates are well separated, as soon as the switch S is closed the battery will cause a momentary rush of electrons round the circuit from plate A, which is connected to the positive terminal of the battery, through the battery towards plate B, where they will crowd together ; the galvanometer pointer will be deflected. The current flowing will stop as soon as the potential difference between the plates is equal to the terminal P.D. of the battery. The two plates will now be oppositely charged. Plate B will have a surplus of electrons which will repel others trying to arrive. Some of the atoms of plate A have lost electrons, and are therefore positive charges, which, by their attraction, prevent any more electrons from moving away. Equilibrium is thus established.

These two oppositely-charged plates produce an electric field in the dielectric separating them, and a displacement of electrons, or displacement current, will occur within the atoms in the dielectric, in the direction from the negatively-charged plate B to the positively-charged plate A.

(b) Let the two plates be suddenly brought closer together.

The negative charge on plate B overcomes to some extent the effect of the positive charge on plate A and *vice versa*, so that the potential difference between the two plates is momentarily lowered, the forces holding the electrons in check are decreased, and another momentary electron movement takes place until equilibrium is again established, and the P.D. between the plates is again equal to the terminal P.D. of the battery.

Thus, the closer the plates are together the greater is the charge which may be concentrated on one or other for the same P.D. between them.

(c) Suppose we break the switch S. Each plate is now left charged with a certain quantity of electricity, A positively and B negatively. The sum of these charges is algebraically zero. When the term " charge on a condenser " is used, it refers to the charge on one of the plates.

(d) If the battery B is now short-circuited and the switch S again closed, the electrons will rush back from the negative plate to the positive plate until they are equally distributed round the circuit, and there will be a deflection of the galvanometer pointer in the reverse direction.

The electrons in the dielectric, which were strained towards the positive plate, will return to their normal orbits.

There will thus be a momentary conduction current (paragraph 40) round the circuit, and a displacement current (paragraph 42) through the dielectric.

Clearly, the greater the voltage applied to the condenser the greater will be the electric flux density in the dielectric.

The greater the flux-density the greater will be the amount of electrical energy stored in the condenser.

D

167. A condenser is illustrated diagrammatically as in Fig. 48.   A useful mechanical analogy to a condenser is furnished by a steel spring. When the spring is compressed or extended, potential energy is stored up in it and is liberated when the spring is allowed to return to its normal size. Similarly, in the case of a charged condenser, lines of electric flux fill the space between the plates. These lines are in a state of tension and try to make themselves as short as possible. When the plates are joined by a wire, the ends of these lines can come together in the wire. While they are thus shortening, the potential energy they represent is given up and sustains a current in the wire (*cf.* " R."13).

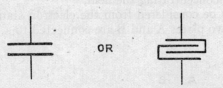

Condenser of the order of jars or centimetres.	Relatively larger condenser often of the order of microfarads.

FIG. 48.

168. **Units of Capacity.**—The formula for capacity

$$C = \frac{Q}{V}$$

will give different units for capacity according to the units in which charge and potential (or P.D.) are measured.

In the electrostatic system a charged body has unit capacity if its potential is one E.S.U. of potential when it is given a charge of one E.S.U.   This unit is called **the centimetre.**

In the practical system, charge is measured in coulombs and potential in volts.   The practical unit of capacity derived on this system is called **the Farad** (symbol F).

Definition.—A charged body has a capacity of one farad if it is raised to a potential of one volt when it is given a charge of one coulomb.

A condenser thus has a capacity of one farad if the P.D. between its plates is one volt when the charge on either plate is one coulomb.

A farad is, for convenience, subdivided into the following smaller units :—

1 farad = 10^3 (a thousand) " **millifarads** " (*m*F) = 10^6 (a million) " **microfarads** " (µF).
     = 10^9 " **millimicrofarads** " (*m*µF)   = 10^{12} " **micromicrofarads** " (µµF).
     = 9×10^8 (nine hundred million) **jars.**   = 9×10^{11} **absolute units or cms.**

For 1 cm. = $\dfrac{1 \text{ E.S.U. of charge.}}{1 \text{ E.S.U. of P.D.}}$ = $\dfrac{\dfrac{1}{3 \times 10^9} \text{ coulomb}}{300 \text{ volts}}$ (*see* paras. 95 and 102)

     = $\dfrac{1}{9 \times 10^{11}}$ farad.

It will be seen that 1 jar = 1,000 cms.

Also 1 µF = 900 jars, and 1 jar = $\dfrac{1}{9 \times 10^8}$ F.

The jar is now obsolete as the Service unit, having been replaced by the Farad and its sub multiples.

Example 18.

Find the quantity of electricity in a condenser of 500 jars capacity when charged to a P.D. of 10,000 volts.

Q = CV, where Q is in coulombs, C in farads, V in volts.

$$Q = \frac{500 \times 10,000}{9 \times 10^8} = \frac{500}{9 \times 10^4} \text{ coulomb} = \frac{5}{900} \text{ coulomb} = \frac{1}{180} \text{ coulomb.}$$

The same quantity introduced into a condenser of 1,000 jars capacity (twice as much) would create a P.D. of only half the amount, viz., 5,000 volts.

169. **Specific Inductive Capacity.**—It was seen in paragraph 97 that the field strength due to a charge depended on the material surrounding the charge, and this was expressed in the formulæ derived there by the appearance of the factor K, called the specific inductive capacity (S.I.C.) of the material.

In a material whose S.I.C. is K, the field strength at any point is $\frac{1}{K}$ times the field strength that would be produced *in vacuo* by the same arrangement of charges.

The potential difference between any two points in the field is thus reduced in the same ratio, *i.e.*, it is $\frac{1}{K}$ times what it would be *in vacuo* for the same charges.

It follows that the capacity of the arrangement of charges, which is equal to charge divided by P.D., is K times as great in a material whose S.I.C. is K as it would be *in vacuo*.

The S.I.C. of an insulator may thus be defined as the ratio of the capacity of a condenser with the insulator as dielectric, to the capacity of the same condenser with a vacuum as dielectric. In fact, the S.I.C. of an insulator is found in practice by measurements of capacity.

For the same P.D. between the condenser plates in the two cases the charges on the plates would be K times as great with the insulator as dielectric as with a vacuum as dielectric.

K is equal to unity for a vacuum. In all other materials, except an ionised medium ("P."9), it is greater than unity. It does not appear to vary appreciably with temperature at ordinary temperatures. For dry air at 0° C. and 760 mm. pressure it is 1·00059. It is greater in moist air, but, generally speaking, it may be taken as unity in air to a good approximation.

Approximate S.I.C. values for some dielectrics at ordinary temperatures are as follows :—

Solids :—

Ebonite = 2 — 3·2 (fairly constant).
Vulcanite fibre = 2·5.
Glass = 4 — 10. (Very variable. Pebble glass 5 (about) ; plate glass 7 — 8.)
Shellac = 2·75 — 3·73
Dry paper = 1·5.
Mica = 5.
Ice = 71 (at — 7·5° C.).
Indiarubber = 2·12 — 2·34.
Porcelain 4·4 — 6·8.

Liquids :—

Distilled water K = 80, but its efficiency is very low.
Paraffin = 2 — 2·3 (variable).
Finest vaseline oil = 2 (constant).
Service insulating oil = 2·217.
Petroleum and turpentine = 2·2.

170. **Capacity of a Parallel Plate Condenser.**—The calculation of the P.D. between two parallel plates has already been given (paragraph 103), but is recapitulated here for convenience.

In a condenser consisting of two parallel plates the charge on either plate may be considered as being uniformly distributed over the area of the plates. The lines of force are therefore parallel and the flux density will be uniform.

Let V be the P.D. between the plates, Q the charge on either plate, d cms. the distance between the plates, and A sq. cms. the area of the plates. Q and V are supposed to be measured in electrostatic units.

The flux density D is $\frac{Q}{A}$ lines per sq. cm. The relationship between flux density D and field strength X is given by the formula of paragraph 100, *i.e.*, in the case of a dielectric whose S.I.C. is K,

$$X = \frac{4\pi D}{K}.$$

The P.D. in electrostatic units between the plates is given by the field strength multiplied by the distance between them (paragraph 103).

So that V (in E.S.U.) $= d \times \dfrac{4\pi D}{K} = \dfrac{4\pi Q d}{AK}$.

But if C is the capacity in E.S. Units or centimetres,

$$V = \frac{Q}{C} \qquad \therefore \ C = \frac{AK}{4\pi d} \text{ centimetres.}$$

Hence, in practical units, $C = \dfrac{AK}{4\pi d \times 9 \times 10^{11}}$ farads $= \dfrac{AK}{4{,}000\ \pi d}$ jars.

If A is expressed in square inches, and d in inches,

$$C = \frac{A \times (2 \cdot 54)^2\ K}{4{,}000\ \pi d \times (2 \cdot 54)} \qquad (1 \text{ inch} = 2 \cdot 54 \text{ cms.})$$

$$= \frac{2 \cdot 54\ AK}{4{,}000\ \pi d} \text{ jars} = \frac{2 \cdot 54\ AK}{12{,}570\ d} \text{ jars} = \frac{AK}{5{,}000 d} \text{ jars approximately.}$$

In practice, condensers of large capacity are built up by separating a series of thin flat conducting plates by thin layers of insulating material. Alternate plates are joined together to form one conductor; the remainder, similarly connected together, form the second plate. Such a condenser is equivalent to two large parallel sheets of conductor separated by a large thin sheet of insulating material.

If the number of sheets of dielectric under strain in such a condenser is N, the formula then becomes

$$C = \frac{AKN}{4{,}000\ \pi d} \text{ jars, where A and } d \text{ are in sq. cms. and cms. respectively.}$$

Example 19.

Find the capacity of a condenser of 16 tinfoil plates, 15 cms. by 10 cms., separated by ebonite of S.I.C. $= 2 \cdot 5$ and thickness $0 \cdot 2$ mm.

$N = 16 - 1 = 15$ dielectrics under strain.
$A = 150$ sq. cms.
$d = 0 \cdot 02$ cm.

$$C = \frac{150 \times 15 \times 2 \cdot 5}{4{,}000 \times 3 \cdot 14 \times 0 \cdot 02} \text{ jars} = \frac{150 \times 37 \cdot 5}{80 \times 3 \cdot 14} = \frac{562 \cdot 5}{25 \cdot 12} = 22 \cdot 4 \text{ jars.}$$

171. Energy Stored in a Condenser.—Just as when a magnetic field is created round an inductance a certain amount of energy is stored up, so when a condenser, capacity C, is charged up to a voltage V, energy is stored in the creation of the electric field between the plates. When the condenser discharges, this energy is returned to the circuit. If the condenser is perfectly efficient, there is no expenditure of energy, i.e., all the charge put into the condenser is returned by it.

The energy stored in a magnetic field is comparable to kinetic energy, being associated with current flow, or motion of electrons; in a condenser it is comparable to potential energy, being dependent on the P.D. set up across the plates.

At any time during the charging of the condenser let the P.D. be v. A small charge dq introduced into the condenser at this voltage will mean an amount of work done $= vdq$. The total work done in charging the condenser to its maximum voltage V is found by adding up these small amounts of work done.

Now

$$q = Cv. \quad \therefore \ dq = Cdv, \text{ and so } vdq = Cvdv.$$

The total work done, which is the energy stored in the condenser $= \displaystyle\int_0^V Cvdv = \tfrac{1}{2} CV^2$. If C is in farads, and V in volts, the energy is $\tfrac{1}{2}CV^2$ joules.

The same result can be obtained in a less general manner as follows :—

The total quantity of electricity in coulombs introduced into a condenser of C farads charged to a maximum potential of V volts is given by $Q = CV$ coulombs.

The charging current, if the condenser is charged by a steady current in t seconds, has a value of $\frac{CV}{t}$ amperes.

The average voltage during this time is $\frac{V}{2}$ volts. Therefore the average rate at which work is done is $\frac{CV^2}{2t}$ watts.

The total work done in time $t = \frac{CV^2}{2t}$ watts $\times$ t seconds $= \frac{1}{2}CV^2$ joules.

This is also the amount of energy stored in the condenser when charged.

172. Power Taken in Charging a Condenser.—If a condenser is charged N times a second, a power of $\frac{1}{2}CV^2 \times N$ joules per second will be required. But joules per second = watts.

Hence the power required to charge a condenser N times per second $= \frac{1}{2}CV^2N$ watts.

173. The capacity of a condenser is a fixed quantity.

A condenser may be compared with an iron gas cylinder. To increase the quantity of gas pumped into it an increased pressure must be applied. At first the gas passes easily, but the more gas is pumped in the harder it is to force in more. At any moment the internal pressure equals the applied pressure.

★174. Charge and Discharge of a Condenser through a Resistance.—When a condenser is joined up to a source of steady E.M.F. and the circuit contains resistance, the condenser does not instantaneously acquire a P.D. equal to that of the source ; in other words, it does not acquire its full charge immediately. The investigation of the gradual building-up of the charge to its maximum amount is very similar to the case of para. **158,** where we considered the way in which current in an inductive circuit reaches its maximum value.

In the charging case, suppose the switch just made and a steady voltage V applied to the circuit. The charging current is given by $\frac{V}{R}$ at the beginning of the action, because the condenser has no charge and hence exerts no back E.M.F. As the condenser charges up, however, its voltage acts in opposition to the impressed E.M.F., so that at any instant it is the difference between these voltages that is effective in sending the current through the resistance,

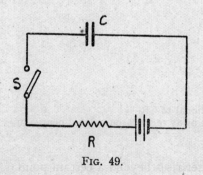

FIG. 49.

i.e., $V - V_e = iR$, where V_e = condenser voltage.

Let q be the instantaneous charge on the condenser.

Then $V_e = \frac{q}{C}$ and $i = \frac{dq}{dt}$. Hence $V = \frac{q}{C} + R\frac{dq}{dt}$.

This may be written as $\frac{dq}{q - CV} = -\frac{dt}{CR}$.

Integrating both sides,

$$\log_e (q - CV) = -\frac{t}{CR} + K,$$

where K is a constant depending on the initial conditions.

These are, in this case, that at $t = 0$, $q = 0$. $\therefore$ K $= \log_e (-CV)$.

$$\therefore \quad \log_e \frac{q - CV}{- CV} = -\frac{t}{CR} \quad \text{or} \quad \frac{CV - q}{CV} = e^{-\frac{t}{CR}}$$

$$\therefore \quad CV - q = CVe^{-\frac{t}{CR}}$$

$$\therefore \quad q = CV\left(1 - e^{-\frac{t}{CR}}\right).$$

CV is the final value of the charge, and so, theoretically, this is only reached after an infinite time. In any practical case this value is nearly reached in a very short time.

As in paragraph 158, we can define a **time constant** for this circuit.

In a time $t = CR$, the charge reaches $(1 - e^{-1})$, or $63 \cdot 2$ per cent. of its final value. This time, $t = CR$, is the time constant of the circuit.

$$\text{Since } i = \frac{dq}{dt}, \; i = \frac{V}{R} e^{-\frac{t}{CR}}.$$

So i has the value $\frac{V}{R}$ at $t = 0$, as stated before, and in a time given by the time constant CR it falls to e^{-1}, or $36 \cdot 8$ per cent., of its maximum value. The charging current decreases to zero as t increases.

Graphs indicating the growth of the charge in the condenser and the decay of the charging current are exactly similar to the growth and decay curves of Fig. 44.

Case of Discharge.—If the two plates of a charged condenser are connected by a conductor of resistance R, a current starts to flow, and continues until the P.D. across the condenser is zero. The stored-up energy is expended in I^2R losses in the resistance.

The equation representing the action can be easily seen, from previous work, to be

$$R \frac{dq}{dt} + \frac{q}{C} = 0.$$

(This is simply the general equation with $V = 0$.)

The solution, assuming the initial conditions that at $t = 0$, $q = CV$, V being the voltage to which the condenser was charged, is given by

$$q = CV e^{-\frac{t}{CR}}$$

This shows that, as might be expected, the charge on the condenser decreases continuously, and in a time $t = CR$, the **time constant** of the circuit, diminishes to e^{-1}, or $36 \cdot 8$ per cent. of its original value.

The discharging current is given by $i = \frac{dq}{dt}$, i.e., $i = -\frac{V}{R} e^{-\frac{t}{CR}}$.

The general shape of the curves of charge and current flowing are therefore both similar to the decay curve of Fig. 44. The negative sign in the expression for i simply means that the current is in the opposite direction to that during charging.

From the solution $q = CV e^{-\frac{t}{CR}}$, the time may be found in which the voltage of the condenser diminishes from V to, say, V_1 .

At the latter voltage

$$q = CV_1 = CV e^{-\frac{t}{CR}}$$

$$\therefore \frac{V_1}{V} = e^{-\frac{t}{CR}}, \text{ or } \frac{V}{V_1} = e^{+\frac{t}{CR}}$$

$$\log_e \frac{V}{V_1} = \frac{t}{CR} \quad \text{or} \quad t = CR \log_e \frac{V}{V_1}.$$

Thus the time required for the voltage to drop from V to V_1 is proportional to CR.

This result is useful in valve theory later on, when considering the leak away of the accumulated charge in a condenser through a grid leak. (*See* " CR " values.)

175. Dielectric Strength.—If the electric strain in a condenser rises beyond a certain point the dielectric is punctured.

In the case of liquids or gases the wound so created heals itself (though, in oil, contamination will occur), but in solids the insulation is punctured, *i.e.*, a hole is formed which only offers the insulation of air, instead of the insulation of the solid dielectric.

The voltage corresponding to that at which the rupture of a plate 1 mm. thick takes place is called the **dielectric strength of the insulator.**

A thin sheet of dielectric is *proportionally* stronger than a thicker one of the same material. That is, a sheet of $\frac{1}{16}$ in. thickness is not twice as strong as one of $\frac{1}{32}$ in., but something considerably less.

The reason for this appears to be that, as the thickness of the dielectric increases, it becomes more difficult to keep the field strength uniform between the plates. Thus, in parts of the field, the field strength becomes considerably greater than that calculated on a basis of uniform field strength, and the insulation breaks down.

For this reason, large condensers are usually built up of several different parts—or sections— connected in series ; this saves space.

The strength of dielectrics is compared with that of air.

A spark of 1 mm. in air at atmospheric pressure between flat metallic surfaces requires 4,300 volts.   A spark of 2 mm. would only require 7,400 volts.   Two plates 1 cm. apart in air require 30,000 volts applied to spark across.   With spark balls the voltage is less the less the diameter of the balls.   Between sharp points the voltage required is much less.

The dielectric strengths of various dielectrics are given in the following table :—

Dielectric.		Dielectric Strength.			Corresponding sparking distance between plates in air at atmospheric pressure.
Crystal Glass	.. ..	28,500 volts	..	..	9 mm.
Indiarubber	.. ..	40,000 „	..	..	13 „
Ebonite	.. ..	50,000 „	..	..	16 „
Mica	.. ..	60,000 „	..	..	20 „
0·1 mm. of mica ...	..	10,000 „	..	..	3 „
Oil (vaseline)	.. ..	6,000-8,000 volts	..		2·4 mm.

It is usual in building condensers to allow a factor of safety of from three to six times the dielectric strength, since the above only gives voltages at which the dielectric is bound to puncture ; it may puncture at a much less voltage if any brush discharge burns the plate or sparking takes place between the contacts.

Dielectrics puncture at lower voltages if subjected to alternating E.M.Fs. as compared with steady E.M.Fs., and the higher the frequency of alternation the lower is the puncturing voltage.

176. Dielectric Efficiency.—Dielectric efficiency is the ratio of the energy output to the energy input, thereby taking account of any waste of energy that occurs during the charge and discharge of a condenser.

If a dielectric is perfect there should be no waste of energy in it.   In most condensers, however, this does not hold good.   The term " **Hysteresis** " is used to cover all the losses, and these may be summed up as :—

(a) **Conductor losses,** or true resistance losses due to the resistances of the plates and leads. These are easily kept low in parallel plate condensers.   They are equivalent to a resistance in series with the condenser.

(b) **Chemical action.**—This may take place if damp is present.   Hence, condenser cases must be properly sealed.

(c) **Leakage losses.**—These may be due to faulty insulation or to corona discharge from points and edges of the condenser plates.

Faulty insulation, which might enable a considerable current to flow through the dielectric, is equivalent to a resistance in parallel with the condenser.

Leakage over the plate edges may be prevented by immersing the condenser in oil and keeping the plate edges well away from the sides of the condenser tank.

Moisture should not be allowed to collect on the surface of a solid dielectric.

(d) Most important is **dielectric absorption.**

When a condenser is charged, the initial rush of current is followed by a relatively small more gradual current, which appears to " soak in " to the dielectric.   The charge on the condenser is therefore dependent on the time during which it is connected to the source of E.M.F., quite apart from considerations mentioned in the last paragraph concerned with the resistance of the charging circuit.   Similarly, when such a condenser is short-circuited, the initial heavy discharge, which should leave it practically uncharged, is an incomplete one.   If the short-circuit is removed and the condenser set aside and again short-circuited a few minutes later, a second discharge can be obtained. This is due to the charge which " soaks into " the dielectric during charging.   If the condenser is charged and discharged periodically, this absorption causes heat to be generated in the dielectric

Hence, with condensers connected in parallel the equivalent capacity is the sum of the individual capacities.

Condensers may be joined both in series to give adequate dielectric strength, and in parallel to give increased capacity.

Example 21.

Given a number of condensers, each capable of standing 1,000 volts and each with a capacity of 1 jar. Find an arrangement suitable for giving a condenser of capacity 2 jars, across which 2,000 volts may be applied.

Two condensers in series will stand the voltage of 2,000 volts, but their capacity will be only $\frac{1}{2}$ jar.

Four such groups in parallel will give a capacity of 2 jars.

Therefore 8 condensers are needed, 2 in series and 4 groups in parallel.

179. Condensers used in Wireless Telegraphy Circuits.—The condensers used in wireless telegraphy fall under three headings :—

    (*a*) **Natural capacity circuits** in which the capacity exists between the wires of the circuit itself, or between the circuit and earth.

    (*b*) **Artificial capacities,** in which a built-up condenser, generally of the parallel plate type, is used.

    (*c*) Combinations of (*a*) and (*b*).

(*a*) **Natural Capacity Circuits.**—Every ordinary electric circuit possesses capacity. In an electric cable the conductor forms one plate of the condenser, the insulation is the dielectric, and the outer lead casing, or the earth, the other plate.

In general, any two wires which are adjacent to each other have capacity to each other.

Thus there is always a certain amount of capacity between the turns of a coil of wire. The combined effect of all the small capacities between turns is spoken of as the " **self-capacity** " of the coil.

Again, a suspended wire has a capacity to earth, the air being dielectric.

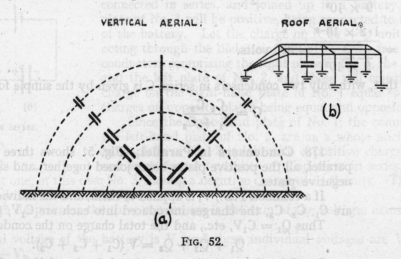

FIG. 52.

The capacity of the wire is therefore very complex, being the sum of the capacities of each portion of it to the earthed points in the neighbourhood as indicated in Fig. 52 (*a*).

This capacity may be increased by arranging wires to form a roof, as in Fig. 52 (*b*).

The total capacity is called the " **natural capacity** " of the wire to earth, and is denoted in the Service by the letter " σ " (sigma).

(*b*) **Artificial Capacities.**—These are used very extensively in wireless telegraphy, in transmitting, receiving, wavemeter circuits, etc. They will be dealt with in due course.

(*c*) In every circuit containing an artificial condenser there must also always be a natural capacity to earth or between leads. This capacity is in parallel with the artificial capacity and must therefore be added to it.

If the artificial condenser is large the capacity of the leads may be neglected, whereas if the condenser is small the latter may be a considerable factor.

If an artificial condenser is inserted in an earthed wire having a natural capacity to earth, it is in series with that capacity and reduces the total capacity value.

180. Receiving Condensers.—Receiving condensers are designed to have a maximum dielectric efficiency and to occupy a minimum of space. Generally, air dielectric is used because of its efficiency. Mica may be used if a large capacity is required.

Such condensers may have a **fixed** or a **variable** value of capacity.

In a fixed condenser the plates, or sets of plates, are rigidly mounted with respect to each other, so that the capacity value does not vary.

In a **variable** condenser there are two sets of plates, one set being fixed, mounted one above the other at equal fixed intervals, and attached to a rigid support. The other set is mounted one above the other at equal intervals on a rotating spindle, and arranged to be rotated into the spaces between the fixed plates so as to overlap them more or less. The greater the overlap the greater the capacity.

A common type of such a variable condenser has plates cut in the form of semicircular segments, as indicated in Fig. 53.

The amount of overlap of area is directly proportional to the **angle** of overlap in this case, and can be measured by a pointer travelling over a scale of degrees and attached to the spindle of the rotating plates.

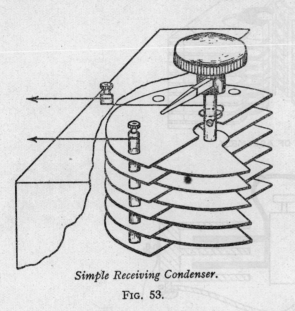

Simple Receiving Condenser.

FIG. 53.

When the condenser is in its minimum position and the plates not overlapping at all the capacity does not fall quite to zero, owing to the fact that a small capacity exists between the edges of the two sets of plates. This is known as edge effect. A curve, known as a calibration curve, may be drawn for such a condenser, showing the capacity graphed against angle of overlap. It is a straight line curve, except for small angles, where, on account of edge effect, it flattens out somewhat.

A typical curve of this type is shown below (Fig. 54).

If it is desired to increase the capacity of a condenser of this type it may be immersed in oil, which has a S.I.C. higher than that of air.

There are other types of variable condenser besides that described above. It is sometimes found convenient to have a condenser whose capacity varies as the square of the angle of overlap, and such a condenser is designed by constructing the plates in a different shape from a semicircle (*cf.* W.4).

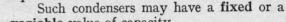

FIG. 54.

Electrolytic Condensers.—These originally consisted of a pair of aluminium electrodes, placed in an electrolyte consisting of a chemical solution of ammonium borate or sodium phosphate. If the combination is connected to a D.C. supply, electrolysis takes place and a thin film of aluminium oxide is formed on the positive plate ; in due course the latter becomes

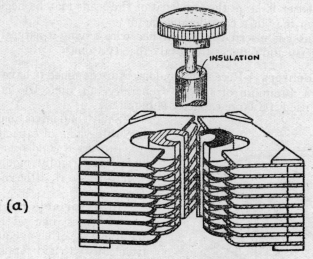

INSULATION

(a)

DETAILS OF ASSEMBLY.

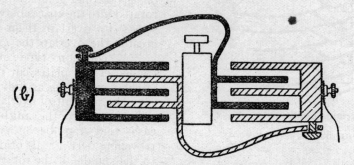

(b)

EXPLANATORY DIAGRAM FOR MAXIMUM CAPACITY.

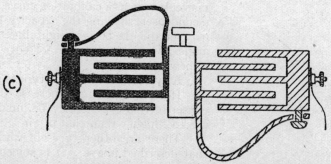

(c)

EXPLANATORY DIAGRAM FOR MINIMUM CAPACITY.

Die-cast Condenser.

FIG. 55.

insulated from the electrolyte, in which state the combination acts as a condenser in which the thin film of aluminium oxide acts as the dielectric. The thinner the film the higher will be the capacity, and capacities of the order of a 1,000 microfarads are easily obtained, the condensers occupying no more space than the paper condensers of 4 or 5 μF capacity.

These condensers cannot be used on raw A.C. supplies, since the anode must be held at a positive potential ; they must always be used in places where there is a D.C. polarising P.D. Their chief application is in connection with rectifying apparatus for supplying power to receivers from A.C. mains. A Service application is seen in Fig. 31 of Section " N."

There is also a newer type of " dry electrolytic condenser." The principle is the same, except that the liquid is replaced by a semi-fluid gelatinous material.

181. Die-cast Condenser.—The type of variable capacity condenser used in the Navy is more economical in space than that illustrated in Fig. 53. It is known as the die-cast condenser.

In this type, illustrated in Fig. 55, there are two sets of moving and two sets of fixed plates, one set of moving plates being connected to one set of fixed plates. Thus, in the position shown in the bottom figure of Fig. 55, the capacity is zero, since the rotating plates are in this case entirely contained between the fixed plates to which they are made common as regards potential.

A rotation through 180° gives the position shown diagrammatically in Fig. 55 (b), in which the capacity is obviously a maximum. The capacity can be made variable to any degree required up to its maximum value by a proportionate rotation.

The great advantage of this form of construction is that, with a condenser of the same superficial area and the same depth, a maximum capacity can be obtained of **double** the value possible with only one set of fixed and one of moving plates. In addition, the depth of the condenser and hence its capacity value can be increased by adding on further units.

182. Transmitting Condensers.—The general considerations that determine the design of transmitting condensers as compared with receiving condensers may be summed up as follows :—

(a) They are much larger in dimensions.

(b) Variability in value is sometimes secured by joining up separate fixed value condenser units in series and parallel, instead of having the condensers themselves continuously variable by rotation.

(a) The increase in the dimensions is accounted for, firstly, by the fact that it is usual to employ larger capacities in transmitting circuits, and secondly, because the question of dielectric strength prohibits the reduction of the distance between the plates to less than a certain amount. To achieve a large capacity value, therefore, the area of the condenser plates must be larger and dielectrics of high S.I.C. must be employed.

(b) An example of such an arrangement is given below. Condensers joined in series can stand higher voltages without danger of rupture of the dielectric, and condensers joined in parallel give an increase in total capacity.

Transmitting Condensers for Spark Sets have dielectrics of ebonite, mica or glass, and are generally arranged with " sections " in series, to give adequate dielectric strength. If a variation of capacity is necessary, the sections are arranged in groups or " elements," whose terminals are brought out of the tank, so that by suitable switches these groups—termed " Elements "—may be arranged in various combinations.

The plates of ebonite or glass condensers are generally immersed in oil, to prevent brushing. Fig. 56 illustrates the construction of such a condenser.

It can be seen that each section comprises, in the case illustrated, six active plates and five active dielectrics under strain.

Between sections are placed ebonite separators, generally of thicker material. The whole element is clamped up between metal plates which are earthed.

Next to the active plate at each end is placed a sheet of dielectric, and next it a conducting plate in electrical connection with the earthed clamping plate, so as to keep the capacity to earth constant.

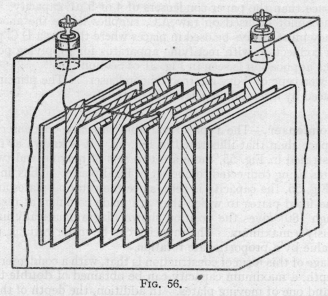

FIG. 56.

The following is an arrangement used in the Navy for securing a certain amount of variability of capacity value, as referred to in (b) above. The separate elements are two condensers, each having a capacity of 10 jars. Leads are taken from these condensers to four terminals, as shown in Fig. 57, and from two of these terminals connections are made to the remainder of the circuit.

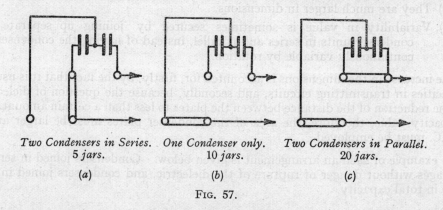

Two Condensers in Series.   One Condenser only.   Two Condensers in Parallel.
    5 jars.   10 jars.   20 jars.

(a)   (b)   (c)

FIG. 57.

By different arrangements of two movable links, which can be inserted between any pair of the terminals, different capacity values can be obtained. Thus in Fig. 57 (a), the two condensers are in series, and the total capacity is $\frac{10}{2} = 5$ jars. In Fig. 57 (b), one condenser only is in circuit, and the capacity is 10 jars. In Fig. 57 (c) the two condensers are in parallel and the total capacity is 20 jars.

Example 22.

You have the following materials available : ebonite $\frac{1}{32}$ in. thick (S.I.C. = 2·5) and dielectric strength sufficient to stand 5,000 volts, and tinfoil sheets 12 in. × 12 in.

You wish to construct a condenser (a) to give a total capacity of 234 jars with its elements arranged in parallel, and (b) to stand 15,000 volts with its elements arranged in series.

(i) How many plates would you require for (a) ?
(ii) What would be the capacity of the condenser in (b) ?

For (b) we shall require three elements in series to stand 15,000 volts.
Hence, capacity of each element, to give 234 jars when the three are joined in parallel will be :—

$$\frac{234}{3} = 78 \text{ jars.}$$

$C = \dfrac{AKN}{5,000d}$. Hence N (the number of dielectrics required) will be equal to $\dfrac{C \times 5,000 \times d}{AK}$

$$= \frac{78 \times 5,000}{12 \times 12 \times 2 \cdot 5} \times \frac{1}{32} = \frac{390,000}{11,520} = 33 \cdot 8 = 34 \text{ dielectrics.}$$

Hence the number of plates required for each element $= 34 + 1 = 35$.
Total number of plates $= 3 \times 35 = 105$ plates.

The capacity of three elements of 78 jars joined in series will be $\dfrac{78}{3} = 26$ jars.

183. The units of the quantities dealt with in Chapters II and III are summarised in the following table, and the conversion factor from one system to another is given in each case :—

TABLE 7.

Quantity.	Symbol.	Practical Unit.	1 E.M.U.	1 E.S.U.	1 E.M.U. in E.S.U.
			In Practical Units.		
Energy	W	1 joule	$1 \text{ erg} = \dfrac{1}{10^7} \text{ joule}$	..	1
Power	P	1 watt	$1 \text{ erg per sec.} = \dfrac{1}{10^7} \text{ watt}$	..	1
Quantity of electricity	Q	1 coulomb	10	$\dfrac{1}{3 \times 10^9}$	3×10^{10}
Potential difference or E.M.F.	V or E	1 volt	$\dfrac{1}{10^8}$	3×10^2	$\dfrac{1}{3 \times 10^{10}}$
Electric field strength	X	1 volt per cm.	$\dfrac{1}{10^8}$	3×10^2	$\dfrac{1}{3 \times 10^{10}}$
Electric flux density	D	1 E.S.U.	3×10^{10}	1	3×10^{10}
Electric flux	Ψ	1 E.S.U.	3×10^{10}	1	$\dfrac{1}{3 \times 10^{10}}$
Magnetic pole strength	m	1 E.M.U.	1	3×10^{10}	$\dfrac{1}{3 \times 10^{10}}$
Magnetic field strength	H	1 gauss (E.M.U.)	1	3×10^{10}	$\dfrac{1}{3 \times 10^{10}}$
Magnetic flux density	B	1 line per sq. cm. (E.M.U.)	1	3×10^{10}	$\dfrac{1}{3 \times 10^{10}}$
Magnetic flux	Φ	1 line (E.M.U.) or maxwell	1	3×10^{10}	$\dfrac{1}{3 \times 10^{10}}$
Magnetic reluctance	S	1 oersted (E.M.U.)	1	$\dfrac{1}{9 \times 10^{20}}$	9×10^{20}
Magneto Motive Force	G	1 gilbert (E.M.U.)	1	$\dfrac{1}{3 \times 10^{10}}$	3×10^{10}
Electric Current	I	1 ampere	10	$\dfrac{1}{3 \times 10^9}$	3×10^{10}
Resistance	R	1 ohm	$\dfrac{1}{10^9}$	9×10^{11}	$\dfrac{1}{9 \times 10^{20}}$
Capacity	C	1 farad $= 9 \times 10^8$ jars	10^9	$\dfrac{1}{9 \times 10^{11}}$	9×10^{20}
Inductance	L	1 henry	$\dfrac{1}{10^9}$	9×10^{11}	$\dfrac{1}{9 \times 10^{20}}$

D.C. MEASURING INSTRUMENTS.

184. In electrical circuits the quantities that commonly require measurement are the currents flowing in, and the potential differences across, various parts of a circuit. The instruments used for these purposes are called ammeters and voltmeters respectively. If it is also desirable to measure power directly, an instrument called a wattmeter, which combines the functions of voltmeter and ammeter, may be used. Wattmeters are not at present used with Naval wireless equipment.

The principles on which both ammeters and voltmeters operate are the same, and the differences that occur are due only to their different functions. The ammeter, being required to measure current, must be inserted in series in a circuit so that the current to be measured will flow through it. It follows also that it must be of low resistance compared with the rest of the circuit, or the extra resistance will alter appreciably the current flowing. This does not apply if the ammeter is permanently in the circuit, but the resistance should still be kept as low as possible to cut down the power loss, (I^2R), in the instrument.

The voltmeter measures P.D. and so must be connected in parallel between the two points in a circuit across which the P.D. is to be measured. It must therefore have a high resistance compared with that of the circuit. This keeps down its power loss (V^2/R) and, if it is not permanently in circuit, prevents its insertion from making an appreciable change in P.D.

An ammeter is thus converted into a voltmeter simply by putting a large resistance in series with the actual measuring part of the instrument.

Example 23.

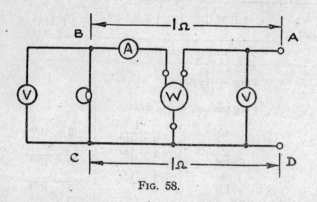

FIG. 58.

Between the two mains AB and CD a lamp of resistance 108 ohms is joined.

The resistance of line A to B is 1 ohm, and the resistance C to D is 1 ohm. The P.D. between A and D is 110 volts. Then the voltmeter V will read 110 volts.

The current flowing will be

$$I = \frac{E}{R} = \frac{110}{108 + 2} = 1 \text{ ampere.}$$

This will be indicated by the ammeter A (which could equally well have been joined in the circuit between C and D).

As the voltage drop A to B and C to D in each case = $I \times R = 1 \times 1 = 1$ volt, the P.D. between B and C = $110 - 2 = 108$ volts; this will be indicated by the voltmeter V_1.

The wattmeter W would read $110 \times 1 = 110$ watts.

185. According to the size of the currents they are designed to measure, current measuring instruments are described as ammeters, milliammeters, microammeters and galvanometers.

Their range of measurement may be greatly extended by the use of shunts, *i.e.*, by adding a resistance in parallel with the instrument (paragraph 67).

Shunts are usually made of a material which has a very small temperature coefficient of resistance *e.g.*, an alloy like manganin. This lessens inaccuracies due to temperature changes, which, by altering its resistance, will alter the readings of the instrument. This also applies to the series resistance in voltmeters.

The ammeter itself then carries only a fraction of the total current, depending on its resistance compared with that of the shunt. The ammeter is graduated to read the total current flowing in the circuit, and so the scale reading will have a different value for every shunt that can be inserted.

Ammeter and voltmeter terminals are always marked + and —, and must be correctly joined in a circuit, *i.e.*, positive terminal to positive lead.

Example 24.

An ammeter of resistance 2 ohms can take a maximum current of 0·5 amps. How can it be adapted to operate as :—

    (*a*) An ammeter reading to 5 amps. ?

    (*b*) A voltmeter reading to 100 volts ?

(*a*) It must be shunted by a resistance which takes 4·5 amps. when the ammeter is taking 0·5 amp. The value of the resistance is therefore $\frac{0·5}{4·5} = \frac{1}{9}$ of the ammeter resistance, *i.e.*, $\frac{2}{9}$ ohm.

(*b*) The P.D. across the ammeter when taking 0·5 amp. is $2 \times 0·5 = 1$ volt. A resistance must therefore be put in series which has a P.D. of 99 volts across it when 0·5 amp. is flowing in it. *i.e.*, $R = \frac{99}{0·5} = 198$ ohms.

186. Types of Instrument.—These may be classified as :—

    (*a*) Hot wire ; (*b*) moving coil ; (*c*) moving iron ; (*d*) electrostatic ; (*e*) rectifier instruments.

With the exception of (*d*), which is only used as a voltmeter, these may all be adapted for use either as ammeters or voltmeters.

Hot-Wire Instrument.—This is shown diagrammatically in Fig. 59. A is a taut wire, through which flows the current to be measured. The wire is of some material of high melting-point and high resistivity, usually platinum-silver. One end of a phosphor-bronze wire F is attached to some point in A near the centre, and its other end to an insulated block E. A silk fibre is attached to F as shown and passes round a pulley P on the spindle carrying the pointer. The fibre is held taut by the pull of the light spring R. When a current flows through A it is heated and expands, allowing the wire F to sag. As a result, the silk fibre in being pulled taut by the spring R rotates the pulley P, and the pointer moves over the scale.

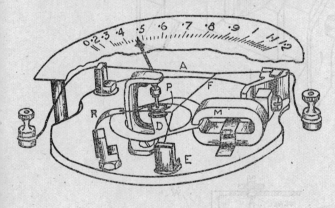

The aluminium disc D, attached to the spindle of the pointer and placed between the poles of the permanent magnet M, acts as a damping device. Movement of the pointer causes movement of the disc, thus producing eddy currents, which oppose the motion causing them and prevent oscillations of the pointer before it takes up its final position.

Since the heating effect, and therefore the expansion of A, is proportional to the square of the current, the scale is not uniform, being crowded at the lower end and open at the upper end.

The principal defect of a hot wire instrument is wandering of the zero, due to changes in the surrounding temperature. These changes produce different expansions in the wire itself and the metal block on which it is mounted, and so the wire may sag and a pointer deflection be produced even if no current is flowing.

It is possible to compensate for this to some extent if the base on which the hot wire is mounted is

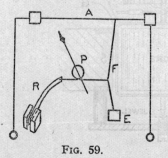

Fig. 59.

arranged to have the same coefficient of expansion as the wire itself.

Hot-wire instruments are also sluggish in action owing to a time lag between the current flowing and the expansion it produces.

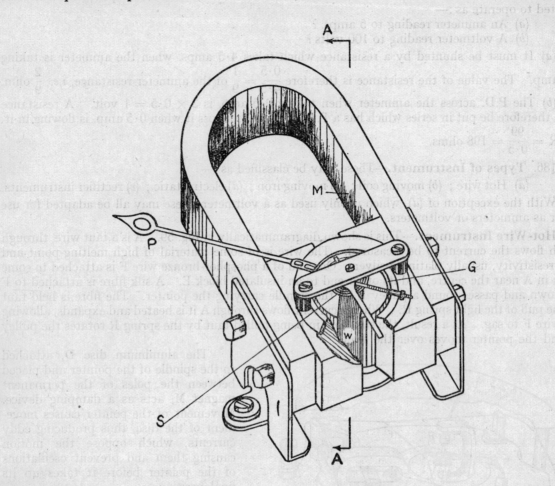

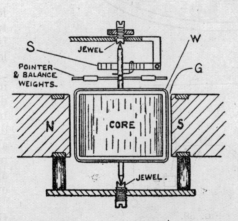

Sectional view at A.A.

Fig. 60.

187. **Moving Coil Instrument.**—If a coil carrying a current is placed in a magnetic field a mechanical force will act on the coil (paragraph 129). A typical instrument making use of this principle is shown in Fig. 60. The coil W is wound on a former of copper or aluminium, inside which is a fixed iron cylindrical core. The former is mounted on pivots so that it can rotate between the poles of a permanent magnet M. This leaves only a narrow air gap G between the poles and the former, so that the field of the magnet is radial and uniform for any position of the coil. Current is led into and away from the coil by one or two phosphor bronze springs S.

Equal forces in opposite directions act on the two halves of the winding, as can be seen by applying Fleming's Left Hand Rule. The coil thus tends to turn about its axis and, as the magnetic field is the same for all coil positions, the coil is subject to a constant torque or turning moment proportional to the current flowing in it. In the zero position there is no twist of the controlling springs. When the coil starts to rotate the springs become twisted and set up a torsional torque opposing the motion and proportional to the angle through which the coil has turned. The coil therefore takes up an equilibrium position in which the resisting torque due to the springs just balances the electrical torque due to the current. Since these torques are directly as the angle of rotation and the current respectively, it follows that the deflection of a pointer attached to the coil is directly proportional to the current and so the scale is uniform.

When in motion the metal former and the winding will have induced E.M.Fs. set up in them, causing currents tending to oppose the motion (Lenz's Law) and so acting as a damping device. The coil and pointer also have very small inertia. The motion of the pointer is, in consequence, " dead-beat."

As the magnetic field in the air gap is strong, the instrument is very little affected by stray magnetic fields. The permanent magnets are specially " aged " so that their strength remains constant for a long period. In consequence, moving coil instruments are the most accurate and satisfactory type for all D.C. measurements.

Rectifier Instruments.—The advantages of moving coil instruments may be extended to the measurement of alternating quantities by incorporating a rectifier in the instrument.

Very satisfactory instruments may be made using metal rectifiers (H.10) ; the A.C. input is rectified by the latter, and the mean value of the D.C. rectified current is measured by the moving coil meter.

In the case of ammeters, the scale is calibrated in R.M.S. values of the input, assuming the latter has a sinoidal waveform. Errors are introduced when the waveform departs from a sine wave shape. Direct reading ammeters may be made for currents up to about 50 milliamps, and higher currents may be measured by employing suitable current transformers. It is similarly easy to employ this principle in the design of low reading A.C. voltmeters.

These instruments are particularly applicable to low current and voltage measurements, the accuracy often being $\pm$ 2 per cent. on frequencies below 20 kc/s. At higher frequencies the shunting effect of self-capacity becomes apparent, and readings are usually low ; for a voltmeter the error may be of the order of 15 per cent. at 100 kc/s.

188. **Moving-Iron Instruments.**—Though not as accurate as the best moving-coil instruments, this type is usually simpler and of more robust construction. Two kinds are in common use, the attracted iron type and the repulsion type.

The operation of these instruments depends on the magnetisation of soft iron by a current and the consequent mechanical forces of attraction or repulsion.

Fig. 61 (a) illustrates the **attracted iron type.** C is a fixed coil carrying the current to be measured and M is a disc of soft iron, eccentrically pivoted and carrying a pointer. When current flows in the coil, M is magnetised. Not being pivoted at its C.G., it is attracted into the interior of the coil, thus causing the pointer to move. The controlling torque may be provided by a spring or a weight.

An air damping device to render the movement " dead-beat " is shown in Fig 61 (b). The block D is hollowed out so that a piston P, mounted on the axis of the moving iron, can travel into it.   The compression by the piston of the air in the hollow provides sufficient resistance to the motion to prevent oscillation of the moving parts.

Provided the disc is not near saturation, its magnetisation is roughly proportional to the current flowing in the coil.   The force of attraction, being proportional to the product of disc magnetisation and coil current, is therefore proportional to the square of the current to be measured.   As in the case of the hot-wire ammeter, the scale will not be uniform, being crowded at the lower end and more open at higher current values.

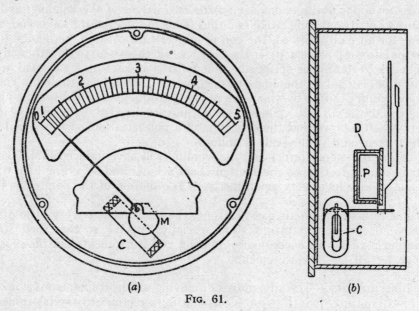

(a)   (b)

FIG. 61.

These instruments are not so sensitive as those of the rectifier type described above.   They are not practicable for low voltage and current measurements.

The **repulsion type** is shown in Fig. 62.   The spindle pivoted at BB, which carries the pointer P, runs down the axis of a cylindrical coil C carrying the current to be measured.   Attached to the spindle is a wedge-shaped piece of soft iron MI, the moving iron.   Inside the coil and bent so as to be parallel to its circumference is the fixed iron FI.   This covers a larger arc than the moving iron and is shaped in such a way that it is much narrower at one end than the other.   When current flows in the coil both irons become magnetised longitudinally in the same direction.   The magnetic effect of the fixed iron is greater at its broader end, and so the moving iron is repelled towards the narrower end, causing movement of the pointer.   The motion is controlled by the spring S and rendered dead-beat, as in the attraction type, by an air dashpot, shown at D.   Z is a zero-adjusting lever.

The force of repulsion is proportional to the product of the pole strengths of the two irons, and as each of these is proportional to the current, when working away from saturation, the movement is proportional to the square of the current.   The non-uniformity of scale which this produces may be minimised over the working region by suitably shaping the irons.

Moving iron instruments are affected by external magnetic fields, and are also liable to hysteresis errors which cause them to read low with increasing currents and high when the current is decreasing. In modern instruments, these errors can be made very small by shielding from external fields in an iron case, and by using for the " irons " a nickel-iron alloy which has negligible hysteresis effects. Particularly in the attracted iron type, the coil C can also be made small, thus minimising temperature effects.

189. **Electrostatic Voltmeter.**—The action of this instrument depends on the force of attraction between two opposite charges, insulated from each other.   A spindle mounted between

pivots carries a pointer and a light aluminium vane V, which can swing between two electrically common brass plates BB. The whole instrument is enclosed in a metal case on an insulating base and provided with a glass window for observing the scale. Apart from the window, the instrument is thus shielded from the electrostatic effects of external charges.

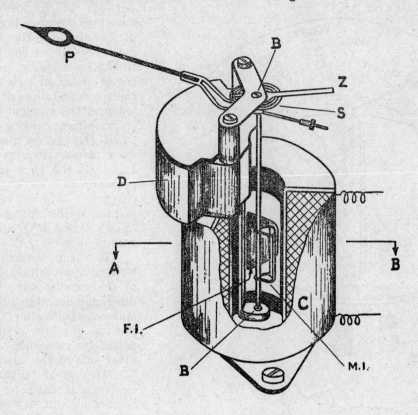

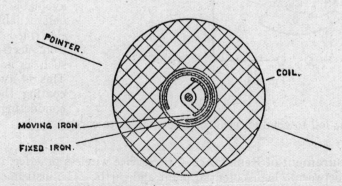

Sectional plan at A.B.

FIG. 62.

The moving vane is generally in conducting communication with the case *via* its spindle, and the brass plates are insulated from the case.

In the uncharged position the long axis of the moving vane is set at some angle to that of the brass plates, as shown in the diagram. When a P.D. is established between the moving and fixed parts they are equivalent to the plates of a condenser and acquire equal and opposite charges, the electrostatic attraction between which draws the moving vane into the space between the brass plates and causes the pointer to move over the scale. The motion is controlled by a spring, and the pointer comes to rest in such a position that the opposing torque due to the spring balances the moment of the electrostatic forces causing motion. The equal charges on the moving and fixed plates are proportional to the P.D. and the force of attraction is proportional to the product of the charges. The movement of the pointer is thus proportional to the square of the P.D. and the scale is not uniform.

In a ship, the instrument should work in any position, but the weight of the moving vane would have a different moment in different positions and so would alter the zero. To prevent this the vane is counterpoised by two small weights on the other side of the axis of rotation.

The great advantage of the electrostatic voltmeter is that it takes no current, and so wastes no energy and does not suffer from temperature defects. It is also unaffected by stray magnetic fields, but the unavoidable use of a glass window renders it liable to errors from external electrified bodies and particularly from electrification of the glass itself, such as is produced by cleaning it. This is avoided to some extent by coating the glass with transparent conducting varnish and fixing on it a strip of metallic foil to conduct electrostatic charges to earth.

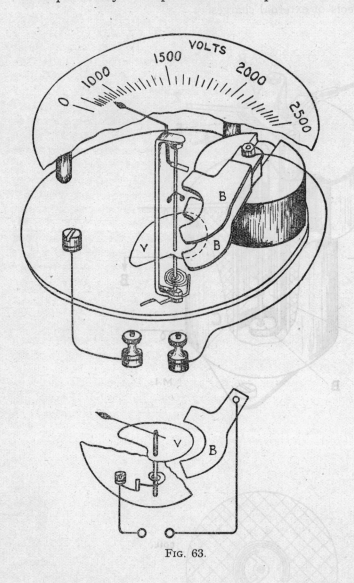

FIG. 63.

190. **Measurement of Resistance.**—In Service wireless practice, it is often necessary to test the insulation between a high potential point and earth. The instrument used for this purpose is called a Megger and reads directly on a scale the resistance between the two points at which it is connected.

The principle of the Megger is shown in Fig. 64. The measuring system consists of two coils mounted at right angles to each other on a common shaft and called the Current or Deflecting Coil and Pressure or Control Coil respectively. They are pivoted so as to be free to move in the magnetic field of a permanent magnet, and wound so that when carrying current they tend to rotate the movement in opposite directions. The pointer thus comes to rest in an equilibrium position determined by the relative values of the currents flowing in the two coils.

The Pressure Coil is connected, in series with a fixed high resistance to adjust the range, directly across the generator. One generator terminal is earthed and the other is connected through the Current Coil and a fixed resistance to the point whose insulation to earth is to be tested. Thus the Current Coil is in series with the unknown insulation resistance across the generator terminals.

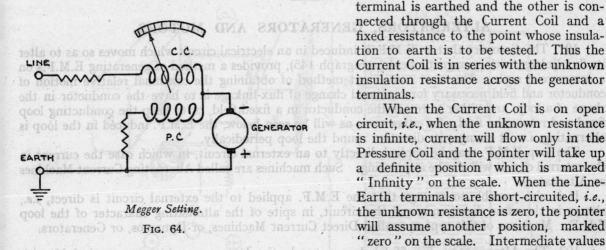

Megger Setting.

Fig. 64.

When the Current Coil is on open circuit, *i.e.*, when the unknown resistance is infinite, current will flow only in the Pressure Coil and the pointer will take up a definite position which is marked " Infinity " on the scale. When the Line-Earth terminals are short-circuited, *i.e.*, the unknown resistance is zero, the pointer will assume another position, marked " zero " on the scale. Intermediate values of resistance will cause the pointer to take up positions on the scale between these two limits, and these positions may be determined by inserting known resistances. The instrument is thus calibrated to read resistance directly.

The generator armature is rotated by hand from a handle outside the instrument. A constant-speed clutch is interposed between the handle and the armature, so that the armature cannot rotate above a certain rate (160 r.p.m. in the Service instrument), no matter how fast the handle is turned. In addition, if the handle is stopped suddenly, a free wheel allows the armature to come to rest slowly so that the generator is not damaged.

The lowest resistance which can be measured accurately on this instrument is about 10,000 ohms. The range may be extended to 0·01 ohm by means of a change-over switch, which gives the circuit of Fig. 65, known as the Bridge Setting.

The principle employed is that of Wheatstone's Bridge (paragraph 73). The unknown resistance forms one arm of the bridge, the fixed resistance in series with the current coil forms another, and a known resistance with various tappings provides the other two arms as shown.

The current coil takes the part of the galvanometer in the ordinary Wheatstone Bridge arrangement. The bridge is balanced

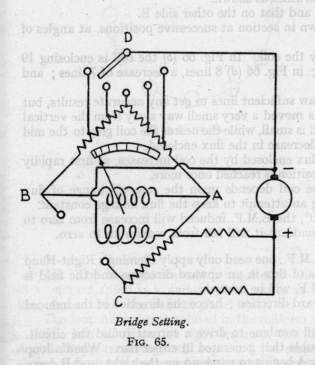

Bridge Setting.

Fig. 65.

when no current flows in this coil. As shown above, the pointer in this case indicates " infinity " on the scale, so that the procedure is to adjust the tapping point until this reading is obtained.

From the point of view of generating E.M.F. we are only interested in the horizontal movement of A, since it is only when moving horizontally that it cuts across the magnetic field, and generates an E.M.F. The length of AD at any instant will, therefore, be a measure of the rate of cutting of lines of flux by A, and therefore of the voltage generated.

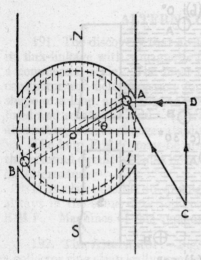

The vertical component CD represents the motion of A parallel to the field, which motion has no effect in generating an E.M.F.

We therefore wish to investigate how AD will vary during a revolution of the bar A.

195. Since CD is perpendicular to the initial position of the conductor, and AC is perpendicular to its direction AB after it has turned through an angle θ, it follows that angle ACD is equal to θ.

Fig. 68 shows the bar in successive positions as the angle θ varies from 0° to 90°.

(a) θ = 0°, DC = AC, and AD = 0 ; no lines of force are being cut and no voltage is being generated.

(b), (c) and (d). The line AD, and therefore the voltage generated, steadily increases.

(e) θ = 90°, AD = AC : therefore the voltage generated is a maximum ;

and so on.

FIG. 67.

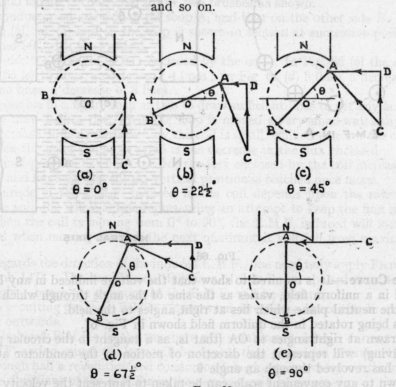

(a) θ = 0°

(b) θ = 22½°

(c) θ = 45°

(d) θ = 67½°

(e) θ = 90°

FIG. 68.

Now $\dfrac{AD}{AC}$ = sine of the angle ACD.

Therefore AD = AC × sin ACD = a constant × sin ACD = **a constant × sin θ**.

AD is proportional to v, the voltage induced at any instant.

Therefore $v = $ a constant $\times \sin \theta$.

If $v = \mathcal{V}$ when A is opposite the centre of the north pole, *i.e.*, when $\theta = 90°$, it follows that the constant in the above expression is equal to $\mathcal{V}$, for $\sin 90° = 1$. $\mathcal{V}$ is the maximum value assumed by v in a revolution.

Hence

$$v = \mathcal{V} \sin \theta \quad \dots \dots \dots \dots \dots \dots \quad (1)$$

Taking figures, let us suppose that $\mathcal{V}$ is 10 volts.

Then from a table of sines we find that v will go through the following values :—

θ:	0°,	10°,	20°,	30°,	40°,	50°,	60°,
v:	0,	1·74,	3·5,	5·2,	7,	7·6,	8·6,

θ:	70°,	80°,	90°,	100°,	110°,	120°, &c.
v:	9·4,	9·8,	10,	9·8,	9·4,	8·6.

A convenient method of plotting the curve $v = \mathcal{V} \sin \theta$ geometrically is shown in Fig. 69.

Let the line OA represent $\mathcal{V}$. Then the line AM $=$ OA $\sin \theta = \mathcal{V} \sin \theta$.

We may now take a horizontal line DE to represent degrees and plot on it the various lengths and directions of the line AM as the point A revolves.

Fig. 69 is a graph of the various values of AM as the line OP revolves through 360°. The dotted lines indicate how the curve is constructed, and should need no further explanation.

When AM comes above the line CD we call it positive in sign. This will be for values of θ lying between 0° and 180°. For values of θ between 180° and 360°, A will be below the line and AM will be negative.

After joining up all the points we have the curve as in Fig. 69.

A curve constructed in this manner is termed a " Sine Curve."

The maximum height of the curve, called its " amplitude," will be equal to OA, which equals $\mathcal{V}$.

At all times the height of the curve $= \mathcal{V} \sin \theta$, so that :—

When $\theta = 0°$ or $180°$, $\mathcal{V} \sin \theta = 0$: when $\theta = 90°$ or $270°$, $\mathcal{V} \sin \theta = \mathcal{V} \times 1 = \mathcal{V}$, or $\mathcal{V} \times -1 = -\mathcal{V}$.

The variation of the curve from zero, to a maximum positive, through zero to maximum negative, and back to zero again, is termed a " Cycle."

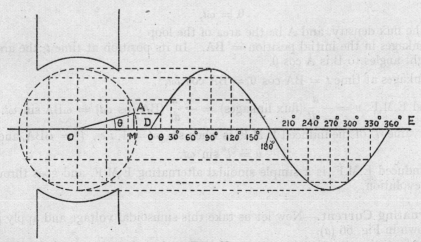

FIG. 69.

196. Frequency.—In every revolution of the armature bar, a cycle of the E.M.F. is completed. Hence, if the bar is revolving at f revolutions per second, f cycles are completed per second.

"Cycles per second " is termed "**Frequency.**"

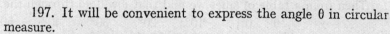
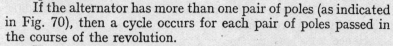
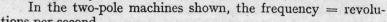

Fig. 70.

In the two-pole machines shown, the frequency = revolutions per second.

If the alternator has more than one pair of poles (as indicated in Fig. 70), then a cycle occurs for each pair of poles passed in the course of the revolution.

Hence, frequency = revs. per sec. × number of pairs of poles.

197. It will be convenient to express the angle θ in circular measure.

Consider a two-pole machine.

In one second f revolutions take place, each of 360°; but 360° = 2π radians.

Therefore in one second f revolutions take place, each of 2π radians.

In one second, 2πf radians are swept out in all.

So 2πf is the number of radians swept out per second.

This is called the "**angular velocity.**"

For brevity, the expression 2πf is denoted by the letter " ω " (a Greek letter called " omega ") Thus ω = 2πf = 6·28 × f.

In a time t secs., the angle θ in radians swept out by the conductor is θ = ωt. Formula (1) in paragraph 195 thus becomes

$$v = \mathcal{V} \sin ωt \quad . \quad . \quad . \quad \text{in volts} \quad . \quad . \quad . \quad . \quad . \quad . \quad . \quad . \quad . \quad (2)$$

If two pairs of poles are fitted, although the armature sweeps out only 360 actual degrees, we have two complete cycles, which require on the curve 720 electrical degrees.

By using " ω " to represent angular velocity, we mean " electrical " angles, without reference to any definite number of poles.

★198. The above results may be obtained much more directly as follows :—

Let the initial position of the loop be on the neutral axis midway between the poles, and after a time t, let it have turned through an angle θ from its initial position. The angular velocity is ω and so

$$θ = ωt.$$

Let B be the flux density, and A be the area of the loop.

The flux linkages in the initial position = BA. In its position at time t, the area of the loop projected at right angles to B is A cos θ.

∴ Flux linkages at time t = BA cos θ = BA cos ωt.

∴ Induced E.M.F. $v = -\dfrac{d}{dt}$ (flux linkages) $= -\dfrac{d}{dt}$ (BA cos ωt) = ωBA sin ωt.

The maximum value $\mathcal{V}$ of the induced E.M.F. is when sin ωt = 1, $i.e.$, $\mathcal{V}$ = ωBA, and we can write

$$v = \mathcal{V} \sin ωt.$$

Thus the induced E.M.F. is a simple sinoidal alternating E.M.F. and goes through one cycle per electrical revolution.

199. **Alternating Current.**—Now let us take this sinusoidal voltage and apply it to the ends of a circuit, shown in Fig. 66 (a).

Suppose, at first, that the circuit contains resistance, but that it is non-inductively wound and has no capacity. A current will flow, which will rise, fall and reverse in step with the voltage impressed on the ends of the circuit, and we can employ Ohm's Law to find the strength of the current.

Hence, the current at any moment

$$i = \frac{\mathcal{V}}{R} \sin \omega t = \mathcal{J} \sin \omega t.$$

200. The Alternator.—A single armature bar would have to be revolved at a tremendous speed in a very dense magnetic field in order to generate an E.M.F. that would be of any use to us.

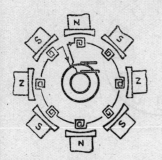

An alternator armature winding therefore consists of several groups of windings arranged in series, separated by the same distance that separates the poles, and so wound that the E.M.F.s induced in all the coils act in the same direction, as in Fig. 71.

In Fig. 72 is illustrated a portion of an armature winding in successive positions as it passes under a pair of poles.

When it starts (a) it is not cutting any flux, and so is generating no E.M.F.

As it moves under the pole pieces, the E.M.F. induced in it rises, till in Fig 72 (c) it is generating a maximum E.M.F. (as shown by the curve above it) because it is cutting across the field at right angles.

As it moves away from the central position the generated E.M.F. will fall off, till it is zero again as in Fig. 72 (e).

FIG. 71.

The right-hand side of the coil will then come under the influence of the north pole and the left-hand side under that of the next south pole (not shown in the illustration), and the E.M.F. will start to rise in the opposite direction.

201. The Armature.—We have previously shown that for a given magnetising force, the total number of magnetic lines produced in a magnet will depend upon the reluctance of the magnetic circuit. The greater part of the reluctance in a magnetic circuit of ordinary dimensions is due to the air gap. It is clear that by reducing the air gap between the poles, we can get a greater density and therefore a greater total number of magnetic lines with the same magnetising force.

This air gap can be reduced in two ways; firstly, by shaping the pole faces in a curve so that they are parallel to the path of rotation of the conductors, and,

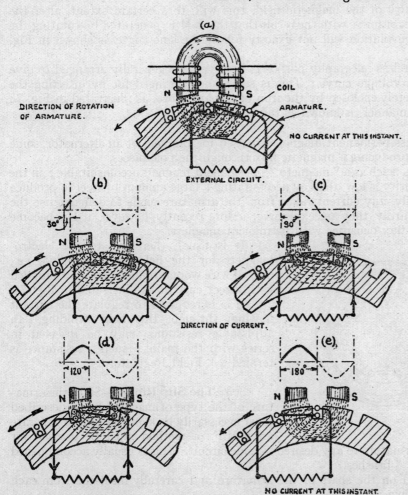

FIG. 72.

secondly, by filling up the space inside the path of the conductors—that is to say, filling up the core of the armature—with iron.

Such an arrangement is shown in Fig. 73 (a), where, as is usual in most dynamos, the conductors are shown embedded in slots in the iron core, thus reducing the gap between the iron of the pole face and the iron of the armature core to a minimum.

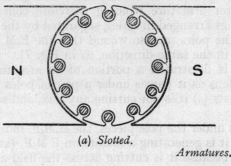 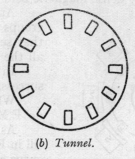

(a) Slotted.   (b) Tunnel.

Armatures.

FIG. 73.

Besides increasing the density of the magnetic field, this will, to a certain extent, alter the distribution of the magnetic lines of force, with the result that the E.M.F. generated by rotating the conductor through a complete revolution will not exactly follow the sine curve as shown in Fig. 69.

Alternators designed for wireless telegraphy purposes, however, are generally arranged to give what is practically a sinusoidal voltage curve. This is sometimes arranged for by inserting the conductors through holes completely enclosed by the iron of the armature, as illustrated in Fig. 73 (b). An armature wound in this manner, is known as tunnel-wound.

202. Pole Winding.—Unless permanent magnets are used for the field of an alternator, some arrangement must be made for producing a magnetic flux through the pole pieces.

Except for special machines (such as a " magneto "), permanent magnets are unsuitable ; in the first place, the magnetic flux density is low, thereby necessitating a large amount of steel to produce a given amount of flux ; secondly, any current taken from the armature tends to demagnetise the poles owing to reaction ; and, thirdly, they are expensive. More recently, however, it has become possible to obtain much higher flux densities with permanent magnets.

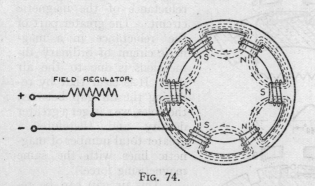

FIELD REGULATOR

FIG. 74.

It is usual, therefore, to use electro-magnets for the fields of a dynamo, i.e., coils of wire wound round cores, and supplied with direct current as illustrated in Fig. 74.

If it is required to regulate the current flowing through the field winding, an adjustable resistance may be inserted in series with the mains ; such a resistance is termed a " Field Regulator."

203. The Slip Rings.—Since the armature of the type of machine being described must necessarily be kept rotating to generate an E.M.F., a method must be devised for connecting the windings of the armature to any desired outside circuit. This is usually accomplished by the use of " slip rings " and " brushes."

Two brass rings are carried on the shaft of the armature and carefully insulated from each other and from the shaft, as shown in Fig. 75.

These rings rotate with the armature, but as they have a smooth surface, connection can conveniently be made to them from a fixed part of the machine by means of carbon "brushes" pressing lightly on the surface of the rings.

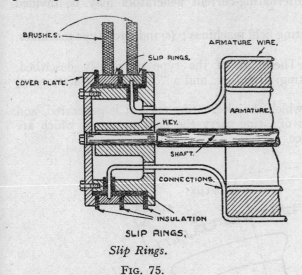

SLIP RINGS.

Slip Rings.

FIG. 75.

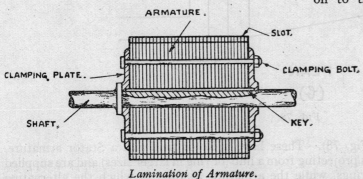

DIRECTION OF EDDY CURRENTS

ARMATURE

DIRECTION OF MOTION

DIRECTION OF MAGNETIC LINES

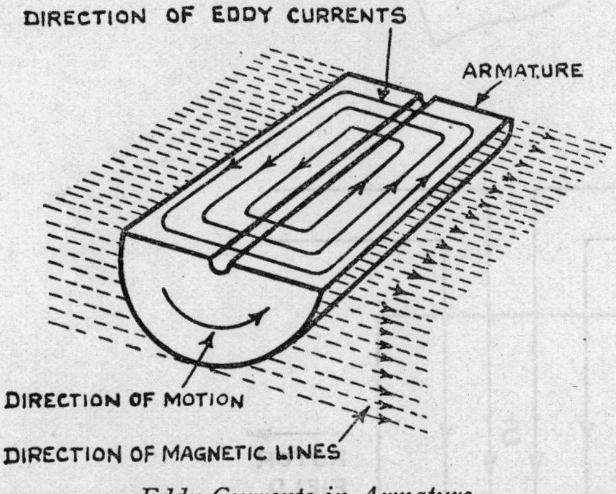

Eddy Currents in Armature.

FIG. 76.

ARMATURE.

SLOT.

CLAMPING PLATE.

CLAMPING BOLT.

SHAFT.

KEY.

Lamination of Armature.

FIG. 77.

One end of the armature winding is then connected to one slip-ring and the other end to the other slip-ring, while the outside circuit to which it is desired to connect the alternator is connected to the two brushes.

204. Eddy Currents.—It has already been seen that the conductors on the armature are embedded in an iron core in order to reduce the air gap in the magnetic circuit of the alternator.

Obviously, this iron core revolves with the conductors in the magnetic field. Since the iron is also a conductor of electricity and is unavoidably cutting the lines of force induced by the field magnets, the result is that E.M.F.s are generated in the iron body of the armature and cause currents to circulate continually in the metal.

These currents are known as Eddy Currents, and since they cannot be utilised they only represent so much wasted energy, and in addition heat up the iron of the armature core to the detriment of the running of the machine. Means must therefore be found to reduce them to a minimum.

The direction of these currents will be found by applying Fleming's "Right Hand Rule," and will be as shown in Fig 76; that is to say, round the core at right angles to the lines of force.

205. Lamination.—To prevent these currents flowing, armature cores are built up of a large number of thin circular plates of iron, separated from each other by very thin paper or varnish. The plates are threaded on to the armature shaft and are clamped together by some suitable means, such as that illustrated in section in Fig. 77.

It will be seen that these sheets of paper, being non-conducting, offer a large resistance to any currents which tend to flow in the iron core in a direction parallel to the shaft, as indicated in Fig. 76.

At the same time they do not increase the reluctance of the magnetic circuit to any great extent, as the lines of force can pass freely down each plate of the armature core without passing through the paper.

206. Alternator Construction.—Practical alternating-current generators may be divided into three classes, thus :—

      (*a*) Rotating armature machines ; (*b*) rotating field machines ; (*c*) inductor-type machines.

207.—(*a*) Rotating Armature Machines.—These are of the type previously described, and are spoken of as having a " Rotor " (or rotating) armature, and a " Stator " (or stationary) field.

A revolving armature carries the winding in which the alternating current is generated, and poles projecting inwards from a yoke in the form of a ring carry the field windings, which are supplied with direct current from an outside source.

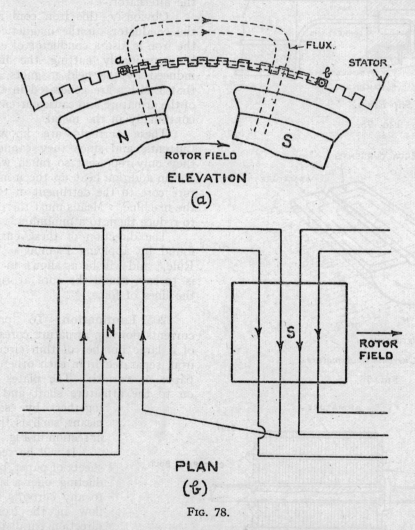

ELEVATION

(a)

PLAN

(b)

FIG. 78.

(*b*) **Rotating Field Machines** (Fig. 78).—These have a Rotor field and a Stator armature, *i.e.*, the magnet coils are carried on poles projecting from a hub (or ring in larger sizes) and are supplied with direct current through two slip-rings, while the armature winding in which the alternating current is generated is wound in slots on the inside of a cylinder enclosing the rotor. Fig. 78 (*a*) and (*b*) show diagrammatically an elevation and plan view respectively of part of the armature winding.

The direction of the induced E.M.F. is obtained by Fleming's Right Hand Rule, but if, as in Fig. 78, the field is moving to the **right**, this is equivalent to keeping the field stationary and moving the armature conductors to the **left**. This must be allowed for in applying the rule, in which the thumb gives the direction of relative motion of the **conductor**. The E.M.F. induced into conductor *a* (Fig. 78 (*a*)) is *into*, and in conductor *b out of*, the paper. In Fig. 78 (*b*) the flux is coming out of the paper from the north pole and going into the paper again in the south pole.

This is a more convenient method of generating a high-voltage alternating current, since the conductors and slip rings of the rotor have to stand only the voltage of the direct current supplied for magnetising the field, while it is much easier to insulate the stator winding, which does not require slip-rings.

208.—(3) **The Inductor Type.**—In the " Inductor " type of alternator both the armature winding and the field magnet winding are wound on projections inside the stator, while the rotor consists of a drum carrying projections of steel or iron material.

Fig. 79 (*a*) illustrates diagrammatically a machine of this type. The armature winding is wound on projections of the stator while, for clearness, the field winding is shown on the legs of the field magnet system. The rotor is simply a soft iron cylinder with projections whose width corresponds to the pole pitch of the stator.

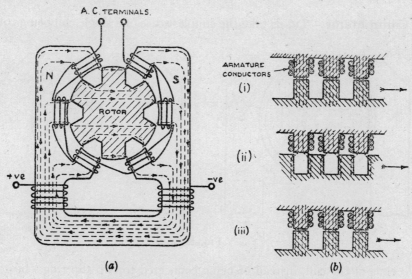

Alternator—Inductor Type—diagrammatic.

FIG. 79.

Fig. 79 (*b*) illustrates the action. The flux is formed into " tufts " each time a rotor pole is opposite a stator pole ((i) and (iii)) : when the poles are in the midway position (ii) the flux is fairly evenly distributed across the air gap. Therefore, considering any one stator pole, the flux is continually spreading out and gathering in again, the spreading out causing one alternation and the gathering in a reverse alternation, and the two together forming one complete cycle.

An E.M.F. is developed in the stator winding and it may be made to have the form of a sine curve.

The frequency is given by the number of revolutions per second of the rotor, multiplied by the number of its projections.

E

The generation of an E.M.F. in this case may also be considered as a result of the variable reluctance of the path of the flux lines, as the air gaps between the stator and rotor poles alter in length during a revolution. The ampere-turns producing the field are a constant quantity and so therefore is the M.M.F. (paragraph 92). **Variation in the reluctance of the magnetic circuit thus produces a variation in the number of lines linking with the armature circuit and an E.M.F. is generated.**

THE DIRECT CURRENT GENERATOR, OR DYNAMO.

209. Exactly the same principles hold good as regards the E.M.Fs. produced in the conductors of the armature of a continuous current dynamo. That is to say, alternating E.M.Fs. are produced in the conductors themselves, but, as we shall show later, these alternating E.M.Fs., instead of being brought straight to the outside circuit through slip-rings, as in the case of the alternator, are taken through an apparatus for automatically reversing their direction, so far as the outside circuit is concerned, at definite intervals.

In order to produce a continuous current in the outside circuit, or, as it may be better considered, in order to produce a continuous E.M.F. at the brushes of the dynamo, an arrangement is provided for reversing the connections of the armature coils at the brushes at the moment when the E.M.F. induced in the coils reverses.

This arrangement is known as the Commutator, and its action is described in the following paragraphs.

210. The Commutator.—Let us take the simplest case of a single coil being rotated, as shown in Fig. 80.

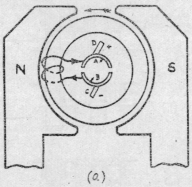 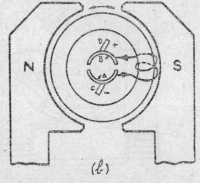

(a)   (b)

FIG. 80.

If the two ends of the coil, instead of being connected to two slip rings, be connected one to each half, A and B, of a divided ring which rotates with the armature, and if the two brushes C and D be fixed in the position shown, it is evident that while the coil is travelling under the N pole of the magnet the half-ring A will be in contact with the brush D and the half ring B with the brush C (Fig. 80 (a)), and, similarly, while the coil is travelling under the S pole of the magnet, A will be in contact with C, and B with D, as shown in Fig. 80 (b).

By tracing the directions of the E.M.F. generated, it will be seen that while the coil is travelling under the N pole, the half ring A will be positive and B will therefore be negative, and similarly, while the coil is travelling under

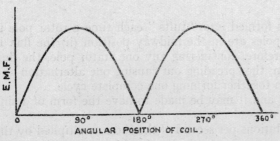

ANGULAR POSITION OF COIL.

FIG. 81.

the S pole, A will be negative and B positive. It follows, therefore, that the brush D will always be in contact with whichever half ring is positive and the brush C with whichever half ring is negative throughout the revolution.

Since the wave form of the E.M.F. generated in the active conductors of the coil takes the form shown in Fig. 69, it is obvious that the curve showing the value of the E.M.F. at the brushes, when the coil is thus connected to a split ring, will take the form shown in Fig. 81.

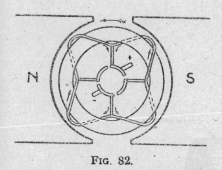

FIG. 82.

Let us develop this arrangement a little further and take a commutator with four segments, connected to four points on the armature winding, as in Fig. 82.

If the position of the brushes is adjusted as shown, it will be observed that each brush short-circuits two segments when the coil attached to these segments is generating no E.M.F. With respect to the brushes, the coils are arranged in two sets of two coils in series, the sets being in parallel with each other. The E.M.F. between the brushes is thus the sum of the E.M.Fs. in the two coils in series on one half of the armature. The individual E.M.Fs. in these coils are shown dotted in Fig. 83. One lags on the other by a quarter of a period, as is evident from Fig. 82. The total E.M.F. of the machine is the sum of these two E.M.Fs., indicated by the full line curve in Fig. 83.

211. Armature Windings.—In practice, an armature winding consists of a great many conductors arranged in slots on an iron core. Each conductor is connected to one segment of the commutator.

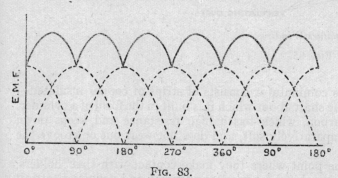

FIG. 83.

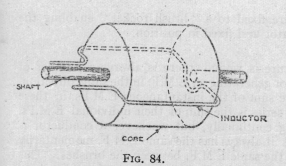

FIG. 84.

The conductors are not in practice arranged as in Fig. 82, which illustrates a "ring-wound" or "Gramme ring" armature, but are wound entirely on the outside of the armature, as in Fig. 84.

All the coils are so arranged that they, together with the commutator segments to which they are connected, form a closed circuit upon themselves, and each coil always comprises part of the circuit; consequently the P.D. between the brushes is half the sum of the average E.M.Fs. induced in all the conductors.

An illustration of one coil, and the way coils are built up on an armature, is given in Fig. 85 (a) and (b).

There are two main types of windings :—

(1) Lap (or parallel) ; and

(2) Wave (or series), with simple and complex forms of each.

The reader is referred to any standard electrical textbook for a description of the various methods of winding an armature.

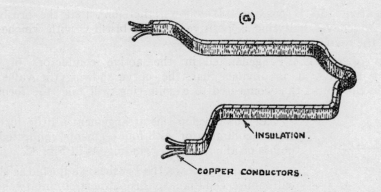

(a)

INSULATION.

COPPER CONDUCTORS.

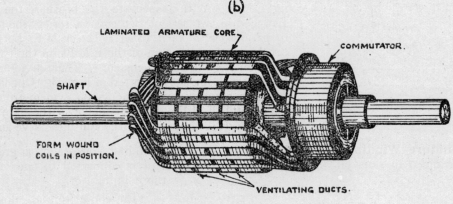

(b)

LAMINATED ARMATURE CORE.

COMMUTATOR.

SHAFT

FORM WOUND
COILS IN POSITION.

VENTILATING DUCTS.

Armature Winding.

FIG. 85.

212. Commutator and Brushes.—The commutator consists of strips of copper insulated—usually by mica—from each other and from the shaft about which it is built in the form of a cylinder.

The brushes are usually of graphitic carbon, which has a high resistance and keeps down sparking, keeps the commutator clean, is comparatively soft, and does not wear out or groove the commutator, but takes its shape.

They are sometimes copper-plated at the point where they make contact with their holders, although this practice is being discontinued in machines for wireless purposes, and definite electrical connection is made by means of a flexible copper wire.

They are held in brush-holders and the latter are fixed to a " brush rocker " enabling the brushes to be shifted all together round the commutator and fixed in position.

213. E.M.F. of Machine.—However the armature is wound there is always a number of conductors in series between the brushes, each conductor generating an E.M.F. in the same direction. The E.M.F. between the brushes at any instant is the sum of the instantaneous E.M.Fs. in these conductors, just as the E.M.F. of a number of cells in series is the sum of their individual E.M.Fs. The E.M.F. of the individual conductors is changing continually, but whenever a conductor is passing through a fixed position relative to the brushes it always has the same E.M.F. momentarily induced, so that there will be, on the average, always the same E.M.F. between the brushes. This will be equal to the average E.M.F. induced in any one conductor in its passage from brush to brush, multiplied by the number of conductors in series between the brushes. It is called the E.M.F. of the machine. As is suggested by a comparison of Fig. 81 and 83, the fluctuation about this mean value becomes smaller as the number of conductors in a series zone becomes greater.

There will be a number of such series zones of conductors in parallel between the brushes; cf. Fig. 82, where there are two such parallel paths. Each series zone produces the same E.M.F., which is the E.M.F. of the machine, and is unaffected by the number of parallel paths; but, as in a series parallel arrangement of cells, the internal resistance of the armature winding is decreased, and its current-carrying capacity increased, by increasing the number of such parallel paths.

214. Calculation of Dynamo E.M.F.—As explained above, the method of doing this is to find the average E.M.F. induced in one conductor in its passage from brush to brush, and multiply the result by the number of conductors between brushes.

Let Φ be the flux per pole. Then in passing under a N pole and the succeeding S pole, a conductor cuts 2Φ lines. If there are p pairs of poles alternately N and S round the armature, a conductor therefore changes its flux linkages by $2p\Phi$ lines in one revolution, and at an armature speed of N revolutions per second, the change of flux linkages per second for each conductor will be $2p\Phi \times N = 2pN\Phi$. Therefore the average induced E.M.F. in any conductor is $2pN\Phi \times 10^{-8}$ volts.

If n is the number of conductors in series between two brushes, the E.M.F. of the machine is thus $E = 2pnN\Phi \times 10^{-8}$ volts.

n and p are constants which depend only on the construction of the machine, and so we may write

$$E = KN\Phi$$

as a formula to cover all machines, the constant K varying with the particular machine considered. Thus in all cases the E.M.F. of a dynamo is proportional to—

(a) the flux per pole, i.e., the field;
(b) the speed.

The general formula for calculating the E.M.F. of a particular machine is

$$E = \frac{2pZN\Phi}{a} \times 10^{-8} \text{ volts,}$$

where Z is the total number of armature conductors, "a" is the number of parallel conducting paths through the armature, and the other symbols have the same significance as before.

For any "lap winding," the number of paths in parallel "a" is always equal to the number of poles; for a simple "wave winding," "a" is always 2.

215. Energy Changes in Armature.—So far, we have been discussing the dynamo purely as a generator of E.M.F. We have now to consider what happens when the E.M.F. is applied to an external closed circuit, and current starts to flow. While the machine is on open circuit no electrical power is being provided, and the horse-power supplied to the armature shaft by the steam engine or other source of mechanical power has only to spin the armature against the torque or resistance to rotation offered by friction, air resistance, etc. As soon as a current starts to flow, electrical power is being supplied to the external circuit, this additional power supply being proportional to the current flowing. The power which must be supplied from the mechanical source thus increases with the current taken from the dynamo.

We may consider this conversion of mechanical power to electrical power from two points of view.

216. On closed circuit a current flows through the armature windings, and so they are current-carrying conductors placed in a magnetic field. Thus each conductor is acted on by a force (paragraph 130) which, by Fleming's Left Hand Rule, is seen to be in the opposite direction to the direction of rotation. This " electrodynamic torque " has to be overcome by the mechanical drive, and so additional power must be supplied for this purpose by the source of power.

We can find the value of the " electrodynamic torque " as follows :—

If the torque is T foot-pounds, the power on the shaft required to overcome it at N r.p.s. is $\frac{2\pi NT}{550}$ H.P. This mechanical power is completely converted to electrical power E.I_a watts, where E is the E.M.F. generated by the dynamo and I_a is the armature current.

Therefore, expressing mechanical and electrical power in the same units (1 H.P. = 746 watts), we have

$$\frac{2\pi NT}{550} = \frac{EI_a}{746}$$

or

$$T = \frac{550\ EI_a}{746 \times 2\pi N}.$$

We have seen that $E = KN\,\Phi$ (para. 214) and substituting this value gives

$$T = \frac{550\ KN\,\Phi I_a}{746 \times 2\pi N} = \frac{550K}{746 \times 2\pi} \times I_a\,\Phi$$

$$= K_1 I_a\,\Phi,$$

where K_1 is a constant depending on K, *i.e.*, on the particular machine.

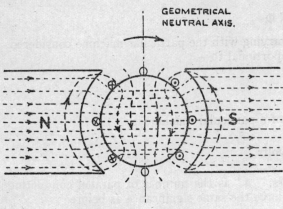

GEOMETRICAL
NEUTRAL AXIS.

COMPONENT FIELDS.

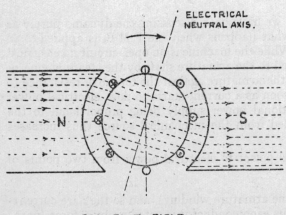

ELECTRICAL
NEUTRAL AXIS.

RESULTANT FIELD.
FIG. 86.

This shows that the " electrodynamic torque " is independent of the speed and depends only on the field flux and the armature current.

217. Armature Reaction.—We can also consider the problem from the point of view of the flux distribution. The current flowing in the armature windings produces a magnetic field, and, along with the original field, this produces a resultant field in which the flux lines are distorted from their original direction. This distortion in the case of a dynamo is shown in Fig. 86. The flux, instead of being approximately uniform over the pole surfaces, tends to crowd into the forward pole tip in the direction of rotation, and is correspondingly weakened in the hindward tip. The line along which any coil is enclosing maximum flux and generating no E.M.F., the " electrical neutral axis," has advanced relatively to the axis of symmetery between the poles or " geometrical neutral axis " through a certain angle in the direction of rotation.

We have seen (paragraph 210) that the aim in commutation is to reverse the current in coils when no E.M.F. is being produced in them *i.e.* in coils on the " electrical neutral axis." The brushes must therefore be advanced in the direction of rotation from their original position on the geometrical neutral axis.

This will change the distribution of current in the armature windings, and so the flux distribution and electrical neutral axis will alter again. Thus, the brushes must be advanced still further in the direction of rotation until the field due to the armature current is perpendicular to the resultant field.

218. Fig. 87 represents the original state of affairs. AB is the flux due to the field magnets, BC is the flux due to the armature current. We advance the brushes through an angle CBC′ so that the armature field is perpendicular to AC, the original resultant field. The armature field, however, retains its original strength and is now represented by BC′, which is not perpendicular to AC′ the new resultant field. Thus, the brushes must be advanced through another angle C′BC″, until the armature field is perpendicular to the final resultant field AC″, as shown in Fig. 87.

The amount of this " armature reaction " is obviously proportional to the armature field, and so varies with the current taken from the machine.

The armature field BC″ can be resolved into two components :—

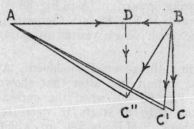

FIG. 87.

(*a*) A cross-magnetising component DC″. It is this component which produces the flux distortion.

(*b*) A demagnetising component BD in opposition to AB. Thus the field magnet flux is weakened as the current increases and the E.M.F. generated by the machine falls off.

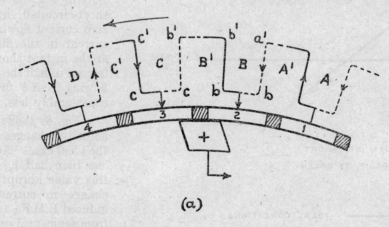

(a)

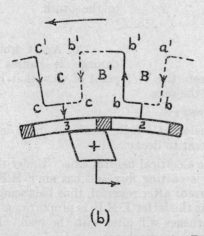

(b)

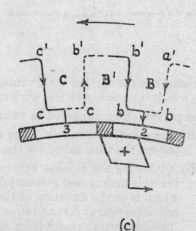

(c)

FIG. 88.

219. **Sparking.**—Sparking at the brushes is caused by the self-inductance of the armature windings. Fig. 88 (*a*) shows some of the coils in the neighbourhood of the positive brush joined to their corresponding commutator segments. Fig. 88 (*b*) shows the instant just before commutation of coil B commences. The current in *bb'* is upwards. Fig. 88 (*c*) shows the instant just after commutation of coil B is finished. The current in *bb'* is now in the opposite direction. In each case the current is half the armature current (in a two-brush machine), the other half, in the same direction to the brush but in the opposite direction in the armature, being provided via coil C before commutation and via coil A after commutation of coil B. Thus the current in coil B has to be changed by an amount equal to the whole armature current during the time that the brush is short-circuiting the junction B' of coils B and C. Fig. 88 (*a*) shows the middle instant of this interval.

Under ideal conditions, half the armature current would be flowing upwards in *bb'* in Fig. 88 (*b*), zero current in Fig. 88 (*a*), and half the armature current downwards in Fig. 88 (*c*) ; the current would then have been reversed uniformly in the interval in which the brush passes over the insulating segment of the commutator.

In practice, owing to the self-inductance of the armature winding, this reversal is delayed. At the instant just after that shown in Fig. 88 (*b*), when the current from *b* to *b'* starts to decrease, a back E.M.F. is set up which prevents the current from falling to zero in Fig. 88 (*a*). When B' is short-circuited, instead of having zero current flowing, there is still a current in the direction *bb'c*, and at the instant shown in Fig. 88 (*c*), instead of half the armature current flowing from *b'* to *b*, the current is considerably less.

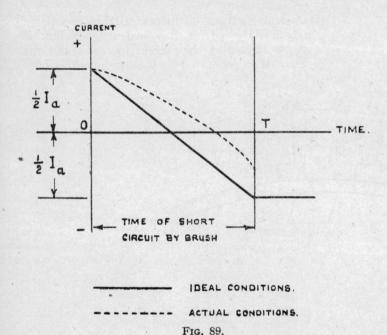

IDEAL CONDITIONS.

ACTUAL CONDITIONS.

FIG. 89.

Fig. 89 shows how the current actually changes compared with the ideal case. At T the current is less than half I_a, and has to take this value abruptly. This sudden change in current causes a big induced E.M.F., and a spark passes from segment 3 over the insulation to the brush.

220. Apart from the obvious damage it causes to the commutator, sparking has the further disadvantage from the W/T point of view that H/F oscillations are produced, which interfere with the working of the sets.

It may be prevented or mitigated in various ways :—

(*a*) By using carbon brushes. The inclusion of a high resistance in an inductive circuit lessens the time taken for the current to decay.

(*b*) By advancing the brushes beyond the electrical neutral axis. Under these conditions the coil undergoing commutation is cutting flux and has an E.M.F. induced in it which is in the direction of the current after reversal, thus balancing the E.M.F. of self-induction at commutation. As the latter E.M.F. is proportional to the current, the appropriate position for the brushes will alter with the load. For this reason the method is not employed on modern machines.

(c) By means of interpoles. These are small poles placed halfway between the main poles and having their field coils in series with the armature windings, so that the flux they produce is proportional to the armature current. Thus the induced E.M.F. in coils passing under them is proportional to the armature current, and automatically balances the reactance volts of the coil being commutated, if the interpoles are of correct strength and their flux linkages are in the correct direction, *i.e.*, so as to produce an E.M.F. in the coil in the direction of its current after reversal. Interpoles must therefore be wound so that an N interpole comes before an N main pole in the direction of rotation.

Interpoles also serve another useful purpose, as the flux they produce balances that due to the current in the armature windings, thus neutralising armature reaction, and mitigating the fall in E.M.F. at large currents due to the demagnetising component.

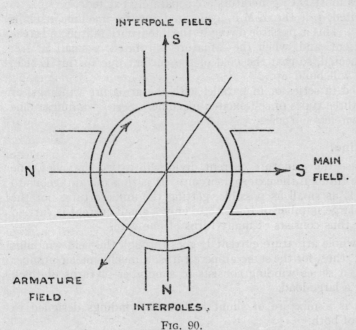

Fig. 90.

221. Types of Machine.—Dynamos are usually classified according to the way in which the magnetic flux is produced. The simplest method is to use permanent magnets, but the difficulty of constructing these to produce sufficient flux for large machines confines their use to the small dynamos called "**magnetos.**" All large machines employ electromagnets. They

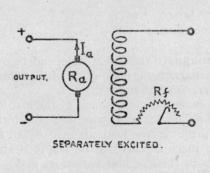

SEPARATELY EXCITED.

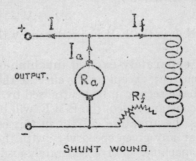

SHUNT WOUND.

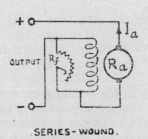

SERIES-WOUND.

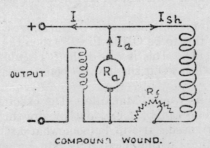

COMPOUND WOUND.

Fig. 91.

may be separately-excited or self-excited. Separate excitation involves the use of an independent source of E.M.F. for the field coils, and is now mainly confined to alternators and low-voltage generators. For Naval wireless purposes most D.C. generators are separately excited.

D.C. machines are usually self-excited, *i.e.*, the E.M.F. generated by the machine itself is used to obtain a current in the field coils. This is possible owing to the retentivity of iron and steel. Some residual magnetism is always present, and, when the armature is rotated, a small E.M.F. is generated. If the field coils are connected, so that the field of the current due to this E.M.F. reinforces the residual field, the E.M.F. will build up.

The field windings may be connected in series or in parallel with the armature windings, or there may be a mixture of both, giving three types of self-excited machine. Series windings alone are never used on generators for Naval wireless purposes.

222. Types of Self-excited Machine.

    (1) **Shunt wound.**—In this case the armature current divides into two branches, one through the field and one through the external circuit. It is thus advantageous to keep the shunt current I_f as small as possible, getting the ampere turns for the required flux by using a large number of turns. As only a small current is carried by the shunt winding, it thus consists of many turns of fine wire.

    (2) **Series wound.**—Here the whole armature current I_a goes through the field windings and the external circuit ; thus, for the same ampere turns, a much smaller number of coils is necessary, *i.e.*, a series winding consists of a number of turns of thick wire, capable of carrying a large load.

    (3) **Compound wound.**—This is a mixture of shunt and series windings designed to combine the advantages of both.

The potential difference V at the terminals of the machine will depend in each case on the current I_a taken from the armature. If the armature resistance is R_a, the potential drop in the armature is $I_a R_a$. In addition, there is a drop of potential of one or two volts due to the resistance of the brushes. This varies to some extent with the electrical contact they make. We may call this potential drop V_B.

$$\therefore \quad V = E - I_a R_a - V_B,$$

where $E = KN\Phi$ is the E.M.F. produced by the machine.

223. In a **separately-excited machine or magneto** the flux is independent of variations of the armature current, except for the effect of the demagnetising component of the armature reaction, which, as we have seen, can be neutralised by interpoles and other devices.

Thus, at constant speed, the E.M.F. will be a constant independent of the load current, which is the same as the armature current in this case. The curve showing how the terminal volts of the machine at any given speed vary with the current in the load circuit is called a *characteristic curve* of the machine. For a separately-excited machine this will be nearly a straight line, as shown in the figure, except near the origin, owing to the irregular variations of V_B in this region. Thus, the terminal volts fall off slowly as the load current increases. The machine has a " falling characteristic."

A generator is designed not to be run above a certain load, called the " full load " of the machine. If we assume this to be OM in Fig. 92, then the fall in terminal voltage from no load (OR) to full load (MQ) is PQ. This is called the " **regulation** " of the machine, and is said to be " good regulation " when PQ is small and " poor regulation " when PQ is large.

224. **Shunt-wound Machine.**—The exact nature of the building up of the E.M.F. in a self-excited machine can be found out by drawing the magnetisation curve, *i.e.*, the B-H curve, at any given speed. It will be somewhat as in Fig. 93. Owing to retentivity, B has a definite value when the exciting field H is zero. Hence, an E.M.F. is produced which sends current through the field windings, and so produces an exciting field H and an increase in B. As the

E.M.F. is proportional to B at a given speed, and H is proportional to the shunt current I_f, the B-H curve is also the E-I_f curve if the scales are suitably altered. The machine is

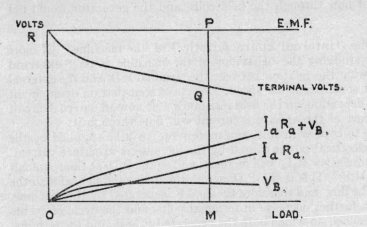

Characteristics of Separately excited Machine.

FIG. 92.

supposed to be on open circuit in this discussion, so that all the armature current goes through the field windings. The size of I_f thus depends on the resistance of the armature, R_a, and shunt windings, R_f. If V_B is the brush drop, the fall of potential round the circuit is $V_B + I_f (R_a + R_f)$. As long as the generated E.M.F., E, is greater than this, the current will tend to increase to that value which makes

$$E = V_B + I_f (R_a + R_f).$$

If we plot $V_B + I_f (R_a + R_f)$ against I_f, we shall get a curve OQT, as shown in Fig. 93. It is practically a straight line except near the origin, and its slope depends on $R_a + R_f$. The only thing we can vary is R_f, and so the slope of the line alters as we alter R_f. The line will have a steeper slope if R_f is increased.

Consider the value of I_f shown by OM in the figure. For the particular value of R_f considered, PM is the generated E.M.F. and QM $= V_B + I_f (R_a + R_f)$. Thus, the E.M.F. is greater than the fall of potential round the circuit by PQ, and so I_f will increase, and E will increase with it. This goes on till the point T is reached. At T the generated E.M.F. is just sufficient to keep the current OS flowing in the field coils, for it is exactly balanced by the fall of potential round the circuit.

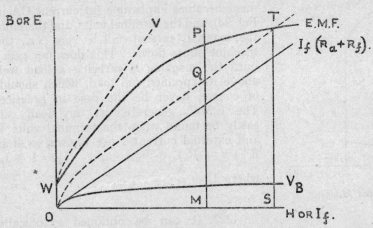

Internal characteristic of Shunt-wound Machine.

FIG. 93.

Thus, there is no tendency for the field current to increase over OS, and the corresponding E.M.F., S.T., is the steady E.M.F. to which the machine will build up. For any given machine it is obvious that the position of T depends on the slope of OQ, i.e., on the value of R_f. As we increase R_f, the slope of OQ increases, and the point in which it cuts OP moves nearer to the origin, i.e., the steady E.M.F. built up becomes smaller. It is obvious that there is a limiting value of R_f above which the machine will refuse to build up any E.M.F. beyond that due to the residual magnetism. OWV shows the slope of the fall of potential line for a value of R_f above this limiting value. The E.M.F. is limited to OW.

225. Thus, in starting up a shunt-wound generator two points should be observed :

(a) The field regulator resistance should be adjusted to such a value that the slope of OQ is small enough for the machine to excite. Generally, machines excite even with all the resistance in the circuit.

(b) No external circuits should be connected across the terminals until the E.M.F. has built up, otherwise part of the armature current is diverted from the field circuit, thus reducing I_f. For instance, if the output terminals were short-circuited, no current whatever would flow through the field coils, and the generator would not excite.

226. The above curve is called the "**internal characteristic**" of the machine. Of more importance from the point of view of studying the behaviour of the machine is its "**external characteristic.**" This is a curve showing the relation between the terminal P.D. and the external load current taken from the machine at some particular speed. We have seen that on open circuit the E.M.F. builds up to a steady value, depending on the field resistance. If now an external circuit be connected across the terminals, a part of the armature current will flow through it.

The armature current will increase to cope with this, and more power will be supplied by the prime mover to provide the increase in electrical power caused by the increase in armature current. The fall of potential in the armature windings ($= R_a I_a$) will increase, and so the P.D. at the terminals will decrease for the same generated E.M.F. This is the P.D. across the field windings, and so the field current will be lessened. Hence, the flux, and therefore the E.M.F. generated by the machine, will fall off. Due to this there will be a further decrease in terminal volts, and the cycle of events will repeat itself until a steady state is reached, in which both the generated E.M.F. and the terminal volts have smaller values than at no-load, the actual values depending on the armature current. The curve showing how the terminal volts vary with the external current can be plotted from experimental measurements of these two quantities for various loads, and is shown in Fig. 94.

When the external current becomes very large, i.e., if the machine is being overloaded, the terminal volts fall off rapidly, and increased difficulty is experienced in getting a field current large enough to produce an E.M.F. which will keep the terminal volts up. Eventually this adjustment becomes impossible (at current OA in Fig. 94), and the terminal volts, and therefore the external current, fall to zero, i.e., the machine shuts down. This does not occur until the machine is carrying a load well above its specified full load, which should, of course, never be the case in practice. The E.M.F. generated at any load can easily be found when the terminal volts V and external current I are known, as it is

$$E = V + R_a I_a + V_B, \quad \text{and} \quad I_a = I + I_f,$$

where $I_f = \dfrac{V}{R_f}.$

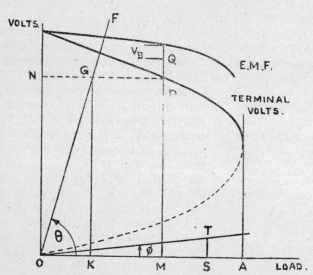

External characteristic of Shunt-wound Machine.

FIG. 94.

227. It can be obtained graphically from the external characteristic as follows. Consider the particular working point P on the characteristic (Fig. 94). The machine is delivering an output current OM or NP and the terminal volts are MP or ON. The field current is obtained from the relation MP $= R_f I_f$. If we draw a straight line OF, making an angle θ with the current axis, where $\tan \theta = R_f$, it cuts NP at G; GK = PM and GK = OK tan θ = $R_f \times$ OK. Thus, OK represents, to scale, the field current for terminal volts PM. If we make MS = OK, then OS = OM + OK = I + I_f = I_a, the total armature current. We now draw another resistance line OT, which makes an angle ϕ to the current axis such that tan $\phi = R_a$. TS = OS tan ϕ = $I_a R_a$ = potential drop in armature.

$\therefore$ E = PM + TS (= PQ) + V_B for the particular external current OM. In this way every point on the E.M.F.—external current characteristic may be plotted, and a curve obtained as shown.

228. **Series-wound Machine.**—In this machine the field current is also the external current, or at least proportional to it. (The field coils may have a rheostat in parallel for regulating purposes.)

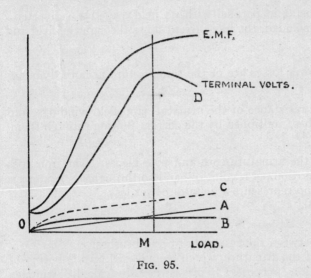

FIG. 95.

Thus, the curve connecting generated E.M.F. and external current at any particular speed will have the same shape as the magnetisation curve of the machine. A typical curve is shown in Fig. 95. To find the lost volts in the machine, draw a line OA, making an angle, whose tangent is $(R_a + R_f)$, with the current axis. Any point on this line gives the armature drop for the corresponding current. If to this be added the voltage drop at the brushes given by the corresponding ordinate of curve OB, we get the curve OC giving the resultant lost volts in the machine. The terminal p.d. (V) = generated E.M.F. (E), less lost volts, and so is given by the curve OD. This is the external characteristic of the machine, which would be obtained by experimental test. It is a " rising characteristic."

229. **Compound-wound Dynamo.**—In many cases it is desirable that the terminal volts should be independent of the external current being taken by the machine, *i.e.*, that it should have a " level characteristic." As a shunt-wound machine has a falling characteristic and a series-wound machine a rising one, it is obvious that a suitable combination of both will give either a practically level characteristic or a very slowly-rising one. The former is called a " level compounded " machine and the latter an " over-compounded " one.

It is also possible to obtain a level characteristic from a shunt-wound machine by suitably adjusting the series winding on the interpoles.

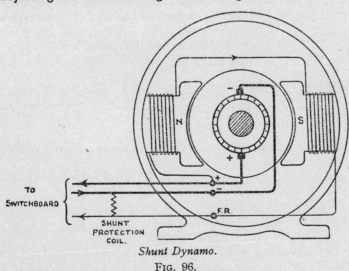

Shunt Dynamo.
FIG. 96.

230. **Voltage Regulation of Self-excited Machines.** — The terminal volts of a well-designed compound-wound machine are independent of the external current, *i.e.*, the regulation is automatically nearly perfect. The same effect can be obtained for shunt and series-wound machines by altering (*a*) the speed, (*b*) the resistance in the field winding. Generally, the speed is kept constant at all loads by means of a " governor," and method (*b*) is used to adjust the voltage.

For a shunt-wound machine, the rheostat is in series with the field windings. As resistance is cut out I_f increases, and therefore

the flux and generated E.M.F. increase.

Fig. 96 illustrates a shunt dynamo, showing windings and connections.

In parallel with the field regulator, a shunt protection coil is sometimes provided on the dynamo. Its object is to prevent the circuit of the highly inductive field magnet winding from being broken, as might happen in the leads to the field regulator or in the latter itself, thus obviating the voltage failing altogether, and sparking or arcing at the break, with risk of fire and possibly danger to life.

A series-wound machine may have a rheostat in parallel with its field, called a " diverter." The smaller the amount of diverter resistance included, the less current flows through the field and the smaller is the E.M.F. generated.

231. Losses in D.C. Machines.—The power losses are of the same nature in both dynamos and motors, and may be classified as follows :—

   (*a*) **Copper losses,** due to the ohmic resistance of the armature and field windings, and also to the P.D. across the brushes, multiplied by the current flowing through them.

   (*b*) **Iron losses** caused by :—
     (i) Hysteresis (paragraph 89) in the armature core and pole pieces. The iron goes through p cycles of magnetisation per revolution, and so through pN hysteresis loops per second. Each loop represents a definite power loss.
     (ii) Eddy currents (paragraph 204).

   (*c*) **Mechanical losses** due to :—
     (i) Friction at the bearings and between the commutator and brushes.
     (ii) Air resistance to the motion of the armature, which is increased by the boring of the armature for ventilation purposes. This is usually called " windage loss."

232. Dynamo Efficiency.—This may be regarded from various points of view. First, we have a conversion from mechanical power in the prime mover to electrical power in the machine. This gives the " **mechanical efficiency.**"

$$= \frac{\text{Total watts generated}}{\text{Mechanical power supplied.}}$$

Of this total electrical power generated, a part is lost due to the causes considered in paragraph 231. The rest is available for the external circuit. From this is derived the idea of " **electrical efficiency.**"

$$= \frac{\text{Watts available in external circuit.}}{\text{Total watts generated}}$$

Finally, we have the overall or " **commercial efficiency** "

$$= \frac{\text{Watts in external circuit.}}{\text{Mechanical power supplied}}$$

It will be easily seen from these definitions that **commercial efficiency = mechanical efficiency × electrical efficiency.**

The mechanical power supply will generally be given in H.P., and to perform the above calculations it must be converted to watts by the formula 1 H.P. = 746 watts.

In a good dynamo the commercial efficiency may be as much as 95 per cent. Where the source of power is an electric motor, this efficiency is usually of the order of 75 per cent.

233. Calculation of Efficiency.—The quantities which can be obtained experimentally are the H.P. on the armature shaft, the terminal volts V and output current I, and the resistances of the armature and field windings, R_a and R_f respectively. The efficiencies should therefore be expressed in terms of these quantities.

Let E be the E.M.F. generated, I_a the armature current, and I_f the field current :—

(1) Series Machine.

$$I_f = I_a = I,$$
$$\text{and } E = V + I (R_a + R_f).$$
Mechanical power supply $= HP \times 746$ watts.
Total watts generated $= EI = VI + I^2 (R_a + R_f).$
Watts in external circuit $= VI.$

$$\therefore \text{ Mechanical efficiency} = \frac{VI + I^2 (R_a + R_f)}{HP \times 746}$$

$$\text{Electrical efficiency} = \frac{VI}{VI + I^2 (R_a + R_f)}$$

$$\text{Commercial efficiency} = \frac{VI}{HP \times 746}$$

(2) Shunt Machine.

$$I_a = I + I_f \text{ and } I_f = \frac{V}{R_f}$$

$$E = V + R_a I_a = V + R_a\left(I + \frac{V}{R_f}\right)$$

Mechanical power supply $= HP \times 746$ watts.

Total watts generated $= EI_a = VI + \frac{V^2}{R_f} + R_a\left(I + \frac{V}{R_f}\right)^2$

Watts in external circuit $= VI.$

$$\therefore \text{ Mechanical efficiency} = \frac{VI + \frac{V^2}{R_f} + R_a\left(I + \frac{V}{R_f}\right)^2}{HP \times 746}$$

$$\text{Electrical efficiency} = \frac{VI}{VI + \frac{V^2}{R_f} + R_a\left(I + \frac{V}{R_f}\right)^2}$$

$$\text{Commercial efficiency} = \frac{VI}{HP \times 746}$$

Example 25.

What horse-power is required to drive a 150-kilowatt dynamo when it is developing its full-rated load, if the machine has a full-load commercial efficiency of 91·5 per cent ?

$$\frac{91 \cdot 5}{100} = \frac{150 \times 1,000}{746 \times \text{H.P.}}$$

$$\therefore \text{H.P.} = \frac{150 \times 1,000 \times 100}{746 \times 91 \cdot 5} = 220.$$

234. Rating of Dynamos.—The rating of a dynamo is the kilowatt-power-load that the machine will carry continuously without excessive (1) heating, (2) sparking, or (3) internal voltage drop.

Thus, if a maker puts a label on a machine he sells :—

" 500 amps, 100 volts, 2,400 revs."

he infers—

(a) that if the machine is kept revolving at 2,400 r.p.m. it will always generate a terminal P.D. of 100 volts ;

(b) that it will stand a maximum current output of 500 amps. without developing any of the faults referred to above.

THE MOTOR.

235. The electric motor is a machine for the conversion of electrical energy into mechanical energy, and so its function is exactly the reverse of that of a generator.

When a conductor carrying a current is placed in a magnetic field, it experiences a mechanical force, the direction of which is given by Fleming's Left Hand Rule (paragraph 130). The armature conductors of a D.C. generator are situated in the magnetic field of the poles, so that if a current is passed through them by applying an external E.M.F. to the brushes, they will be acted on by mechanical forces, and the armature will be set in rotation. By the use of belting or other devices, the rotation of the armature may be caused to turn a flywheel or do other useful mechanical work, the ultimate source of which is the electrical energy supplied by the external E.M.F.

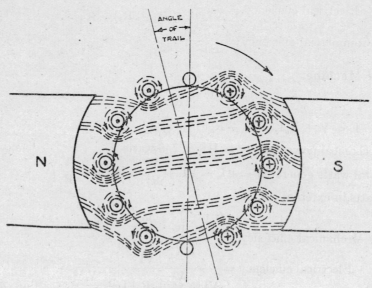

Illustrating Action of a Motor.

FIG. 97.

236. The same machine can therefore be made to act as a dynamo by supplying it with mechanical power, or as a D.C. motor by supplying it with electrical power ; as regards types of armature, and field windings and arrangements, we have thus exactly the same classification for motors as for generators.

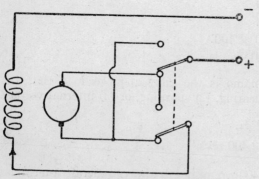

Reversing Switch for Small Series Motor.

FIG. 98.

The application of Fleming's Left Hand Rule shows that, if both the current and the external field are reversed, the direction of the mechanical force is unchanged ; in order to reverse the direction of rotation of a motor, the leads must be interchanged either in the armature circuit or the field magnet circuit, but not in both.

237. Torque.—We have already calculated the electrodynamic torque on an armature carrying a current I_a when the flux per pole is Φ, and found it to be proportional to ΦI_a (paragraph 216). This is therefore the value of the driving torque in a motor.

As the flux is proportional to the field current I_f and the permeability μ, we may also write $T \propto \mu I_a I_f$.

238. Back E.M.F.—As soon as the armature starts rotating, its conductors will begin to cut flux, and so an E.M.F. will be induced in them just as in a generator.

Lenz's Law tells us that the induced E.M.F. will be in such a direction as to oppose the rotation which is producing it ; the rotation is caused by the external current supply to the armature, and so the induced E.M.F. will act so as to cut down the current, *i.e.*, it will act in opposition to the applied E.M.F. This can also be seen by applying the Right Hand Rule to any conductor. This " Back E.M.F." has the same value as if the machine were running as a generator, *i.e.*, $E = KN\Phi$ (paragraph 214) and so is proportional to the speed N.

239. The effect of the torque is to produce an angular acceleration of the armature, *i.e.*, to increase N. This causes an increase in the back E.M.F. and cuts down the armature current, thus decreasing the torque.

The torque opposing rotation, due to friction and air resistance, also increases with the speed. Thus the nett torque available to accelerate the armature decreases as the speed increases. Eventually a speed is reached at which the frictional torque exactly balances the driving torque (decreased by the decrease in armature current), and there will be no further tendency to accelerate. The motor will run at this steady speed until the conditions change.

This speed may be altered in three ways :—

(1) The terminal volts may be altered. This is unlikely, as the supply is usually constant voltage.
(2) The resistance in the field regulator may be altered.
(3) The opposing mechanical torque may be altered by causing the rotating armature to do mechanical work, *e.g.*, by running a belt round the shaft, which drives a pulley or flywheel.

240. **Armature Reaction in Motors.**—Just as in generators, the flux due to the armature current combines with the field magnet flux to produce a resultant field which is not symmetrical about the geometrical neutral axis. Fig. 97 shows that in the case of the motor the electrical neutral axis lags behind the geometrical neutral axis in the direction of rotation. Hence, in motors, the brushes must be set at a lagging angle, as opposed to a leading angle in the case of generators. To effect sparkless commutation the lagging angle must be increased, or interpoles may be used. For a motor, the polarity of an interpole must be the same as that of the main pole immediately behind it in the direction of rotation.

241. **Energy Conversion in Armature.**—In the case of a motor we have to consider the efficiency of conversion of electrical energy into mechanical energy. The following notation will be used :—

V = applied volts across armature.
I_a = armature current.
R_a = armature resistance.
I_f = field current producing flux.
T = driving torque on shaft.
E = back E.M.F.
N = speed.

The electrical power supplied to the machine $= VI_a$.

By Kirchhoff's Law, $V = I_a R_a + E$.

$\therefore VI_a = I_a{}^2 R_a + EI_a$, where $I_a{}^2 R_a$ is the copper loss in the armature. The residue of power EI_a represents the electrical power directly converted to mechanical power.

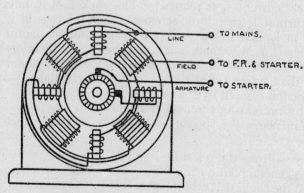

Shunt Motor with Interpole Windings.

FIG. 99.

The efficiency of the motor is $\eta = \dfrac{\text{mechanical power output}}{\text{electrical power input}} = \dfrac{EI_a}{VI_a} = \dfrac{E}{V}$.

It is therefore greater the more nearly equal the back E.M.F. is to the applied volts, *i.e.*, the smaller the armature current. Thus a motor is most efficient when running light and taking least power (VI_a) from the mains. As the load increases, the efficiency falls off.

242. Motors, like dynamos, are classified according to the nature of the magnetic field excitation. Thus we may have separately excited, shunt, series and compound-wound motors. Separately excited and shunt motors behave very similarly in practice, for in each case the field coils are directly across the applied voltage and so the flux is independent of the motor variables.

As mentioned in paragraph 239, the speed (N) of a motor may be altered by variations of torque or load (T), field flux (Φ), and applied voltage (V).

A detailed investigation of the effect on the speed of variation of these three quantities is fairly complicated. We may simplify the argument by considering what happens in each case if two of them are kept constant and only one is varied at a time. A further simplification in obtaining a general idea of how the speed of a motor varies under these conditions is to assume that the back E.M.F. (E) remains an approximately constant proportion of the applied voltage. This is justifiable in the practical case, because it was seen in the last paragraph that for efficient running the back E.M.F. (E) must be nearly equal to the applied E.M.F. (V). The variation in back E.M.F. is much smaller than the other variations considered. Since the power converted to mechanical power is EI_a watts, we may thus assume that power output $P \propto I_a$. Actually there is a slight decrease in proportional power output as I_a increases, for the back E.M.F. falls off slightly. Expressed in mechanical quantities the power output is equal to the torque on the shaft multiplied by the speed of the motor, and so $P \propto NT$.

It follows therefore that $NT \propto I_a$.

The other general relations we have already obtained are

$$T \propto I_a I_f$$

and

$$E \propto N\Phi \propto NI_f.$$

243. Speed Variation of Shunt Motor.

(*a*) **Variation of flux (and therefore I_f) only.**—Since E remains approximately constant and $E \propto NI_f$ it follows that N varies inversely as I_f. Thus if the field current is decreased, the speed increases and *vice versa*.

The action is approximately as follows. Suppose that while the motor is running at a steady speed the field current I_f is reduced. The back E.M.F. falls momentarily and the armature current I_a therefore increases. This increase in I_a more than makes up for the fall in I_f, and so the torque increases and the motor is speeded up. This increases the back E.M.F. again and diminishes I_a and therefore the torque. When the torque is reduced to its former constant value the motor is thus running at a higher speed than before. The back E.M.F. is nearly the same as before, the fall in I_f being nearly compensated by the increase in speed.

The field current is decreased by increasing the field resistance and *vice versa*. Thus increase of field resistance increases the speed ; decrease of field resistance decreases the speed.

(*b*) **Variation of load (torque T) only.**—From the relation $T \propto I_a I_f$ it follows that if I_f is constant, then $T \propto I_a$. The general relation $NT \propto I_a$ therefore shows that in this case N is constant. Owing to the slight decrease in back E.M.F. as I_a increases, the speed falls off slightly for large armature currents, but practically the shunt motor may be looked upon as a constant-speed machine for varying load.

(*c*) **Variation of applied voltage (V) only.**—If I_f and T are kept constant, it follows from the relation $T \propto I_a I_f$ that I_a remains constant and so the back E.M.F. (E) must increase as the applied voltage increases. $E \propto NI_f$; thus for constant I_f the speed increases with the back E.M.F. and therefore with the applied voltage.

This is a possible method of varying the speed in a separately excited motor, but is hardly practicable in a shunt motor, for any increase of V increases I_f correspondingly, and the strengthened flux counterbalances the effect on the speed of the increase in applied voltage.

244. Series Motor.—The flux in this case depends on the armature current, which is also the field current, or proportional to it. The flux therefore varies according to the magnetisation curve of the machine. At saturation and above, the flux is approximately constant, as in the shunt motor, so that for large armature currents the behaviour of the series motor approximates to that of the shunt motor.

Below saturation the flux Φ may be taken as approximately proportional to the field current I_f, which, in the case of the series motor, is proportional to I_a, the armature current. Thus the relation $T \propto I_f I_a$ becomes $T \propto I_a{}^2$. As the general relation $NT \propto I_a$ still holds, it follows that N must be inversely proportional to I_a, and therefore inversely proportional to the square root of the load ($\sqrt{T}$). In other words, as the load increases, the speed decreases and *vice versa*.

When running light (I_a and therefore T small), N will be very large. Hence, in order to avoid dangerous starting speeds, a series motor should always be started on load. By keeping N small, this also gives a big starting torque, so that a series motor is used where quick starting up on load is desirable, *e.g.*, in electric traction.

To increase the speed with a constant load, the relations $T \propto I_f I_a$ and $NT \propto I_a$ show that N varies inversely as I_f. To keep the load constant, I_a must increase as I_f decreases, so that a method has to be devised of varying the field current without affecting the armature current correspondingly. A controller is used which changes the field windings from a series to a parallel arrangement. For instance, in a four-pole machine, the four field windings in series gives the lowest speed. For successive increases of speed the field windings are arranged two in series, two in parallel, and finally all in parallel. A resistance in parallel with the field windings, called a " Diverter," may also be used to decrease the field flux.

Example on Speed Variation (26).

The particulars of a shunt motor are shown in Fig. 100. It is required to find the speed of this motor when a resistance of $2 \cdot 5$ ohms is inserted in the field regulator, the load remaining unaltered, and assuming that the flux is proportional to the field current.

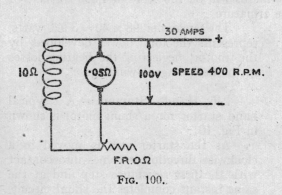

30 AMPS +

10Ω ·05Ω 100V SPEED 400 R.P.M.

−

F.R. 0Ω

FIG. 100.

At 400 r.p.m., $I_f = 100/10 = 10$ amps.

$\therefore \quad I_a = 30{-}10 = 20$ amps.

$\therefore R_a I_a = 20 \times \cdot05 = 1$ volt.

$\therefore$ Back E.M.F. $= 99$ volts.

Back E.M.F. $= KNI_f = 400 \times 10 \times K$.

$$\therefore K = \frac{99}{4,000}.$$

At final speed, $I_f' = 100/12\cdot5 = 8$ amps.

Load is unaltered, *i.e.*, $T \propto I_a \Phi \propto I_a I_f$ is constant,

$$\text{i.e., } I_a' I_f' = I_a I_f$$

$$I_a' \times 8 = 20 \times 10.$$

$\therefore I_a' = 25$ amps. $\therefore R_a I_a = \cdot05 \times 25 = 1\cdot25$ volts,

and new back E.M.F. $= 100 - 1\cdot25 = 98\cdot75$ volts.

i.e., $KN' I_f' = 98\cdot75$

$$\frac{99}{4,000} \times 8 \times N' = 98\cdot75.$$

$$\therefore \quad N' = \frac{98\cdot75 \times 4,000}{8 \times 99} = 500 \text{ r.p.m. nearly,}$$

245. Starting Resistance.—The armature resistance of a motor is made as small as possible, to diminish the power loss in the armature, and is only designed to carry the armature current at the normal running speed. At this speed the back E.M.F. ($= KN \Phi$) is nearly as large as the applied voltage, so that the armature current is small. When the motor is starting up there is no back E.M.F., the full supply voltage will be across the armature, and the consequent heavy current will burn out the armature winding. This is prevented by inserting a large resistance in series with the armature winding when starting the motor, and cutting it out as the speed increases. The arrangement for doing this is called a motor starter. In addition to performing this primary function it also embodies, in general, other safety devices. The starting resistance may be cut out by hand or by automatic methods, giving two types of starter.

Example 27.

Let the armature resistance of a certain machine be $\cdot 05$ ohm and the applied voltage 100 volts. Suppose at full speed the back E.M.F. developed = 98 volts.

Then the armature current $= I_a = \dfrac{100-98}{\cdot 05} = \dfrac{2}{\cdot 05} = 40$ amps.

If the full 100 volts were applied to the armature when it was at rest, a current of $\dfrac{100}{\cdot 05}$ = 2,000 amps. would flow, which would certainly burn it out if it did not blow a fuse.

Consequently we must use a starting resistance (R_s) to limit this current to (say) 60 amps., as follows :—

$$I_a = \frac{V}{R_a + R_s} \text{ or } R_s = \frac{V}{I_a} - R_a = \frac{100}{60} - \cdot 05 = 1 \cdot 66 - \cdot 05 = 1 \cdot 61 \text{ ohms.}$$

Hence we shall need a resistance in the starter of $1 \cdot 61$ ohms, which will be cut out gradually as the machine gathers speed and starts generating a back E.M.F.

A current is needed at starting rather larger than when the machine has reached its normal speed, on account of the inertia of the armature.

The power taken from the mains $= V \times I$. Of this, a power $I_a^2 \times R_a$ will be expended in heating losses in the armature.

The power developed by the motor, including that available at the motor shaft for driving the load and expended in friction, windage, eddy current and hysteresis losses $= E \times I_a$.

In the above example, the power taken from the mains will be $100 \times 40 = 4,000$ watts. Of this, $40^2 \times \cdot 05 = 80$ watts is expended in heating the armature.

The remainder, $98 \times 40 = 3,920$ watts, represents the total power developed by the motor, neglecting the heating losses in the field magnet windings.

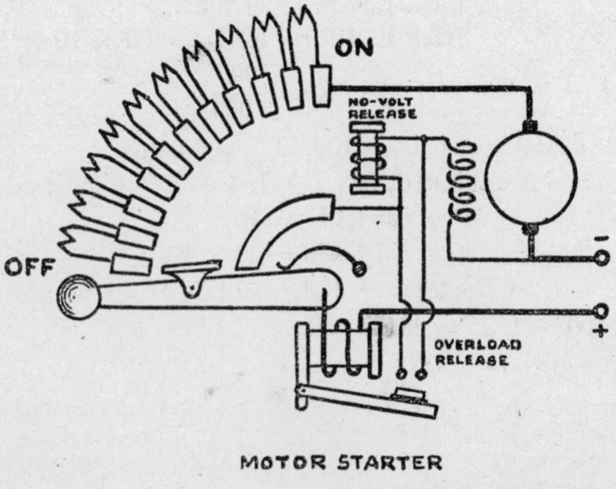

246. Hand Starter.—A typical hand starter for a shunt motor is shown in Fig. 101.

As the starter arm is moved in a clockwise direction it comes into contact with the first resistance step and at the same instant completes the shunt circuit, the full voltage being applied to the field winding. The resistance in the armature circuit is gradually cut out. When the starter arm is at "ON" the starting resistance is completely cut out of the armature circuit, and so by this time the motor should be near its normal speed. A spring control prevents the starter arm

MOTOR STARTER

FIG. 101.

from being moved over too fast. At " ON " the arm is held against this spring by a small electro-magnet energised by the field circuit, and called the " **no-volts** " **coil**. Should the supply fail, this coil ceases to be energised, and the arm returns to the " OFF " position under the action of the spring, thus disconnecting the motor from the supply.

If the supply current exceeds a definite value, the " **overload release** " **coil** attracts a pivoted conducting arm, which short-circuits the no-volts coil, thus disconnecting the motor as above.

In neither case can the motor be restarted without the starting resistance being in the armature circuit, and so damage to the armature windings is prevented.

247. Automatic Starter.—The automatic starter enables a machine to be switched on or off from one or more positions remote from the starter by simply making or breaking a switch. A typical Service automatic starter is shown in Fig. 102. The starter arm (12) cuts out the starting resistance (19) from the armature circuit, but does not insert the resistance (19) in the motor field circuit, as in the case of some hand starters.

Action.—When the " ON " push (27) is made by the operator the circuit is completed from positive, through line terminal, reducing resistance (1) and main contactor solenoid (2) to negative. The reducing resistance (1) adjusts the value of the current in the contactor solenoid (2) according to the input voltage used, and is therefore of different value for varying voltages.

When the main contactor solenoid (2) is energised, it attracts the armature of the anti-rolling stop (34) and allows the main contactor to be pulled on. The anti-rolling stop (34) prevents the contactor from making accidentally when the ship rolls, or by concussion during gun fire, etc.

Three contacts are closed when the contactor is pulled on.

The magnetic blow-out contact (5) makes first, as it is required to break last and allow the blow-out coil (4) to perform its function of blowing out any arcing which may occur at the main contact (7).

The secondary contact (6) makes next and completes the circuit from the contactor through the eddy current brake field coil (8), the economy resistance switch (9), the starting solenoid bobbin (10), and the " ON " push (27). At this stage the economy resistance (16) is short-circuited by the economy resistance switch (9).

The main contact (7) of the contactor makes last and short-circuits the magnetic blow-out coil (4), completes the circuit directly to the motor field (23), and through the whole of the starting resistance (19) to the motor armature (24).

The starting solenoid (10) being energised, the core moves upwards, performing the following functions :—

    (a) The self-sustaining switch (11) is allowed to close and thus provides an alternative path through the " OFF " push (28) for the starting solenoid current, and allows the " ON " push (27) to be released. The " ON " and " OFF " pushes are operated against the tension of a spring. In the normal position the " ON " push (27) is broken and the " OFF " push (28) made.

    (b) By the link mechanism shown, the contact arm (12) is forced sideways against the stops of the starting resistance (19), first making contact with the uppermost stop (13), and then with the other stops in order, and so cutting out the starting resistance (19) in steps.

    (c) The gearing between the horizontal link and the pinion on the axle of the copper armature (18) sets the armature in rotation. It moves between two pole faces (17), energised by the coil (8), and so has eddy currents induced in it, which tend to stop its motion. It thus acts as a brake on the upward motion of the starting solenoid core and governs the rate at which the starting resistance is cut out. The strength of the braking action is adjusted by varying the distance apart of the pole faces (17).

Applications of motor generators in the Service are, among others—to supply the low power switchboard (20 volts) for bells, telephones, fire-control, etc. ; for supplying constant current to searchlights at reduced voltage ; for charging secondary batteries, etc.

249. The Motor Alternator.—The motor alternator consists of a motor and alternator on one shaft, as illustrated diagrammatically in Fig. 104.

The motor is fitted with a starter, and sometimes with a field regulator if variation in speed (and therefore frequency) is required : a separate regulator is supplied for the alternator field current.

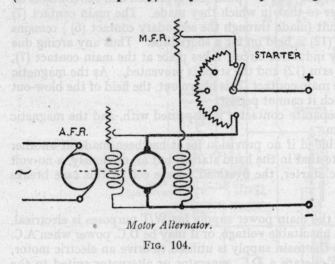

Motor Alternator.

FIG. 104.

The motor field regulator controls the speed of the motor, hence the speed of the alternator, and hence the alternating frequency, and also the voltage to a certain extent.

The alternator field regulator controls the density of the alternator flux and hence the alternating voltage independently of frequency.

250. Motor-Booster.—This is a particular type of motor generator, consisting of a motor and a generator (the " booster "), keyed to the same shaft. The generator is in series with the supply mains, and so the voltage generated is proportional to the supply current, and will assist or oppose the

supply voltage according to the method of connecting up.

The commoner uses of the booster are :—

(1) To make up for the voltage drop in a long transmission line ;

(2) To provide an additional voltage where the main supply voltage is insufficient.

These two uses are essentially the same, and are illustrated by the arrangement shown in Fig. 105.

It will be seen that the positive terminal of the booster is connected to the negative main, so that the booster acts just like an additional cell in a battery. Further, as the current in the leads increases, the booster field, and therefore the booster E.M.F., also increases, compensating for the increased IR drop in the leads.

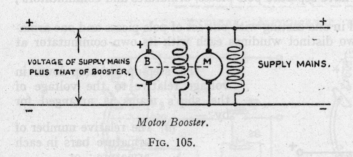

Motor Booster.

FIG. 105.

251. Automatic Voltage Control of Alternators.—The output voltage of an alternator depends on the speed of the machine, and the flux, *i.e.*, the field current. Variations in either or both of these are caused by :—

(a) Fluctuations of supply voltage. These alter both the speed and the field current, and may be large in ship practice.

(b) Variations in output current such as are produced, for instance, by switching over from two valves to one in a transmitter. This alters the reaction of the alternator armature and therefore the flux.

The object aimed at in automatic control is to produce such variations of the alternator field current as will automatically compensate for these effects.

The necessary variations of field current are obtained by means of the " reversing booster " and " contactor " circuits shown in Fig. 106.

The reversing booster is a small generator with two oppositely-wound fields.   When the supply voltage and alternator output are steady these fields have equivalent ampere-turns and neutralise each other, so that no booster E.M.F. is generated.

If the alternator voltage rises above normal, the " opposing " booster field is made to take a larger current by the operation of the contactor, and the booster generates an E.M.F. acting against the supply voltage to the alternator field.   The alternator field current is thus reduced and the output voltage falls.   If it drops below normal, the reverse occurs ; the " assisting " booster field is made to predominate and the booster E.M.F. augments the supply voltage to the alternator field.   The alternator field current rises, and therefore the output voltage.

252. These processes are made automatic by means of the contactor circuit shown inside the dotted rectangle in Fig. 106.

The outer ends of the booster fields are brought to two contacts A and B, across which is the combined resistance of R_{3a} and R_{3b}.   This ensures that the circuit to either booster field is never broken during the operation of the contactor.   The common point of R_{3a} and R_{3b} is joined to the pivot F of a conducting arm DE, which rocks about F so that either D makes contact with A, in which case R_{3a} is short-circuited, or E makes contact with B, short-circuiting R_{3b}.

The movement of the contactor arm is mechanically controlled by a spring.   It is electrically controlled by an electro-magnetic system across the alternator output terminals.   The pull of this system thus varies with the alternator output.   The other details of the contactor circuit perform subsidiary functions which are explained below.

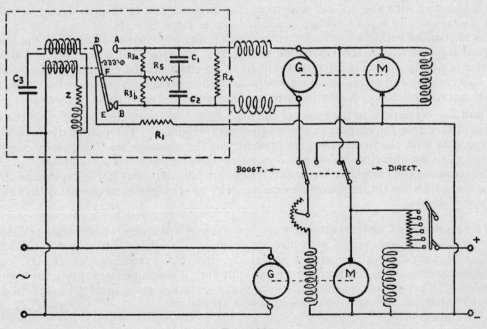

FIG. 106.

Action.—Suppose the supply voltage is switched on.   Contacts AD will then be closed. R_{3b} is in the path through the opposing field, but R_{3a} in the parallel path through the assisting field is short-circuited.   Hence the assisting field predominates, and the corresponding increase in alternator field current quickly raises the output voltage.   When it rises above normal, the attraction of the electromagnetic system overcomes the pull of the spring, and the contactor arm swings over to the position shown in the diagram, breaking contact at A and making it at B. Thus R_{3b} is short-circuited and R_{3a} is brought into circuit. The opposing field is now the stronger, and the booster generates an E.M.F. against the supply voltage.

The alternator field current falls and the output voltage likewise. The pull of the spring now overcomes the attraction of the magnet, the contactor arm swings back to its former position, and the sequence of events is repeated. Thus, under working conditions, the contactor arm is continually and rapidly vibrating and the output voltage is kept approximately constant.

The booster circuit is unsymmetrical, as one of the parallel paths contains the armature resistance and the booster E.M.F. Hence, for correct adjustment of the currents in the two field windings, the resistances R_{3a} and R_{3b} are not equal. Their most suitable values are found by experiment when the design is being arranged.

253. C_1, C_2 and R_5.—Whenever contact is broken by the contactor arm rocking, a large current is suddenly brought to zero, and, owing to the self-inductance of the circuit, arcing is liable to occur at the gaps. To obviate this the condensers C_1 and C_2 are put in parallel with the gaps at A and B respectively. It will be seen that, together with the self-inductances of their respective circuits, these condensers constitute oscillatory circuits and may produce undesirable oscillatory currents if sparking takes place at the gaps. As R_{3a} and R_{3b} are in parallel with these oscillatory circuits, their equivalent series resistances $\left(\dfrac{1}{\omega^2 C_1^2 R_{3a}} \text{ and } \dfrac{1}{\omega^2 C_2^2 R_{3b}} \text{ respectively} \right)$ do not provide sufficient damping. A resistance R_5 in series in both oscillatory circuits is therefore added, large enough to make the condenser discharges non-oscillatory.

R_1 and R_4 are auxiliary resistances, which keep the voltage generated by the booster within suitable limits.

R_1 is in series with the booster and contactor circuits, and is chosen of such a value that a suitable fraction of the supply voltage is applied across these circuits.

R_4 is in parallel with the contactor circuit and limits the current changes in the booster field windings as R_{3a} and R_{3b} are short-circuited in turn. If R_4 were itself a short-circuit, alterations in the resistance of the contactor circuits would have no effect on the currents in the booster fields, while if R_4 were removed such alterations would have their maximum possible effect. R_4 is selected so that the actual effect has a suitable intermediate value between these extremes.

C_3 and Z.—Variations in the speed of the main motor will vary the frequency of the alternator voltage, and therefore the current in the magnet field windings. The pull of the magnetic system would thus alter with the frequency. To prevent this the windings are " frequency compensated." One winding has an inductive resistance Z in series and the other has a condenser C_3. When the frequency increases the current in the inductive circuit falls, but that in the capacitive circuit rises. The reverse occurs when the frequency decreases. The total magnetising current is thus independent of frequency changes.

254. **The Rotary Converter.**—A rotary converter is a machine with one set of field magnets, usually shunt wound and excited with direct current.

It has only one armature with a uniformly distributed winding (as in D.C. machines), which has connections to a commutator at one end, and, if single phase, tappings to two slip rings at the other. In a two-pole machine these tappings are taken at points 180° apart, in a four-pole machine 90° apart, in an eight-pole machine 45° apart, etc.

Its uses are :—

(a) Supplied with D.C. at the commutator end, it runs as a D.C. motor, and A.C. is tapped off from the slip rings. This is the **Service application.**

(b) Supplied with A.C. at the slip rings, it runs as a motor, and D.C. is obtained from the commutator end. This is the common application in commercial work.

(c) If the armature is revolved by an engine, both A.C. and D.C. may be obtained simultaneously. It is then called a " Double Current Generator."

255. Action.—Running as a D.C. motor and delivering A.C.

It is necessary to understand clearly how the back E.M.F. of a motor varies, so we recapitulate the statements given in paragraph 238.

The " Gramme ring " type of armature is illustrated (Fig. 107) for simplicity, its winding being easier to represent than that of a drum armature.

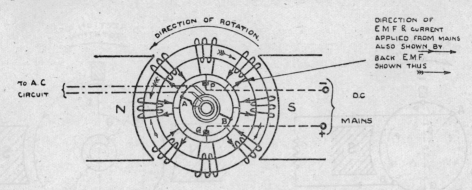

DIAGRAMMATIC REPRESENTATION OF A ROTARY CONVERTER.

FIG. 107.

When a motor is running, the armature conductors have E.M.Fs. induced in them (the dynamo action), which by Lenz's Law oppose the E.M.F. applied by the mains.

The sum of the instantaneous E.M.Fs. induced in all the inductors under either pole is called the " back E.M.F." ; this is of constant value for a given field magnet flux, speed and load.

The sets of inductors under each pole, at any instant, are in parallel with respect to the D.C. brushes bearing on the commutator (this should be traced out in Fig. 107).

The back E.M.F. (E) will be a little less than the applied voltage (V)—say, 98 volts with 100-volt mains ; *i.e.*, 98 volts of those applied balance the back E.M.F., and the other two volts supply the ohmic drop in the armature resistance.

Thus the applied voltage $V = E + I_a R_a$.

256. The variations of P.D. between the tapping points A and B (which is the voltage applied to the A.C. circuit) as the armature rotates may now be considered.

Fig. 108 (*a*) is a further simplification of Fig. 107, drawn to assist in the following explanation. Only four armature bars are shown, namely, the pair lettered A and B, which are connected through the slip rings to the A.C. circuit, and the pair lettered P and Q, which are in connection with the D.C. brushes at any instant.

For the purpose of this elementary treatment of the rotary converter, the IR drop in the armature will be neglected ; in most cases it will be very small owing to the low armature resistance.

Thus we will assume that $E = V$.

When A and B are on the neutral line they will obviously have the P.D. of the mains, (V) or (E), and maximum current will flow in the A.C. circuit. The **maximum** A.C. voltage will be equal numerically to the D.C. voltage, hence we have R.M.S. A.C. voltage = D.C. volts/$\sqrt{2} = 0\cdot707$ × D.C. volts.

When A and B have moved through an angle θ from the neutral line, the **potential of B with respect to P will be**

$$V - (\text{back E.M.F. in BQ} + \text{IR drop in BQ}).$$

In the diagram, the arrows marked " *e* " indicate the direction of the back E.M.F. Ignoring the IR drop, this becomes $V - E_{BQ} = E - E_{BQ}$.

Similarly, the potential of A with reference to the same point P will be equal numerically to the back E.M.F. in AP ; this may be represented by E_{AP}, which is equal to E_{BQ}.

Hence, the P.D. between A and B = $(E - E_{BQ}) - E_{AP} = E - 2E_{BQ}$.   This may also be written :—

P.D. between A and B = V — (back E.M.F. from B to Q + back E.M.F. from A to P).

Mathematically it may be shown that the P.D. between A and B is equal to $E \cos \theta$.   A simple vectorial explanation is provided by Fig. 108 (b).

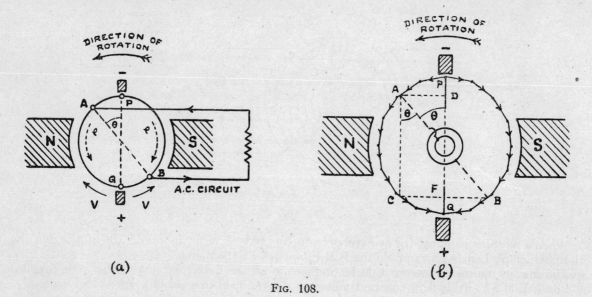

FIG. 108.

The back E.M.F. in the two halves of the armature winding may be considered to be the vector sum of a number of small E.M.Fs. indicated by the arrows of Fig. 108 (b).   When A and B are on the neutral line, the P.D. across the A.C. slip rings will be the same as that of the D.C. supply, and also equal to the vector sum of the small component E.M.F.s   The figure represents a **vector polygon** and, by well-known mechanical principles, the **closing side** PQ, which is also the diameter of the armature, represents the resultant back E.M.F.   The contribution of each small component vector towards the total back E.M.F. is represented by its projection upon the diameter PQ.

When A and B have moved through the angle θ, the vectors still indicate the relative direction of the back E.M.F., and we require to know the instantaneous P.D. between A and B.

From the diagram it is easily deduced that the A.C. voltage between the slip rings is always given by—

V — (back E.M.F. from B to Q + back E.M.F. from A to P).

But the back E.M.F. from B to Q is equal numerically to its projection FQ upon the diameter, and the back E.M.F. from A to P is equal numerically to its projection PD.   Hence we have the geometrical relations—

$$E_{AB} = PQ - (FQ + PD) = DF = AC = E \cos \theta \quad \ldots \ldots \quad \text{(since AB = PQ).}$$

Hence, $E_{AB} = E \cos \theta$.

Fig. 109 shows $E \cos \theta$ plotted, and represents the variations in the P.D. between A and B for one revolution.   This curve is a cosine curve, which is merely a sine curve moved 90° to the left so that the P.D. follows a sine law, tracing out one cycle in each revolution.

The following points should be specially noted :—

(1) When A and B are under the D.C. brushes, $\theta = 0$; therefore $E_{AP} = 0$, and the P.D. = E = V.

(2) When A and B are centrally under the poles ($\theta = 90°$) E_{AP} will be equal to $\frac{1}{2}$ E, so that $E - 2E_{AP} = E \cos 90° = 0$.

(3) A, when between 0° and 90°, has a higher potential than B.

(4) When θ = 180° and A is under the negative brush, the P.D. = — E = — V, and so on for the next half revolution.

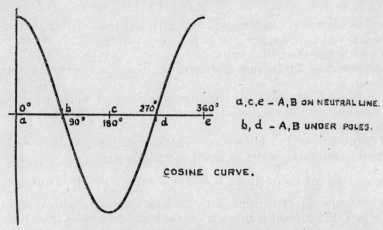

a, c, e – A, B ON NEUTRAL LINE.

b, d – A, B UNDER POLES.

COSINE CURVE.

VOLTAGE BETWEEN SLIP RINGS.

FIG. 109.

257. As regards the currents : in the position of A and B shown in Fig. 108, the motor current will follow the course ... positive brush, PAQ and PBQ in parallel, to the negative brush ; the alternating current will follow the course ... positive brush, PA, external circuit, BQ, to negative brush.

Both the motor and the alternating currents are supplied by the mains. Thus the portions of the winding AP and BQ will carry, at this stage, more current than the other portions, causing additional and varying field distortion and armature reaction.

When A has passed beyond the centre of the left pole piece it will be negative to B, and the course of the alternating current will be :—

Positive brush, PB, external circuit, AQ, to negative brush.

258. **Armature Reaction.**—The armature reaction of a rotary converter, as in dynamos and motors, has important effects in practice.

The A.C. circuit may consist of :—

(1) A pure resistance load ;
(2) A combined resistance and capacity load ;
(3) A combined resistance and inductive load ;
(4) A combined resistance, capacity and inductive load.

The combined armature reactions are rather complicated to follow, and no attempt will be made here to describe them.

Their effects, in so far as their results affect the practical running of machines is concerned, may be summarised as follows :—

(1) A pure resistance load causes a small resultant cross-magnetising field and a slight decrease of speed.

(2) A purely inductive load causes a demagnetising field and consequently an increase of speed.

(3) A pure capacity load causes a magnetising field and consequently a decrease of speed.

Combinations of these loads give a resulting speed retardation or acceleration, depending on which preponderates.

259. Frequency, Voltage and Current.—The frequency of the alternating current delivered by a rotary converter, as with an alternator, is equal to $\dfrac{R.P.M.}{60} \times$ pairs of poles.

The maximum value of the voltage will be a little less than that of the D.C. mains and can never exceed it.

The " R.M.S. value " (*see* next Chapter) will be a little less than ·707 of that of the D.C. supply, *e.g.*, in the case of a 100-volt D.C. supply, the R.M.S. alternating voltage which will be given by a rotary converter is a little less than 70·7 volts.

The relations between the alternating and direct currents can be found approximately from considerations of power.

If there were no losses in the machine the alternating output would equal the direct current input (in watts). Assume, for the sake of argument, a perfectly efficient machine running at 15 amperes on 100 volts direct.

The input is 1,500 watts or 1·5 kilowatts. The alternating volts are 70·7 R.M.S., so that 70·7 × R.M.S. current = output in watts = input = 1,500 watts.

The alternating current has therefore an R.M.S. value $\dfrac{1,500}{70\cdot7} = 21\cdot23$ amperes.

This is greater than the direct current, a result which at first sight appears peculiar. It is accounted for by the fact that current is taken from the mains as well as from the rotary converter. The excess of output current over input will not be quite so marked as is shown by this example, owing to the efficiency of the machine not being 100 per cent., but it is at any rate a factor which may have to be taken into account.

260. With a rotary converter, a normal-type starter and a motor field regulator are provided.

As with a motor, when resistance is inserted in series with the field, the machine speeds up ; thus the frequency of the alternating voltage will be increased.

The value of the voltage remains approximately the same, since it depends on the applied voltage, and is approximately 65 per cent. of that of the D.C. supply.

261. Advantages and Disadvantages of the Rotary Converter.—For W/T purposes, rotary converters are used for moderate power and frequency only.

They are lighter than motor alternators, as they have one armature only, but labour under the disadvantages :— .

    (*a*) That they can only give an R.M.S. voltage less than that of the D.C. supply ;
    (*b*) That it is very difficult to make them for high frequencies ;
    (*c*) That the output is not insulated from the input.

262. Polyphase Alternating Current Systems.—Up to the present we have only considered the production of single phase A.C., but the majority of modern A.C. systems are what is known as polyphase (or multi-phase) systems.

It will be shown later that, with single phase systems, the power absorbed by an A.C. circuit, supplied with a sinoidal voltage, continually varies throughout the cycle and is actually negative during a part of the time, unless the current and voltage are exactly in phase. This means that if this power is supplied by an alternator running at a steady speed the electrical torque will fluctuate between a high positive and a lower negative value. If, however, the windings of such an alternator are duplicated, triplicated or sextuplicated, this variation of torque can be overcome, and a larger ratio of power output to weight can be obtained. The alternator arranged in this way becomes equivalent to two, three or six alternating sources, having the peculiarity that there is a fixed and definite relation between the time phases of the voltages.

In a two-phase alternator there are two equal sources and the difference of time phase is 90° ($\pi/2$). In a three-phase one there are three sources and the difference of time phase is 120° ; for six-phase alternator there will be six separate wave forms spaced $2\pi/6$ apart.

Three-phase currents are very widely used in the commercial world in the transmission of power over long distances, on account of the fact that they require conductors of less total cross section for the conveyance of equivalent power than single phase currents.

In the production of the D.C. power supplies required by the transmitters and receivers of a wireless installation, three-phase power rectifiers have the advantage that the requisite smoothing circuits are simpler than in the single phase case.   (*Cf.* H.5, 16.)

263. **Three-phase Current.**—It will be noticed in the diagrams of alternators in Figs. 71 and 72 that there are portions of the armature which do not carry any winding.

In a three-phase alternator we fit three separate and distinct windings into the armature, spacing them symmetrically round its circumference, *i.e.*, with similar poles 120° apart.

We thus generate three separate alternating voltages.   These three wave forms will not be in step with one another, but will rise to their maximum values in succession, as shown in Fig. 110. They are said to differ in phase by 120°.

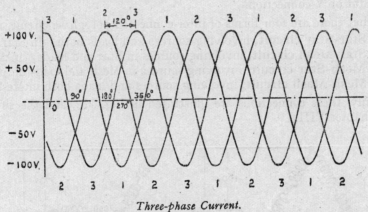

Three-phase Current.

FIG. 110.

An inspection of these curves will show that when No. 1 is zero, Nos. 2 and 3 are equal and opposite ; when No. 1 is maximum Nos. 2 and 3 are each of half the amplitude of No. 1, and are both of opposite sign to No. 1 ; in fact, that at any moment the sum of the three *voltages* is zero.   In consequence, as will be explained later, with balanced loads (paragraph 265) only three wires are required to carry the currents instead of six, as might have been expected.

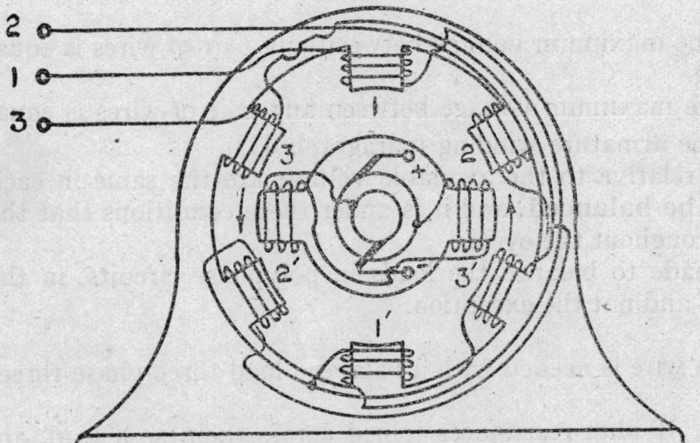

264. **The Three-phase Generator.** — Three-phase generators are usually of the revolving field type (paragraph 207). Fig. 111 gives a diagrammatic picture of a typical machine.

It will be noticed that the poles of the armature are wound alternately right and left-handed, and that similarly wound poles are 120° apart.

The direction of the voltage induced as the field sweeps round will depend on the direction in which each pole is wound.

Three-phase Generator, or Synchronous Motor.

FIG. 111.

Fig. 111 should be compared with Fig. 72. It shows the instant of maximum E.M.F. in 1 ; later on, when the rotor poles are opposite 1, the E.M.F. in 1 will be zero. Similar reasoning may be applied to 2 and 3, and a zero of E.M.F. is always obtained in a stator winding that has a rotor pole opposite to it.

The rotor field must be imagined as spreading out a good deal more than would be expected from Fig. 111, and as influencing adjacent poles ; actually, in practice, the stator would have more than three pairs of poles, and the rotor more than one.

265. Inter-connection of Polyphase Systems.—Each phase may supply a separate circuit, a pair of line wires being required for each. But the number of wires may be reduced, and a, saving in copper thereby effected if the phases are inter-connected.

In general, both the armature windings of motors and generators, and the loads joined between the wires may be connected up in one of two ways, viz. :—

(a) The Delta or mesh connection.
(b) The Star or Y connection.

This implies that there are four forms of inter-connected polyphase circuit, namely :—

(i) The **Star-Star circuit,** involving sources and loads both " in Star."
(ii) The **Star-Mesh circuit,** involving sources in Star and loads " in Mesh."
(iii) The **Mesh-Star circuit,** involving sources in Mesh and loads in Star.
(iv) The **Mesh-Mesh circuit,** involving sources and loads both in Mesh.

For the sources only, these connections are illustrated in Fig. 112, and the subject is treated in further detail in Chapter VIII.

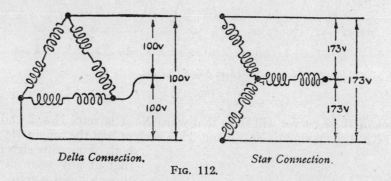

Delta Connection.   *Star Connection.*

FIG. 112.

With the phases in Delta connection the maximum voltage between any pair of wires is equal to that generated in one armature winding.

With the phases in Star connection the maximum voltage between any pair of wires is equal to $\sqrt{3}$, or 1·732 times that generated in one armature winding (paragraph 433).

If the current supplied and its phase relative to the available voltage are the same in each group of circuits, then **the load is said to be balanced,** and it is under these conditions that the power supplied by the source is uniform throughout the cycle.

Although **conscious effort is always made to balance the loads in polyphase circuits,** in the general case unbalanced loads form the rule and not the exception.

266. In order to explain why no return wire is needed with a balanced load three-phase three-wire system, Fig. 113 has been inserted.

The generator windings, and the three 10-ohm resistances joined across them as a load, are both star-connected (*Cf.* paragraph 435).

At the moment illustrated the voltage across No. 1 winding is assumed to be 100 volts positive ; at the same moment the voltages across Nos. 2 and 3 windings will be — 50 volts, as can be seen from Fig. 110.

If a fourth wire were joined up as shown dotted, there would be a current of 10 amps. flowing from right to left in it, counterbalanced by the two currents of 5 amps. due to windings 2 and 3. Consequently no current would flow along the dotted wire, and it may be dispensed with.

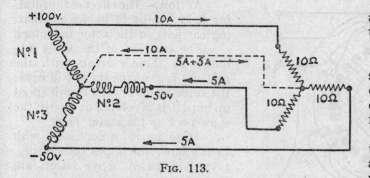

FIG. 113.

This really means that each wire acts as a common return for the other two in turn. (*Cf.* paragraph 433.)

267. The Rotating Field.—A special advantage that three-phase currents possess is the fact that they can be made to produce a rotating field.

Just as they are generated by the use of a rotating field, so when they are applied to a motor they produce a rotating field.

Consider the effect of the three-phase currents shown in Fig. 114, as applied to the field of the Induction Motor shown in Fig. 115 ; remember that a positive current through a right-hand pole will produce the same polarity as a negative current through a left-hand pole.

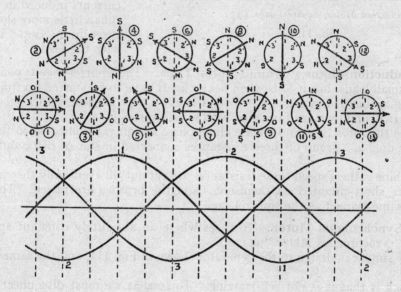

Diagram of Rotating Field.

FIG. 114.

Moment 1.   Field of poles 1, 1′ zero ; fields of poles 2, 2′ and 3, 3′ equal ; resultant midway between 2, 2′ and 3, 3′.

Moment 2.   Field of poles 2, 2′ maximum ; fields of poles 1, 1′ and 3, 3′ symmetrical on either side ; resultant across 2, 2′.

Moment 3.   Field of poles 3, 3′ zero ; fields of poles 2, 2′ and 1, 1′ equal ; resultant midway between 2, 2′ and 1, 1′.

Moment 4.   Field of 1, 1′ maximum ; fields of poles 2, 2′ and 3, 3′ symmetrical on either side ; resultant across 1, 1′ ; and so on.

Thus the position of maximum field strength will rotate at the same frequency as that of the applied alternating current.

268. The Induction Motor ; Squirrel-cage Type.—A very simple type of motor is that illustrated in Fig. 115. The rotor simply consists of a number of copper inductors joined together at each end.

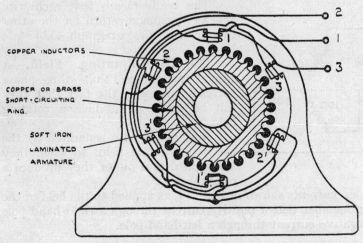

COPPER INDUCTORS

COPPER OR BRASS
SHORT·CIRCUITING
RING.

SOFT IRON
LAMINATED
ARMATURE.

Induction Motor, Squirrel-cage Type.

Fig. 115.

Action.—The effect of the rotating field will be to induce alternating currents in the rotor inductors.

The reaction of the fields produced by these currents with the rotating field of the stator will cause the rotor to move, and it will speed up until it is revolving at nearly the same pace as the stator field.

This is in accordance with Lenz's Law, which, put colloquially, says that all inductive effects are suicidal in tendency.

The rotor would like to run at exactly the same speed as the stator field, but then there would be no currents induced in it. It therefore runs a little more slowly, and "slip" is set up. "Slip" increases slightly with the load.

269. The Induction Motor ; Wound Rotor Type.—The squirrel-cage type is very useful for comparatively small loads, but it fails when heavy loads have to be started up from rest.

For starting against heavy loads a "Wound Rotor" type is used. (In England the majority of motors of 10 H.P. and over are furnished with wound rotors.)

In this type the rotor is wound with a three-phase winding, connnected to three slip rings.

The starter used is a group of three resistances connected in star or delta and joined between the slip rings.

As the machine gathers speed these resistances are cut out till eventually they are out of circuit, the windings are short-circuited on themselves and the brushes are raised. The machine then behaves in the same manner as the squirrel-cage.

270. The Synchronous Motor.—In cases where an absolutely constant speed is required, without slip, a "Synchronous Motor" is used.

This is very similar in design to the generator shown in Fig. 111, and the same diagram may be used.

Its drawback is that it is not self-starting. To start it we must disconnect the three-phase supply from its stator, and rotate it mechanically by the use of (say) an induction motor on the same shaft, until its rotor field is revolving at the same frequency as that of the three-phase supply.*

If then the three-phase supply is switched on to the stator, the rotating field of the stator will drive the rotor round without any slip.

If, however, current is switched on without these precautions, a heavy short-circuit current flows which may damage the machine.

271. It may be useful to remember that three-phase generators and synchronous motors with stator armatures have two slip rings supplied with D.C. ; wound rotor induction motors have three slip rings, and squirrel-cage induction motors have no slip rings.

* Synchronous motors are sometimes started by connecting them directly to the mains, the eddy currents induced in their field systems and in copper grids fitted in slots in the pole faces being sufficient to run them up to speed, as induction motors, on no load. This involves taking a very large current from the mains, and for machines of large size, auto-transformers (paragraph 371) are employed to reduce the voltage applied to the stator windings on starting.

CHAPTER V.

ALTERNATING CURRENT.

272. General Principles.—In the preceding chapter we saw that electric currents are generated in two different forms, viz., direct current and alternating current. The former is generated by means of a D.C. dynamo, and the latter, for W/T purposes, by means of an (motor) alternator or a rotary converter.

In this chapter we are particularly concerned with the latter—alternating current—measurement, and its behaviour under various conditions.

Radio and Audio Frequencies.—So far we have been speaking of alternating current as being produced by an alternator, and its frequency as depending upon the number of poles of the alternator and its speed of revolution.

Such currents are spoken of as " **audio-frequency** " (A/F) currents.

In wireless telegraphy, we meet with alternating currents ranging from, say, 10,000 cycles per second, up to, say, twenty to thirty million per second, produced by means of transmitting arcs and transmitting or receiving valves, by methods which will be described later.

Such currents are spoken of as " **radio-frequency** " (R/F) or " oscillatory " currents. The division between radio- and audio-frequency currents is not at all sharply defined, and both kinds obey exactly the same laws, if we assume that they follow, or approximate, to the Sine Law.

In Chapter VII, a method of producing a high frequency oscillation by means of a " spark oscillator " is described. The high frequency current there described is slightly different in form, since it starts at a maximum amplitude and dies away to zero, but it also obeys the laws laid down in this chapter.

For our immediate purpose, then, we shall consider that we can obtain currents at any frequency we like, without explaining how they are produced in practice.

In diagrams, the source of alternating current will be represented as in Fig. 116 (*a*), which indicates " a source of alternating E.M.F. of any required frequency."

273. Measurement of Alternating Current.—In measuring the value of an alternating current, it is not convenient to measure its **maximum** value, *i.e.*, the value it reaches at the top of each half cycle of the current curve.

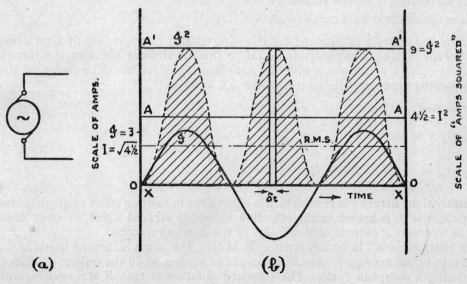

(a)   (b)

Fig. 116.

If an alternating current were passed through a D.C. measuring instrument whose pointer deflection was proportional to the first power of the current flowing, the rapid alternations in value would not be followed by the pointer of the instrument ; it would simply register the average value of current, which would be zero, as is obvious from the shape of the curve which represents the variation of an alternating quantity with time. The value of any current may, however, be measured by its heating effect upon a conductor of given resistance, and therefore a hot wire ammeter (described in Chapter III) is suitable for our purpose.

The heating effect is independent of the direction in which current is flowing, positive or negative, and so, even although the actual value of the current is continuously changing, an indication will be given by the instrument of the average heating effect, and hence of the magnitude of the current.

We shall deal first of all with a current whose wave form is assumed to be sinusoidal, and is therefore represented by the formula.

$$i = \mathcal{J} \sin \omega t.$$

In Fig. 116 (b) is drawn a curve showing an alternating current of this type for which $\mathcal{J}$, the maximum value in each half-cycle, is 3 amperes.

The power expended in producing heat by a current of i amperes in a resistance of R ohms is i^2R watts.

Let the resistance in this case be 1 ohm.

The instantaneous rate at which heat is produced is given by $i^2 \times 1$ watts, i.e., i^2 watts. So that, if we draw the dotted curve, which represents i^2 and so rises each half-cycle to a maximum value of 9, it will represent the variations in the power expended in watts.

The total amount of heat produced, or the total **energy dissipated,** is given by summing up the small amounts of energy dissipated at each instant, i.e., by summing the products of the instantaneous powers multiplied by the small intervals of time during which they are available.

This is simply, therefore, the area contained between the dotted curve and the axis, which area gives the total energy in joules, the axis being an axis of time.

If now we had been considering the total energy which would be dissipated by a direct current of 3 amps. during the same time t, it would be given by $9t$ joules. Graphically, it would be the area enclosed between the horizontal line A'A', where OA' = 9, and the axis.

Hence we have :—

Energy dissipated by A.C.   = Area under the dotted curve.
Energy dissipated by D.C. of 3 amps. = Area A'A'XX.

But, by inspection, from the symmetry of the figure :—

Area under the dotted curve = $\frac{1}{2}$A'A'XX.

Therefore, **the energy dissipated by the alternating current is half that dissipated by a direct current having a magnitude equal to the maximum value of the former.**

The direct current which would give the same heating effect would be such that the rectangle AAXX represented the energy dissipated, where AX = $4\frac{1}{2}$ = $(I_{dc})^2$.

In symbols—

$$I_{dc} = \sqrt{4\tfrac{1}{2}} = \sqrt{\frac{9}{2}} = \frac{3}{\sqrt{2}} = \frac{1}{\sqrt{2}} \times \text{maximum value of the A.C.}$$

$$\text{or, } I_{dc} = \frac{1}{\sqrt{2}} \mathcal{J} = 0\cdot707 \mathcal{J}.$$

This **equivalent direct current,** which is equivalent in heating effect to an alternating current whose amplitude is $\mathcal{J}$, is known as the **effective value,** or **virtual value,** or **root mean square value** of the alternating current, and is $0\cdot707$ of the maximum value.

" Root mean square " is usually written **R.M.S.** The name is derived from the fact that it is the square root of the average (or mean) value of the squares of all the different values the current can take during a complete cycle. The standard notation is that R.M.S. values are written in

" square " capitals, as I, maximum values in " curly " capitals, as $\mathcal{J}$, and instantaneous values in small letters, as i.

$$I = 0 \cdot 707 \mathcal{J} \quad \text{and} \quad \mathcal{J} = \sqrt{2}\, I = 1 \cdot 414\, I.$$

It is obvious that a sinusoidally varying quantity is determined in magnitude by either its maximum value or its R.M.S. value.

Alternating voltages are likewise measured by either maximum values or R.M.S. values, the relationship between them being as before.

An A.C. voltmeter measures R.M.S. values only, so that if it reads 200 volts, the voltage is rising and falling between zero and a maximum value of $200\sqrt{2} = 282 \cdot 8$ volts.

For power calculations, and for finding the sizes of cables necessary to carry currents, we are concerned with R.M.S. values of current and voltage ; while for determining the thickness of insulation necessary, the strength of a dielectric, or the instant at which a spark gap breaks down, we are concerned with maximum values of voltage.

Remember, that in any calculations where current and voltage are interdependent, if we start with a *maximum* value of voltage the answer will be given as a *maximum* value of current, and *vice versa*.

274. R.M.S. Value of an A.C. Superimposed upon a D.C.—This is a case of some importance in W/T theory, where the current in the anode circuits of valves is frequently a combination of steady and alternating currents.

Let the D.C. current be represented by I_1 and the A.C. current be given by $\mathcal{J} \sin \theta$. Hence—

Total instantaneous current $= i = I_1 + \mathcal{J} \sin \theta$.

The power dissipated is proportional to the square of this quantity.

$$\therefore \quad i^2 = (I_1 + \mathcal{J} \sin \theta)^2 = I_1{}^2 + 2\,I_1 \mathcal{J} \sin \theta + \mathcal{J}^2 \sin^2 \theta.$$

Over a complete cycle the second term $2\,I_1 \mathcal{J} \sin \theta$ has an average value of zero, and therefore contributes nothing towards the heating effect.

The first and last terms are the ones producing power dissipation. Fig. 117 is a graph of i^2 plotted against time ; essentially it is the same as Fig. 116 (b), the base line of the latter being displaced a distance corresponding to $I_1{}^2$. It is a convenient representation of the sum $I_1{}^2 + \mathcal{J}^2 \sin^2 \theta$.

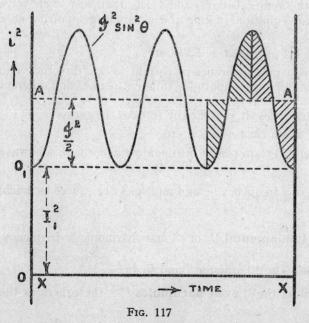

FIG. 117

As in the case of Fig. 116 (b), the area under the curve represents the energy dissipated. With reference to Fig. 117, the direct current which would give the same heating effect would be such that the rectangle AAXX represents the energy dissipated in a given time, where $AX = I_1{}^2 + \mathcal{J}^2/_2$. From this we get the R.M.S. value—

In symbols $\quad I = \sqrt{I_1{}^2 + \dfrac{\mathcal{J}^2}{2}}.$

Considering the numerical example $i = 4 + 3 \sin 2t$, the R.M.S. value of this current is given by

$$I = \sqrt{16 + \frac{9}{2}} = \sqrt{\frac{41}{2}} = 4 \cdot 52 \text{ amps.}$$

Hence an A.C. ammeter placed in a circuit in which there is a direct current of 4 amps. having an A.C. of peak value 3 amps. superimposed upon it, would read 4·52 amps.

★275. **Alternating Current Measurement.**—The results of the last paragraph can be quickly and accurately obtained by methods utilising the calculus, and also extended to cases where the waveform is not sinusoidal.

(a) **R.M.S. value of a pure sine-wave alternating current.**

Let the current be $i = \mathcal{J} \sin \omega t$.

The energy dissipated in a resistance R ohms during a small time $dt = i^2 R dt$ $= \mathcal{J}^2 R \sin^2 \omega t \, dt$.

Total energy dissipated in a complete cycle

$$= \int_0^{\frac{2\pi}{\omega}} \mathcal{J}^2 R \sin^2 \omega t \, dt \;=\; \mathcal{J}^2 R \int_0^{\frac{2\pi}{\omega}} \frac{1 - \cos 2\omega t}{2} \, dt \quad \ldots \text{(since } \cos 2A = 1 - 2\sin^2 A\text{)}$$

$$= \mathcal{J}^2 R \left[\frac{t}{2} - \frac{\sin 2\omega t}{4\omega} \right]_{t=0}^{t=\frac{2\pi}{\omega}} \quad = \mathcal{J}^2 R \cdot \frac{2\pi}{2\omega} = \frac{\mathcal{J}^2 R}{2} \times \text{time of complete cycle.}$$

A direct current of value I would dissipate as much energy in the same time if

$$\text{I}^2 R \times \text{time of complete cycle} = \frac{\mathcal{J}^2 R}{2} \times \text{time of complete cycle.}$$

$$\therefore \; \text{I}^2 = \frac{\mathcal{J}^2}{2}, \text{ and } \text{I} = \frac{\mathcal{J}}{\sqrt{2}} = 0\cdot707\mathcal{J}.$$

(b) **Average Value of Current per half-cycle.**—This is sometimes required, and the value is obviously

$$\frac{\displaystyle\int_0^{\frac{\pi}{\omega}} \mathcal{J} \sin \omega t \, dt}{\dfrac{\pi}{\omega}} = \frac{\left[\dfrac{-\cos \omega t}{\omega} \right]_0^{\frac{\pi}{\omega}}}{\dfrac{\pi}{\omega}} = \mathcal{J} \times \frac{2}{\pi} = 0\cdot637\mathcal{J}.$$

(c) **Alternating Current not sinusoidal.**—Many alternating quantities met with in A.C. work are not pure sine waves in form, although repeating themselves at definite intervals. By a well-known theorem called Fourier's Theorem, any such wave form can be represented by an equation (taking the alternating quantity as a current) of the form :—

$$i = \text{I}_0 + \mathcal{J}_1 \sin (\omega t + \phi_1) + \mathcal{J}_2 \sin (2\omega t + \phi_2) + \text{etc.}$$

The term I_0 simply indicates that there is a preponderance of current in one direction, and superimposed on this are sinusoidal variations of different amplitudes, different periods and different phases.

As we are only considering alternating quantities, it is sufficient to take the terms

$$i = \mathcal{J}_1 \sin (\omega t + \phi_1) + \mathcal{J}_2 \sin (2\omega t + \phi_2) + \text{etc.,}$$

each of which has an average value of zero over a certain period of time, just as a single sine wave has.

These frequencies are seen to be made up of a frequency $\dfrac{\omega}{2\pi}$ and multiples of it, twice as much, three times as much, etc.

The frequency $\dfrac{\omega}{2\pi}$ is known as the " **fundamental** " or " first harmonic " frequency, $2 \times \dfrac{\omega}{2\pi}$ as the " second harmonic," $3 \times \dfrac{\omega}{2\pi}$ as the " third harmonic," and so on.

The second, fourth, sixth, etc., are known as the " **even harmonics** "; the others as the " **odd harmonics.**"

The result of combining a fundamental wave and its second harmonic is shown in Fig 118 (*a*), and that of combining a fundamental wave and its third harmonic (*i.e.*, an odd one) is given in Fig. 118 (*b*).

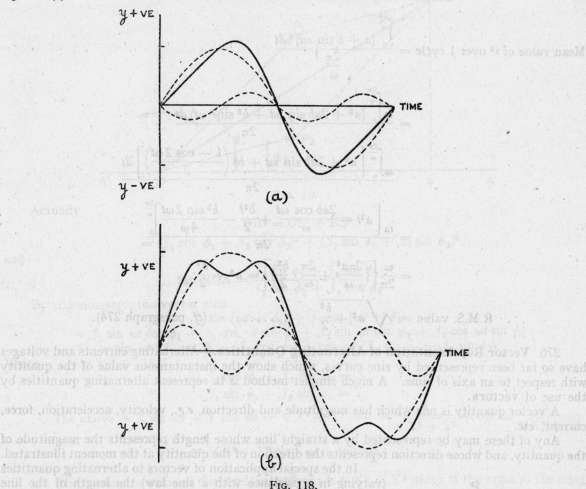

FIG. 118.

The R.M.S. value of such complicated waveforms can be worked out as in section (*a*) of this paragraph.

R.M.S. value = square root of the mean value of the square of the current = square root of

$$\frac{\int_0^{\frac{2\pi}{\omega}} [\mathcal{J}_1 \sin(\omega t + \phi_1) + \mathcal{J}_2 \sin(2\omega t + \phi_2) + ----]^2 \, dt}{\frac{2\pi}{\omega}},$$

which works out to be the square root of

$$\frac{\mathcal{J}_1{}^2}{2} + \frac{\mathcal{J}_2{}^2}{2} + ----$$

$$\therefore I = \sqrt{\frac{\mathcal{J}_1{}^2}{2} + \frac{\mathcal{J}_2{}^2}{2} + \frac{\mathcal{J}_3{}^2}{2} +} = \sqrt{I_1{}^2 + I_2{}^2 + I_3{}^2 + ---}$$

where I_1, I_2, etc., are the separate R.M.S. values of the fundamental and the harmonics.

Vectorially, of course, the two quantities i and $\dfrac{di}{dt}$ are represented by two lines at right angles

to each other, the vector representing $\dfrac{di}{dt}$ being in length ω times that representing i.

RESISTANCE, INDUCTANCE, CAPACITY, AND SERIES COMBINATIONS OF THESE IN ALTERNATING CURRENT CIRCUITS.

277. Resistance in an Alternating Current Circuit.—If between the slip rings of an alternator giving an alternating voltage of sine form, represented by $v = \mathcal{V} \sin \omega t$ volts, we join a resistance of R ohms, as in Fig. 121 (a), then the current flowing through the circuit (neglecting any inductance of the armature winding) will be given by $i = \dfrac{v}{R}$ amperes.

$$i = \frac{v}{R} = \frac{\mathcal{V}}{R} \sin \omega t.$$

If we put $\mathcal{J}$ for $\dfrac{\mathcal{V}}{R}$, the maximum value of the current, the current waveform is $i = \mathcal{J} \sin \omega t$.

The current and voltage rise and fall simultaneously, as illustrated in Fig. 121 (b), and obviously they are in phase with each other. The thin curve represents the voltage, drawn to a scale of volts, and the thick curve the current, drawn to a scale of amperes.

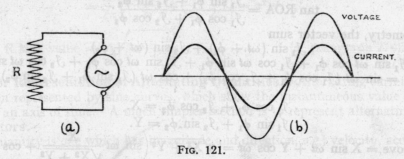

FIG. 121.

Represented vectorially, the two vectors would be laid off along the same line.

278. Effect of Inductance on an Alternating Current.—We shall now discuss the effect of inductance in an alternating current circuit.

Let us first recall what we have already learnt about the effects of inductance.

If current is switched on to an inductance, the inductance sets up a counter E.M.F. which opposes the rise of the current.

When the current is switched off, the inductance sets up a counter E.M.F. which tends to make the current continue flowing.

The reason for this action is that as the current increases through the coil, a magnetic field is set up round it, and work has to be done on the coil in order to create this magnetic field.

When the current is stopping, the magnetic field ceases to be maintained by the current, and the energy that was stored in the magnetic field is restored to the circuit.

Hence the counter E.M.F. **opposes the rise** and **opposes the fall** of a current, alternately **taking energy and returning it intact** to the source, twice in each complete cycle of current. The mean expenditure of energy is zero and the current is described as " **Wattless** " (*cf.* paragraph 325).

The unit of inductance is the **Henry,** which is the inductance of a coil of such a form that when the current through the coil is increasing or decreasing at the rate of one ampere per second, the induced E.M.F. is equal to one volt.

279. Rate of Change.—It follows from the above that what we are concerned with is the **rate of change of the current** ; when the current is changing most quickly the greatest E.M.F. will be induced, and when it is not changing at all, there will be no E.M.F. induced.

Let us join up a coil (L), which is supposed to have inductance without resistance, to a source of alternating E.M.F., as shown in Fig. 122, and assume that an alternating current is flowing through the inductance as shown in Fig. 123 (a).

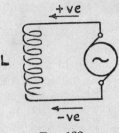

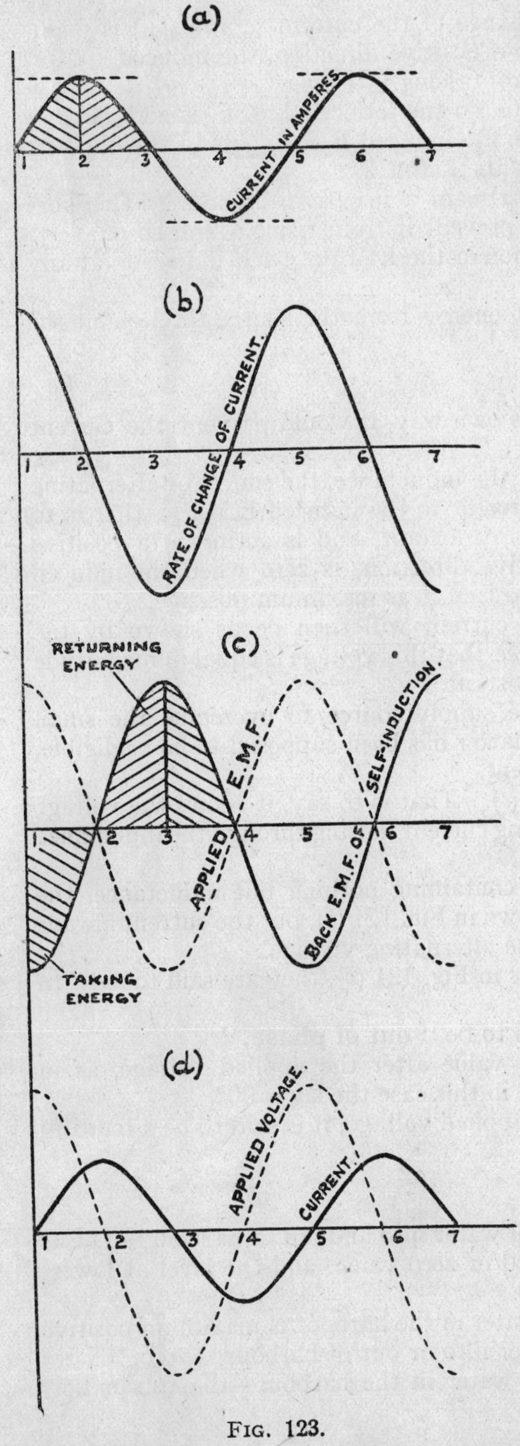

FIG. 122.

Fig. 123 (a) shows a curve where time is plotted horizontally and current strength vertically ; hence, if the current makes a big change in a short time, the slope of the curve during that period will be steep. On the other hand, if the current makes but little change in a long time, the slope will be slight ; thus the slope of the current curve is an indication of its rate of change.

From an inspection of Fig. 123 (a), it can be seen that at moments 1, 3, 5 and 7, the slope is steepest. At moments 2, 4 and 6, the current is not changing at all—neither increasing nor decreasing—and the **slope** of the curve is zero, as indicated by the dotted line.

Fig. 123 (b) is a curve giving the **rate of change of current** in amperes per second, drawn to any suitable scale.

At moment 1, Fig. 123 (a), the current is increasing very rapidly in a positive direction. This is indicated at 1 in Fig. 123 (b), which shows a maximum rate of change in a **positive** direction (above the axis) at this moment.

At moment 2, Fig. 123 (a), the current has just stopped increasing and is just going to decrease. Exactly on the top of the curve it is not changing at all. This is indicated at 2, Fig. 123 (b), i.e., zero rate of change.

At moment 3, Fig. 123 (a), the current is falling very rapidly through zero, and rising very rapidly in the other direction. That is the current is changing very rapidly in the opposite direction to that at moment 1. This is indicated at 3, Fig. 123 (b); and so on.

Hence Fig 123 (b) is a curve indicating the **rate of change** of the current shown in Fig. 123 (a).

280. Induced E.M.F.—Since the E.M.F. induced in any inductance, through which the current of curve (a) is flowing, depends on the rate of change of that current, this E.M.F. will rise and fall in

FIG. 123.

time with curve (*b*), being maximum when curve (*b*) is maximum, and zero when curve (*b*) is zero.

Its direction—positive or negative—can easily be determined by remembering that it always opposes the rise and fall of current through the inductance.

In curve (*c*) the full line curve represents this induced E.M.F.

At moment 1 it is maximum because the rate of change of the current (curve (*b*)) is maximum, and as the current (curve (*a*)) is trying to rise in a positive direction, the induced E.M.F. is acting in a negative direction, trying to prevent it from rising.

At moment 2 the rate of change of the current is zero, so the induced E.M.F. is zero also.

Between moments 2 and 3 the current wants to fall, so the induced E.M.F. acts in the opposite direction to that in which it was acting between moments 1 and 2.

Between moments 3 and 4, the current is trying to rise in a negative direction. Therefore the induced E.M.F. acts in a positive direction trying to prevent it from rising ; and so on.

Hence curve (*c*) shows the relative strength and direction of the E.M.F. of self induction at any instant.

The shaded areas represent the giving and taking of energy from the source throughout the cycle.

281. **Applied E.M.F.**—If the induced E.M.F. had its own way, it would prevent the current from rising and falling at all.

In order, therefore, to make the current flow through the inductance, the source of alternating current has to apply a voltage which is equal and opposite to the induced E.M.F. ; that is to say, a voltage which is equal to the induced E.M.F. at any instant, and is acting in a positive direction when the induced E.M.F. is acting in a negative direction, is zero when the induced E.M.F. is zero, and is maximum negative when the induced E.M.F. is maximum positive.

The applied voltage from the source of alternating current will then be as shown by the dotted curve shown in Fig. 123 (*c*). It can be seen at once that this voltage is equal in magnitude and opposite in direction to the induced E.M.F. at any instant.

In addition, a small voltage will be required from the supply source to overcome the small resistance which must be present in the coil. But as the latter has been supposed to be negligible, we shall neglect this small additional voltage for the present.

Fig. 123 (*d*) shows the combination of curves (*a*) and (*c*). That is to say, it shows the voltage applied by the alternating source and the resulting alternating current flowing through the inductance L.

From this diagram it can be seen that in a circuit containing nothing but inductance, the current and voltage do not rise and fall together, as was shown in Fig. 121 (*b*), but the current always comes to its maximum value a quarter cycle later than the alternating voltage.

When the current and voltage rise and fall together, as in Fig. 121 (*b*), they are said to be " **in phase.**"

When they do not rise and fall together, they are said to be " **out of phase.**"

When the alternating current reaches its maximum value after the applied voltage, as in Fig. 123 (*d*), the current is said to **lag** behind the voltage ; in this case the lag is 90°.

Conversely, when it reaches its maximum **before** the applied voltage, it is said to be a **leading** current.

282. An almost parallel example is given by the flow of water into and out of harbour. Let us call the level of water in a harbour at half tide the normal or zero value, and the level at lowest ebb the maximum negative value.

At the top of the flood and at lowest ebb the level of water in the harbour is maximum positive or maximum negative ; at these moments the flow of water into or out of harbour is zero.

At half-tide—the moment of normal or zero level of water in the harbour—the ebb or flow current is maximum.

Thus, curves representing these two variables—the current at the mouth of the harbour, and the level of water in the harbour—would be a quarter of a cycle out of phase, and just like Fig. 123 (d).

283. Voltage and Current in an Inductive Circuit.—The results obtained in the preceding five paragraphs, as regards phase relationship of current and voltage in a purely inductive circuit, can be arrived at much more quickly by using a mathematical treatment, and at the same time, a formula giving the relationship between current and voltage amplitudes can be found.

The problem, as before, is to investigate the voltage necessary to send an alternating current through an inductance, where self-induction exercises a continuous effect.

Let the current be $i = \mathcal{J} \sin \omega t$, where $\omega = 2\pi f$.

From Chapter III, the induced E.M.F. is given by $-L\dfrac{di}{dt}$, that is $-L \times$ rate of change of current; the result will be in volts, if L is in henries, i in amperes, and t in seconds.

In this case $-L\dfrac{di}{dt} = -\omega L \mathcal{J} \cos \omega t = \omega L \mathcal{J} \sin\left(\omega t - \dfrac{\pi}{2}\right)$.

The E.M.F. of self-induction lags, therefore, by $\dfrac{\pi}{2}$, or 90°, on the current flowing.

Now, in the case we are considering, where the resistance is neglected, the applied E.M.F. has just to overcome this counter E.M.F. to keep the current flowing.

Thus the applied E.M.F. $= +\omega L \mathcal{J} \cos \omega t = +\omega L \mathcal{J} \sin\left(\omega t + \dfrac{\pi}{2}\right)$ **leading** by 90° on the current flowing. It is itself sinusoidal, and has the same frequency as the current. This applied E.M.F. has an amplitude $\omega L \mathcal{J}$ volts, L being in henries and $\mathcal{J}$ in amperes.

From the other point of view, if a sinusoidal voltage whose amplitude is $\mathcal{V}$ volts is applied to an inductive circuit, whose inductance is L henries, at a frequency of f cycles per second, the resulting current flowing will be, in amplitude,

$$\mathcal{J} = \frac{\mathcal{V}}{\omega L} = \frac{\mathcal{V}}{2\pi f L} \text{ amperes,}$$

and will **lag** 90° behind the voltage.

Because of the constant relationship between maximum and R.M.S. values for both alternating currents and voltages, we may conclude that a similar formula will hold for R.M.S. values.

Thus a voltage of R.M.S. value V volts, under the same conditions as above, will give a current of R.M.S. value I amperes, where

$$V = \omega L I = 2\pi f L I, \text{ or } I = \frac{V}{\omega L} = \frac{V}{2\pi f L}.$$

In phase relationship, the current lags 90° on the voltage.

In many practical cases, R.M.S. values are of more interest than peak values, but the latter are sometimes of importance ; in simple numerical problems, an " A.C. voltage of 100 volts " will normally mean 100 volts R.M.S., unless otherwise stated.

284. Inductive Reactance.—This relationship between voltage and current resembles the relationship expressed by Ohm's Law. **The expression " ωL " takes the place of R and has the same effect in determining the value of the current flowing.** As, however, the energy expended in creating the magnetic field round an inductance is restored when the magnetic field collapses, there is no expenditure of energy involved in the introduction of an inductance into a circuit, such as there would be were resistance introduced.

ωL, or $2\pi f L$, is termed " **Inductive Reactance,**" and is denoted by the symbol X_L.

Resistance dissipates energy in the form of heat. **Reactance** diminishes current by setting up an opposing E.M.F., and therefore controls a source of alternating E.M.F. without waste.

The unit in which it is measured must be the same as the unit of resistance, the ohm, since it is a relationship between voltage and current. In its physical sense it is not, of course, a true ohmic resistance, but it is convenient in calculations to give it simply the name " ohm."

Example 28.

Find the value of the current flowing through an inductance of 0·5 henry, of negligible resistance, if an alternating voltage of 200 volts is applied at a frequency of 50 cycles per second.

$$I = \frac{V}{2\pi fL} = \frac{200}{2 \times 3\cdot14 \times 50 \times 0\cdot5} = \frac{4}{3\cdot14} = 1\cdot27 \text{ amps.}$$

Example 29.

Find the value of the current flowing through an inductance of 200 mics, with an applied voltage of 1,000 volts at a frequency of 500,000 cycles per second.

$$200 \text{ mics} = \frac{200}{10^6} \text{ henries.}$$

$$X_L = \omega L = 6\cdot28 \times 500,000 \times \frac{200}{10^6} = 6\cdot28 \times 5 \times 10^5 \times \frac{200}{10^6} = 628 \text{ ohms.}$$

$$I = \frac{V}{X_L} = \frac{1,000}{628} = 1\cdot6 \text{ amperes.}$$

285. Vectorial Representation.—The method of vector representation of alternating quantities can be used to show the preceding results with greater simplicity than in Fig. 123.

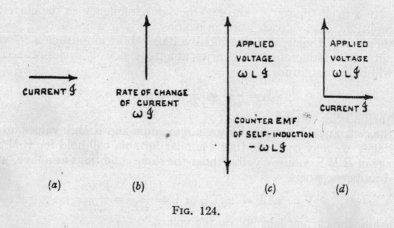

FIG. 124.

In Fig. 124 (a) above, the alternating current $i = \mathcal{J} \sin \omega t$ is represented simply by a line whose length represents $\mathcal{J}$ amperes.

The rate of change of current $\dfrac{di}{dt} = \omega \mathcal{J} \sin\left(\omega t + \dfrac{\pi}{2}\right)$ is shown in Fig. 124 (b) by a line of length $\omega \mathcal{J}$, leading the current by 90°.

The E.M.F. of self-induction, $- L \dfrac{di}{dt}$, or $- \omega L \mathcal{J} \sin\left(\omega t + \dfrac{\pi}{2}\right)$, or $\omega L \mathcal{J} \sin\left(\omega t - \dfrac{\pi}{2}\right)$, is re-Presented by a line, length $\omega L \mathcal{J}$, lagging 90° on the current.

The applied voltage, which must be equal and opposite at each instant, *i.e.*, $+ \omega L \mathcal{J} \sin\left(\omega t + \dfrac{\pi}{2}\right)$, is shown also in Fig. 124 (c).

Fig. 124 (d) shows the applied voltage and current flowing in an inductive circuit on one diagram, the current **lagging** 90° on the voltage ; more usually, the vectors will be labelled in R.M.S. values, I and ωLI, etc.

286. Inductances in Series and Parallel (*cf*, paragraphs 149 and 150).

(a) Series.

If two inductances L_1 and L_2 are joined in series, the total applied voltage necessary to send a current J through both inductances will be given by $\omega L_1 J + \omega L_2 J$, the two separate voltages being simply additive, because each leads 90° on the current.

$$\mathcal{V} = \omega (L_1 + L_2) J.$$

The two inductances in series are therefore equivalent to one inductance L, where $L = L_1 + L_2$, *i.e.*, inductances in series are additive.

(b) Parallel.

If two inductances L_1 and L_2 are joined in parallel and an alternating voltage $\mathcal{V}$ is applied to them (Fig. 125), then currents of J_1 and J_2 will flow through them respectively, these currents both lagging by 90° on the voltage and hence in phase with one another, and additive.

The total current

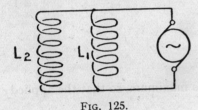

FIG. 125.

$$J = J_1 + J_2 = \frac{\mathcal{V}}{\omega L_1} + \frac{\mathcal{V}}{\omega L_2} = \frac{\mathcal{V}}{\omega} \left(\frac{1}{L_1} + \frac{1}{L_2} \right).$$

The inductances in parallel are therefore equivalent to a single inductance L, where

$$\frac{1}{L} = \frac{1}{L_1} + \frac{1}{L_2}, \text{ or } L = \frac{L_1 L_2}{L_1 + L_2}.$$

Hence, inductances in parallel are additive by the reciprocal law, as is the case with resistances.

287. Resistance and Inductance in Series.—So far, we have only considered two cases :—

(a) where the circuit contains nothing but **resistance**. Here $J = \dfrac{\mathcal{V}}{R}$, and current and voltage are in phase ;

(b) where the circuit contains nothing but **inductance**. Here $J = \dfrac{\mathcal{V}}{\omega L}$, and the current lags 90° behind the applied voltage.

Now, although in practice we often get cases where the inductive reactance is so small compared with the resistance, or the resistance is so small compared with the inductive reactance, that the smaller item can be neglected, yet, as a rule, we have to consider both the inductance and the resistance of the circuit.

In the case shown in Fig. 126 the applied voltage has to do two things :—

(1) overcome the iR drop in the circuit ;

(2) overcome the counter E.M.F. of the inductance of L henries $\left(- L \dfrac{di}{dt} \right)$.

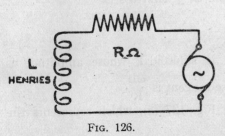

FIG. 126.

Fig. 127 (b) shows the conditions under these circumstances.

The thick line curve indicates the rise and fall of the current.

The voltage forcing the current through the resistance R is indicated by the curve $v = iR$. It is in phase with the current.

The voltage overcoming the counter E.M.F. of the inductance L is indicated by the curve $v = \omega L i$, which leads the current by 90°. The necessary total voltage from the alternator in order to supply these two voltages simultaneously can be found by adding the ordinates of the two curves together at every instant, taking account of their directions ; the result is shown by the curve marked "**Applied voltage.**"

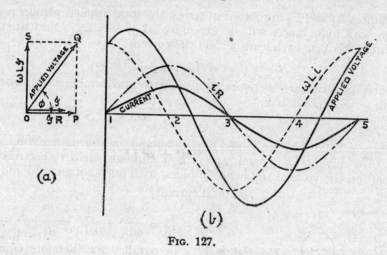

FIG. 127.

It will be seen that :—

(a) At moment 1 the iR curve is zero and the $\omega L i$ curve is maximum, so that the applied voltage required $= \omega L \mathcal{J}$.

(b) At moment 2 the iR curve is maximum and the $\omega L i$ curve is zero, so that the applied voltage $= \mathcal{J}$R.

(c) Between moments 1 and 2 both the iR and the $\omega L i$ curves are positive.

(d) Between moments 2 and 3 the $\omega L i$ curve is increasing in a negative direction, while the iR curve is decreasing, but is still positive ; hence the resultant curve is found by subtracting the ordinates of the $\omega L i$ curve from those of the iR curve.

(e) Between moments 3 and 4 the iR curve and the $\omega L i$ curve are both negative ; hence their ordinates must be added to find the resultant.

It will be seen by comparing maximum positive values that the current is lagging behind the applied voltage by some angle less than 90°.

288. **Value of Applied Voltage.**—Instead of the laborious graphical method above, the results, trigonometrical and vectorial, of paragraph 276, can be utilised to give the value and phase relationship of the applied voltage necessary to send an alternating current $\mathcal{J}$ through a resistance R and an inductance L in series. Trigonometrically, the necessary voltage is given by

$$v = i\text{R} + \text{L}\frac{di}{dt}$$

$$\therefore \quad v = \mathcal{J}\text{R} \sin \omega t + \omega \text{L} \mathcal{J} \sin\left(\omega t + \frac{\pi}{2}\right) = \mathcal{J}\text{R} \sin \omega t + \omega \text{L} \mathcal{J} \cos \omega t$$

$$= \mathcal{J} \sqrt{\text{R}^2 + \omega^2 \text{L}^2} \sin\left(\omega t + \tan^{-1}\frac{\omega \text{L}}{\text{R}}\right)$$

(using paragraph 276), and is therefore a voltage which is sinusoidal, whose amplitude is $\mathcal{J}\sqrt{\text{R}^2 + \omega^2 \text{L}^2}$, and which leads the current by an angle whose tangent is $\dfrac{\omega \text{L}}{\text{R}}$.

Vectorially, the same result is obtained by considering Fig. 127 (a), which represents the vectorial addition of the two vectors $\mathcal{J}$R and $\omega L \mathcal{J}$.

The vector $\mathcal{J}$R, in phase with and therefore drawn in the same direction as the vector representing the current, is shown by OP.

The vector $\omega L \mathcal{J}$, leading the current by 90° and therefore drawn as shown at right angles to the current vector, is shown on the same scale by OS.

The summation is carried out by completing the rectangle OPQS and drawing the diagonal OQ. OQ is then the vectorial representation of the applied voltage which is equivalent to the separate voltages $\mathcal{J}R$ and $\omega L \mathcal{J}$. Its length is given by

$$\sqrt{OP^2 + PQ^2} = \sqrt{(\mathcal{J}R)^2 + (\omega L \mathcal{J})^2} = \mathcal{J}\sqrt{R^2 + \omega^2 L^2}.$$

This is the amplitude $\mathcal{V}$ of the voltage required.

Hence

$$\mathcal{V} = \mathcal{J}\sqrt{R^2 + \omega^2 L^2}, \quad \text{or} \quad \mathcal{J} = \frac{\mathcal{V}}{\sqrt{R^2 + \omega^2 L^2}}$$

In R.M.S. values, $V = I\sqrt{R^2 + \omega^2 L^2}$, or $I = \dfrac{V}{\sqrt{R^2 + \omega^2 L^2}}$.

Also from the figure, if $\phi =$ the angle QOP,

$$\tan \phi = \frac{PQ}{OP} = \frac{\omega L \mathcal{J}}{\mathcal{J}R} = \frac{\omega L}{R}.$$

Hence the current lags on the voltage by an angle whose tangent is $\dfrac{\omega L}{R}$ or $\dfrac{\text{Reactance}}{\text{Resistance}}$

Also $\omega L \mathcal{J} = \mathcal{V} \sin \phi$, and $\mathcal{J}R = \mathcal{V} \cos \phi$.

289. Impedance.—The expression $\sqrt{R^2 + (\omega L)^2}$ is called the **Impedance** of the circuit, and is denoted by the letter **Z (ohms)**. It may be defined as the ratio of the maximum value of the voltage to the maximum value of the current (irrespective of the fact that these may not occur at the same instant). Being a ratio of voltage to current it is measured in ohms, though not necessarily a true ohmic resistance (*cf.* paragraph 284). Ohm's law for A.C. circuits now appears in the forms

$$\mathcal{V} = \mathcal{J}Z \quad \text{and} \quad V = IZ.$$

Example 30.

Let an alternating voltage $\mathcal{V} = 100$ volts at a frequency of 25 cycles per second be applied to a circuit of resistance 1·5 ohms and of inductance ·01 henry. Find (*a*) the current flowing, and (*b*) the angle of lag :—

(*a*) $\omega = 2\pi f = 2\pi \times 25 = 50\pi = 157$ radians per sec.

Reactance $= X_L = \omega L = 157 \times \cdot 01 = 1 \cdot 57$ ohms.

Resistance $= 1 \cdot 5$ ohms.

Impedance $Z = \sqrt{R^2 + X_L^2} = \sqrt{1 \cdot 5^2 + 1 \cdot 57^2}$

$\qquad\qquad = \sqrt{2 \cdot 25 + 2 \cdot 46} = \sqrt{4 \cdot 71} = 2 \cdot 17$ ohms.

$$\mathcal{J} = \frac{\mathcal{V}}{Z} = \frac{100}{2 \cdot 17} = 46 \text{ amperes.}$$

(*b*) $\operatorname{Tan} \phi = \dfrac{X_L}{R} = \dfrac{1 \cdot 57}{1 \cdot 5} = 1 \cdot 047.$

From a table of Tangents, ϕ is seen to be an angle of $46^\circ 19'$.

So we have a current of 46 amps. lagging 46°, or ·13 of a cycle, behind the E.M.F. of 100 volts. Plotting these as vectors and as curves, we get Fig. 128 (*a*) and (*b*).

The voltage drop in the resistance

$$= \mathcal{J}R = 46 \times 1 \cdot 5 = 69 \text{ volts.}$$

The voltage balancing the counter E.M.F. of the inductance

$$= \omega L \mathcal{J} = 1 \cdot 57 \times 46 = 72 \cdot 2 \text{ volts.}$$

It seems impossible for the 100 applied volts to supply both these values, but the 69 volts and the 72·2 volts are not supplied at the same instant owing to the phase difference between the resistance and reactance voltages.

Let us take a radio frequency example.

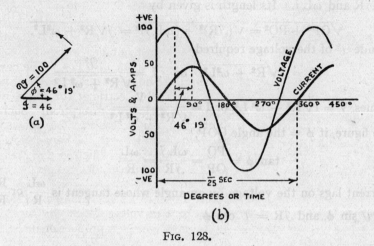

FIG. 128.

Example 31.

Let an alternating P.D., $\mathcal{V} = 100$ volts, at a frequency of 10,000 cycles per second, be applied to a circuit of resistance 20 ohms and inductance 300 mics.   Find (a) the current flowing, and (b) the angle of lag.

$$\omega = 2\pi \times 10{,}000 = 6\cdot28 \times 10^4.$$

$$X_L = \omega L = 6\cdot28 \times 10^4 \times \frac{300}{10^6} = 6\cdot28 \times 3 = 18\cdot84 \text{ ohms.}$$

$$R = 20 \text{ ohms.}$$

$$Z = \sqrt{20^2 + 18\cdot84^2} = \sqrt{400 + 355} = \sqrt{755} = 27\cdot48 \text{ ohms.}$$

$$\mathcal{J} = \frac{\mathcal{V}}{Z} = \frac{100}{27\cdot48} = 3\cdot64 \text{ amps.}$$

$$\mathcal{J}R = 3\cdot64 \times 20 = 72\cdot8 \text{ volts.}$$

$$\omega L \mathcal{J} = 3\cdot64 \times 18\cdot84 = 68\cdot6 \text{ volts.}$$

(b) Tan $\phi = \dfrac{18\cdot84}{20} = \cdot942.$ $\phi = 43^\circ\ 15'.$

Let us try the effect of applying the radio frequency voltage of Example 31 to the circuit given in Example 30.

Example 32.

As before, $\omega = 2\pi \times 10^4.$

$$X_L = \omega L = 2\pi \times 10^4 \times \cdot01 = 6\cdot28 \times 10^2 = 628 \text{ ohms.}$$

$$\cdot R = 1\cdot5 \text{ ohms.}$$

$$Z = \sqrt{1\cdot5^2 + 628^2} = 628 \text{ ohms practically.}$$

$$\mathcal{J} = \frac{\mathcal{V}}{Z} = \frac{100}{628} = \cdot163 \text{ amps.}$$

Tan $\phi = \dfrac{628}{1\cdot5} = 418.$ $\phi = 89^\circ\ 52' = 90^\circ$ practically.

From this example we may deduce that with a radio frequency voltage applied to a circuit where the inductance is large compared with the resistance, the resulting current depends almost entirely upon the value of the inductance and is practically 90° out of phase with the applied voltage.

290. Capacity in an Alternating Current Circuit.—The effect of a condenser joined alone in an A.C. circuit is exactly opposite to that of an inductance ; the current leads in phase on the voltage, as will now be shown.

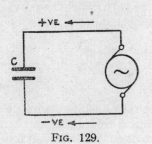

FIG. 129.

Suppose an alternating voltage, whose wave form is sinusoidal, is applied to a condenser C as in Fig. 129. The condenser is supposed to be perfect, *i.e.*, there are no losses due to leakage through the dielectric or across the surface of the dielectric at the edges, no resistances in the leads or plates, and no dielectric absorption. Such conditions cannot be achieved in practice, but losses can be allowed for by assuming resistances in series and parallel with the capacity, and using the theory applicable to such combinations, which is done later. At present, we are only to consider the theoretically perfect condenser.

In such a condenser the law $Q = CV$ is true ; that is, the charge on the condenser at any instant in coulombs is given by the product of the capacity in farads and the voltage applied to it in volts. With no losses, a change of voltage applied to the condenser is instantaneously accompanied by a proportional change in the charge on the condenser. Also the voltage across the condenser due to the charge on it is at every instant exactly equal and opposite to the applied voltage. This condenser voltage may be called the counter E.M.F. of the condenser.

Now, under the conditions that hold when an alternating voltage is applied to the condenser, *i.e.*, a voltage which is always changing, the consequent changes in charge on the condenser must constitute currents flowing into the condenser when the applied voltage is increasing, and currents flowing out of the condenser when the voltage is decreasing. It is very important to distinguish clearly between these two things—quantity, or **charge** on the condenser, measured in coulombs, and **current,** or rate at which this charge is changing, increasing or decreasing, measured in coulombs per second, or amperes.

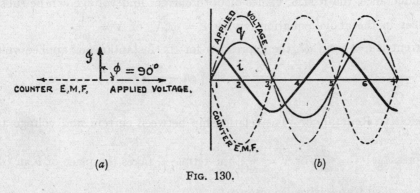

(a)

(b)

FIG. 130.

Fig. 130 (b) shows the conditions when an alternating voltage is applied to the condenser C as in Fig. 129. The curve marked applied voltage is a sine curve.

As this voltage changes, exactly similar changes occur in the charge of electricity introduced into the condenser, and this charge is shown by the curve marked q.

Due to this charge, a counter E.M.F. is set up across the condenser, which is exactly equal to the applied voltage at each instant. This E.M.F. is indicated by the curve marked Counter E.M.F. It is in antiphase with the applied voltage. Between moments 1 and 2 the applied voltage may be said to force an increasing charge into the condenser against the counter E.M.F. ; between moments 2 and 3, as the applied voltage decreases, the counter E.M.F. forces this charge out of the condenser, until at moment 3 the charge is zero.

The same argument holds for the other half of the cycle, during which the condenser is charged in the opposite sense.

From the curve of charge q the current flow may be determined.

At the moment 1, the curve of charge is increasing very rapidly in a positive direction, and the rate of flow of electricity, *i.e.*, the current, has a maximum positive value there.

At the moment 2, the charge is a maximum but is not changing, and at that time, therefore, the current is zero ; similarly for other specified points in the cycle.

The result is, that a curve of current is obtained which is 90° out of phase with either the curve of applied voltage or the curve of charge on the condenser, and in this case the current **leads** on the voltage. The **vectorial representation** is given in Fig. 130 (*a*).

The counter E.M.F. is in antiphase, or 180° out of phase with the applied voltage.

The current, which is the rate of change of the charge, the latter being in phase with the applied voltage, leads on the applied voltage by 90°.

Mathematical Treatment.—The results found above as regards phase relationship of current and voltage in a purely capacitive circuit, can also be deduced by mathematical treatment, and at the same time a formula which gives the relationship between the amplitudes of current and voltage can be obtained.

Given an applied voltage $v = \mathcal{V} \sin \omega t$, the charge q on the condenser is given by

$$q = Cv = C\mathcal{V} \sin \omega t.$$

The current $i =$ rate of change of charge $= \dfrac{dq}{dt} = \omega C\mathcal{V} \cos \omega t = \omega C\mathcal{V} \sin \left(\omega t + \dfrac{\pi}{2} \right).$

So that for an applied voltage $\mathcal{V} \sin \omega t$, a current flows, which is also sinusoidal, with the same frequency as the voltage, and **leading** by 90° on the voltage. The amplitude of the current is $\mathcal{J} = \omega C\mathcal{V}$, or $\mathcal{J} = 2\pi f C\mathcal{V}$, $\mathcal{J}$ being given in amperes, if C is in farads and $\mathcal{V}$ in volts. This may be written

$$\mathcal{V} = \frac{\mathcal{J}}{\omega C} = \frac{\mathcal{J}}{2\pi f C}.$$

As with inductance, the R.M.S. values of **both** current and voltage can be substituted for the maximum values in the above equation, giving $I = \omega CV$, or $V = \dfrac{I}{\omega C}$.

If the current is $i = \mathcal{J} \sin \omega t$, the expression for the instantaneous applied voltage is

$$v = \frac{\mathcal{J}}{\omega C} \sin \left(\omega t - \frac{\pi}{2} \right).$$

291. Capacitive Reactance.—The relationship between current and voltage again resembles Ohm's Law.

In the expression $\mathcal{V} = \dfrac{\mathcal{J}}{\omega C}$, or $V = \dfrac{I}{\omega C}$, the term $\dfrac{1}{\omega C}$ takes the place of R in Ohm's Law, and this term $\dfrac{1}{\omega C}$ is called **Capacitive Reactance.**

It is denoted by the symbol X_C, X being the general term for reactance, inductive or capacitive, and the suffixes L or C indicating which.

The unit in which it is measured must be the same as the unit of resistance, since it expresses the ratio of voltage to current and is therefore the **ohm.** It does not represent a true ohmic resistance, but it is convenient in calculations to give it the name " ohm."

The vector diagram given in Fig. 130 (*a*) can now be completed from the quantitative point of view by giving to the vectors concerned their correct values.

Since, however, we drew the vector diagram for inductance with the current horizontal, the figure may be redrawn as below in a similar manner. For this reason, the reactance $1/\omega C$ is conventionally regarded as a *negative* reactance, inductive reactance ωL being considered *positive*.

The applied voltage lags behind the current by 90°, and as regards amplitude is given by $\dfrac{\mathcal{J}}{\omega C}$.

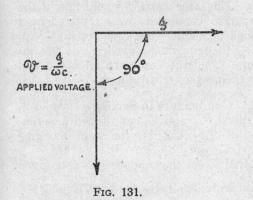

FIG. 131.

292. A Physical Explanation of the Variation of the Reactance of a Condenser.—From the mathematical treatment above it has been shown that—

$$X_C = \frac{1}{\omega C}.$$

i.e., the " reactance " is inversely proportional to the capacity and to the frequency.

Consider first the variation of supply current with capacity. During each half cycle of the alternating supply the voltage across the condenser rises to the peak voltage of the supply. The voltage across the condenser is given by charge/capacity, hence the greater the capacity the greater the charge required and therefore the greater must be the flow of electrons from the supply during each half cycle. This flow of electrons is the **supply current** and we see that, with constant frequency, this increases with increasing capacity, *i.e.*, the " reactance " of the condenser decreases.

If the frequency of the supply is now varied and the capacity of the condenser maintained constant, during each half cycle of the supply voltage the same charge must flow to the condenser. As the frequency of the supply is increased the time available for the charge to flow is decreased and therefore the *rate of flow* (or the current) is increased.

Thus the current increases with increasing frequency, *i.e.*, the reactance decreases.

Example 33.

Find the current flowing through* a condenser of 45 jars if an alternating voltage $\mathcal{V} = 100$ volts is applied at a frequency of 300,000 cycles per second.

$$\omega = 2\pi f = 2\pi \times 300,000 = 1 \cdot 884 \times 10^6.$$

$$X_C = \frac{1}{\omega C} = \frac{1}{1 \cdot 884 \times 10^6} \times \frac{9 \times 10^8}{45} \quad \text{(converting jars to farads†)}$$

$$= \frac{20}{1 \cdot 884} = 10 \cdot 61 \text{ ohms.}$$

$$\mathcal{J} = \frac{100}{10 \cdot 61} = 9 \cdot 4 \text{ amperes.}$$

293. Condensers in Series and Parallel (*cf.* paragraphs 177 and 178).

Condensers in Parallel.—If two condensers, C_1 and C_2, are joined in parallel, as in Fig. 132 (*a*), and an alternating voltage V (using R.M.S. values throughout) is applied to both, currents I_1 and I_2 will flow through C_1 and C_2 such that

$$I_1 = \omega C_1 V \text{ and } I_2 = \omega C_2 V.$$

---

* It is the custom to speak loosely of a current flowing " through " a condenser, when what is meant is a current charging a condenser alternately on either side, or a displacement current flowing in the condenser (*cf.* paragraph 41). No conduction current actually flows through.

† Readers who are not accustomed to the unit of a " jar," still used throughout this book, should remember that 1 jar

$$= 1/900\text{th microfarad, } = 1,000 \text{ centimetres, } = 10/9\text{ths milli-microfarad.}$$

Also see the Prefatory Note.

These currents will both lead by 90° on the applied voltage and will therefore be in phase. The total current flowing from the supply will be $I = \omega (C_1 + C_2) V$.

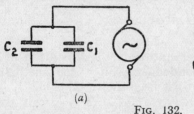 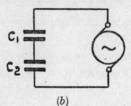

(a)   (b)

FIG. 132.

The same current would flow if the separate condensers were replaced by a single condenser with capacity $(C_1 + C_2)$, i.e., the equivalent capacity of two (or more) condensers in **parallel** is the sum of their separate capacities.

Condensers in Series.—If two condensers, C_1 and C_2, are joined in series, as in Fig. 132 (b), the same charging current I will flow round the circuit, or " through '" each condenser.

The requisite applied voltage to overcome the counter E.M.Fs. of the condensers will be given by $\dfrac{I}{\omega C_1} + \dfrac{I}{\omega C_2}$, the components being additive because the individual voltages are both lagging 90° on the current, and so are in phase.

$$\therefore V = \frac{I}{\omega C_1} + \frac{I}{\omega C_2} = \frac{I}{\omega}\left(\frac{1}{C_1} + \frac{1}{C_2}\right).$$

The same voltage would be necessary to send a current I round a circuit with a single condenser C if $V = \dfrac{I}{\omega C}$.

Hence the equivalent value of the two capacities in series is C, where

$$\frac{I}{\omega C} = \frac{I}{\omega}\left(\frac{1}{C_1} + \frac{1}{C_2}\right) \quad \text{or} \quad \frac{1}{C} = \frac{1}{C_1} + \frac{1}{C_2}.$$

So also a number of condensers in series.

Hence capacities in series have an equivalent value given by the reciprocal law : the reciprocal of the equivalent capacity is the sum of the reciprocals of the separate capacities.

$$\frac{1}{C} = \frac{1}{C_1} + \frac{1}{C_2} + \frac{1}{C_3} + \&c.$$

For two capacities only $C = \dfrac{C_1 C_2}{C_1 + C_2}$.

Note that the rules for finding the equivalent value of capacities in series and parallel are exactly the opposite of those in the case of resistances or inductances.

294. Resistance and Capacity in Series.—The question of finding the voltage necessary to send an alternating current $\mathcal{J}$, or I, using the R.M.S. notation, round a circuit containing resistance and capacity in series, can be tackled by the graphical methods of paragraph 287, or by the shorter and more accurate methods, trigonometrical and vectorial, of paragraph 288.

It is difficult to deduce accurate generalised results from the graphical method, and so attention will be confined to the other methods.

From previous results, the total voltage necessary to maintain an alternating current $i = \mathcal{J} \sin \omega t$ in the circuit above, with resistance R and capacity C, will be given by

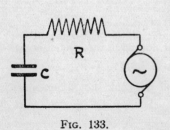

FIG. 133.

$$v = \mathcal{J}R \sin wt + \frac{\mathcal{J}}{\omega C} \sin\left(wt - \frac{\pi}{2}\right) = \mathcal{J}R \sin \omega t - \frac{\mathcal{J}}{\omega C}\cos \omega t.$$

$$= \mathcal{J}\left(R \sin \omega t - \frac{1}{\omega C} \cos \omega t\right) = \mathcal{J}\sqrt{R^2 + \frac{1}{\omega^2 C^2}}\left(\frac{R}{\sqrt{R^2 + \frac{1}{\omega^2 C^2}}} \sin \omega t - \frac{\frac{1}{\omega C}}{\sqrt{R^2 + \frac{1}{\omega^2 C^2}}} \cos \omega t\right)$$

$$= \mathcal{J}\sqrt{R^2 + \frac{1}{\omega^2 C^2}} \sin(\omega t - \phi), \text{ where } \tan \phi = \frac{1}{\omega CR}.$$

The required voltage is therefore sinusoidal, with an amplitude of $\mathcal{J}\sqrt{R^2 + \frac{1}{\omega^2 C^2}}$, and lags behind the current by an angle whose tangent is $\frac{1}{\omega CR}$.

Vectorially, the same result is obtained by considering Fig. 134, which represents the vectorial addition of the two vectors, $\mathcal{J}R$ and $\frac{\mathcal{J}}{\omega C}$.

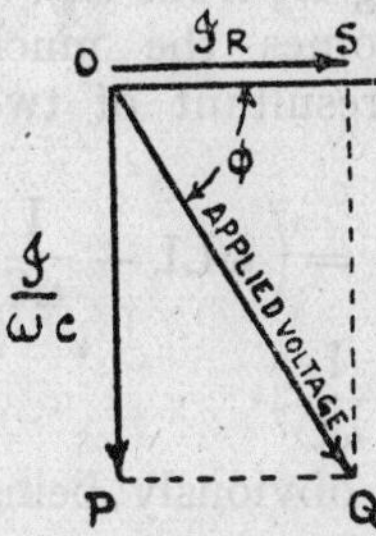

FIG. 134.

The vector $\mathcal{J}R$ in phase with the current vector $\mathcal{J}$ and drawn along the same direction, is shown by OS.

The vector $\frac{\mathcal{J}}{\omega C}$ representing the voltage necessary to maintain the current through the capacity, and therefore lagging 90° on the current, is shown by OP.

The applied voltage is found by completing the rectangle OPQS and drawing the diagonal OQ.

$$OQ^2 = OP^2 + OS^2.$$

Thus the amplitude $\mathcal{V}$ of the voltage required is given by

$$\mathcal{V} = \mathcal{J}\sqrt{R^2 + \frac{1}{\omega^2 C^2}}.$$

Also
$$\mathcal{J} = \frac{\mathcal{V}}{\sqrt{R^2 + \frac{1}{\omega^2 C^2}}}$$

A corresponding result holds for R.M.S. values.

Again, from the figure, if ϕ = angle SOQ,

$$\tan \phi = \frac{SQ}{OS} = \frac{OP}{OS} = \frac{1}{\omega CR}.$$

Hence the current **leads** the voltage by an angle whose tangent

$$= \frac{\frac{1}{\omega C}}{R} = \frac{\text{Reactance}}{\text{Resistance}}.$$

The expression $\sqrt{R^2 + \frac{1}{\omega^2 C^2}}$ is called the **impedance** of the circuit and is denoted by the letter Z. It is measured in ohms.

As in paragraph 289, it may be defined as the ratio of the maximum value of voltage to the maximum value of current.

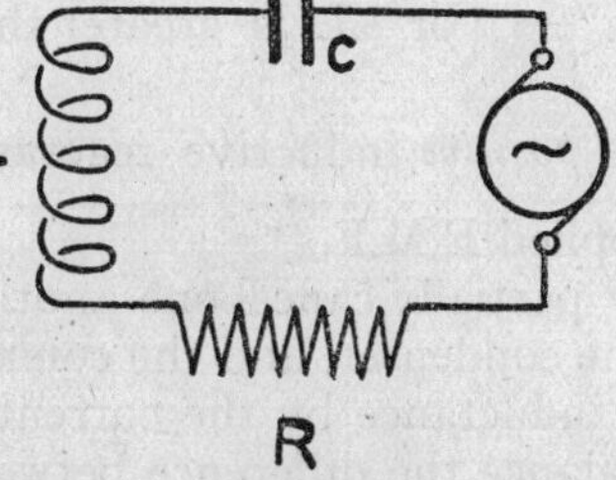

FIG. 135.

295. **Circuits containing Inductance, Capacity and Resistance in Series.**—We now come to the most important problem of all, and one with which we are frequently concerned in wireless telegraphy—namely, the case of a circuit containing **inductance, capacity and resistance in series** (as in Fig 135)

In this case the alternator has three duties to perform ; it has to supply :—

(a) A voltage E_1 (= IR) to drive the current through the resistance R.

(b) A voltage E_2 (= ωLI) to overcome the counter E.M.F. of the inductance L.

(c) A voltage $E_3 \left(= \dfrac{I}{\omega C} \right)$ to overcome the counter E.M.F. of the condenser C.

Let us draw a vector diagram of these three voltages, taking due account of their relative phases (Fig. 136).

The vector E_1 (= IR) is in phase with the current ;

the vector E_2 (= ωLI) is 90° in advance of the current ; and

the vector $E_3 \left(= \dfrac{I}{\omega C} \right)$ is 90° behind the current.

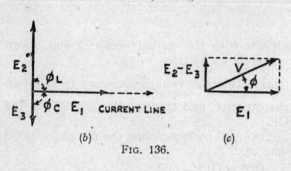

(b)   (c)

FIG. 136.

As E_2 and E_3 are exactly opposite in phase, we can obtain their resultant by subtracting the smaller from the greater (in the case illustrated by subtracting E_3 from E_2).

The problem then becomes the much simpler one of finding the resultant of two vectors—

$$E_1 = IR, \text{ and } (E_2 - E_3) = \left(\omega LI - \frac{I}{\omega C} \right)$$

$$= I \left(\omega L - \frac{1}{\omega C} \right).$$

This is obtained as shown in Fig. 136 (b), the resultant applied voltage (V) obviously being such that—

$$V^2 = E_1^2 + (E_2 - E_3)^2 = I^2 R^2 + I^2 \left(\omega L - \frac{1}{\omega C} \right)^2$$

Therefore

$$V = I \sqrt{ R^2 + \left(\omega L - \frac{1}{\omega C} \right)^2 } \text{ or } I = \frac{V}{\sqrt{ R^2 + \left(\omega L - \frac{1}{\omega C} \right)^2 }}.$$

This is the law for A.C. circuits containing inductance, capacity and resistance in series.

The expression $\sqrt{ R^2 + \left(\omega L - \dfrac{1}{\omega C} \right)^2 }$ is termed the **impedance** of the circuit and is denoted by the symbol Z (ohms).

The tangent of the angle (ϕ) of lag or lead is such that

$$\tan \phi = \frac{I \left(\omega L - \dfrac{1}{\omega C} \right)}{IR} = \frac{X_L - X_C}{R} = \frac{\text{Reactance}}{\text{Resistance}}.$$

As the tendency for the current to lag depends on the value of the counter E.M.F. of the inductance (ωLI volts), and the tendency for the current to lead depends on the counter E.M.F. of the condenser $\left(\dfrac{I}{\omega C} \text{ volts} \right)$, it can be seen that if ωLI is greater than $\dfrac{I}{\omega C}$ (or ωL is greater than $\dfrac{1}{\omega C}$) the resultant current will lag behind the applied E.M.F. ; if the *positive* inductive reactance is less than the *negative* capacitive reactance, the current leads the applied E.M.F.

The fact that the counter E.M.Fs. of the inductance and capacity partially cancel one another means that the counter E.M.F. of the inductance helps to charge up the condenser, and the counter E.M.F. of the condenser helps to create the magnetic field round the inductance by the current it produces ; the assistance of the applied voltage is only required to balance the difference between these two counter E.M.Fs.

A voltmeter, if joined across the inductance, would read ωLI volts, and if joined across the condenser would read $\dfrac{I}{\omega C}$ volts, but if joined across the two would read the difference between the two voltages, i.e., $\left(\omega LI - \dfrac{I}{\omega C} \right)$ volts.

Example 34.

An alternating voltage of 50 volts at a frequency of 158,000 cycles per second is applied to a circuit consisting of an inductance of 900 mics, a condenser of 1 jar, and a resistance of 10 ohms.

Find (a) the current flowing ;
      (b) the phase angle of lag or lead ;
      (c) the P.D. across the inductance ;
      (d) the P.D. across the condenser.

(a) $\omega = 6 \cdot 28 \times 158,000 = 9 \cdot 9224 \times 10^5$.

$$X_L = \omega L = 9 \cdot 9224 \times 10^5 \times \frac{900}{10^6} = 893 \cdot 016 \text{ ohms.}$$

$$X_C = \frac{1}{\omega C} = \frac{1}{9 \cdot 9224 \times 10^5} \times \frac{9 \times 10^8}{1} = \frac{9,000}{9 \cdot 9224} = 907 \cdot 039 \text{ ohms.}$$

$$X_C - X_L = 907 \cdot 039 - 893 \cdot 016 = 14 \cdot 023 \text{ ohms.}$$

$$Z = \sqrt{R^2 + (X_C - X_L)^2} = \sqrt{10^2 + 14 \cdot 023^2} = \sqrt{296 \cdot 645} = 17 \cdot 223 \text{ ohms.}$$

$$I = \frac{V}{Z} = \frac{50}{17 \cdot 223} = 2 \cdot 9031 \text{ amperes.}$$

(b) $\tan \phi = \dfrac{X_C - X_L}{R} = \dfrac{14 \cdot 023}{10} = 1 \cdot 4023 \ldots \phi = 54° \ 30'.$

Since X_C is greater than X_L, ϕ will be an angle of lead.

c) $\omega LI = X_L I = 893 \cdot 016 \times 2 \cdot 9031 = 2,592 \cdot 51 \text{ volts.}$

(d) $\dfrac{I}{\omega C} = X_C I = 907 \cdot 039 \times 2 \cdot 9031 = 2,633 \cdot 22 \text{ volts.}$

296. Resonance.—A question that naturally arises is whether we can arrange matters so that the counter E.M.F. of the inductance exactly balances the counter E.M.F. of the condenser.

This condition is attained if we arrange that—

$$\omega LI = \frac{I}{\omega C}.$$

By dividing both sides of this equation by I we obtain

$$\omega L = \frac{1}{\omega C}, \text{ or } \omega^2 = \frac{1}{LC}, \text{ or } 2\pi f = \frac{1}{\sqrt{LC}},$$

$$\text{or } f = \frac{1}{2\pi \sqrt{LC}}, \text{ where } \begin{cases} \text{L is measured in henries.} \\ \text{C is measured in farads.} \end{cases}$$

This equation is frequently used in wireless telegraphy.

If we arrange to satisfy it, either by altering the applied frequency so that it is equal to $\dfrac{1}{2\pi\sqrt{LC}}$, or by altering the value of the inductance or the capacity of the circuit so that the expression $\dfrac{1}{2\pi\sqrt{LC}}$ is equal to the applied frequency f, then the counter E.M.Fs. of inductance and capacity " cancel out." and none of the applied voltage is required to make good their difference.

That is to say, since $\omega L = \dfrac{1}{\omega C}$, the expression

$$I = \frac{V}{\sqrt{R^2 + \left(\omega L - \dfrac{1}{\omega C}\right)^2}}$$

becomes $I = \dfrac{V}{\sqrt{R^2}} = \dfrac{V}{R}$, and, so far as the applied voltage is concerned, the **circuit behaves as if it comprised resistance only.**

The current neither lags nor leads, but is in phase with the applied voltage, because

$$\tan \phi = \frac{X_L - X_C}{R} = \frac{0}{R} = 0, \text{ and therefore } \phi = 0°.$$

The condition described above is known as "**Electrical Resonance**," and the frequency that satisfies the equation is known as the "**Resonant Frequency.**"

In series circuits, the definition of resonance is that it is the condition under which, for a given applied voltage, the maximum current flows in the circuit ; and of Resonant Frequency is, that it is the frequency at which a given applied alternating voltage will give a maximum value of current.

At such a frequency the impedance equals the resistance and has a minimum value, and the **reactance is zero.**

Physically when the current is a maximum all of the energy $(\frac{1}{2}LI^2)$ is instantaneously in the inductive field ; later, when the current is instantaneously zero, all of the energy $(\frac{1}{2}CV^2)$ is in the condenser. If there were no damping resistance, there would be a continual transfer of energy without loss, and we would have

$$\tfrac{1}{2}LI^2 = \tfrac{1}{2}CV^2. \qquad \text{Now } V = \frac{I}{\omega C}$$

$$\therefore \quad \tfrac{1}{2}LI^2 = \tfrac{1}{2}\frac{CI^2}{\omega^2 C^2} \quad \therefore \quad \omega^2 = \frac{1}{LC}, \text{ as before.}$$

297. Acceptor Circuit.—A circuit comprising inductance and capacity in series, which is in resonance with the frequency applied to it, is said to be an "**Acceptor Circuit,**" for that frequency.

All circuits of the same LC value are obviously acceptor circuits for the same frequency.

For example, if in a certain circuit we double the inductance and halve the capacity the counter E.M.Fs. of each will both be doubled, and they will still " cancel out."

298. As in W/T we are sometimes working in units of mics and jars, and not of henries and farads, it is convenient to turn the above formula into terms of mics and jars, as follows :—

$$f = \frac{1}{2\pi\sqrt{LC}} \qquad \begin{cases} \text{L in henries.} \\ \text{C in farads.} \end{cases}$$

$$\frac{1}{2\pi}\frac{1}{\sqrt{\dfrac{L}{10^6} \times \dfrac{C}{9 \times 10^8}}} = \frac{\sqrt{9 \times 10^{14}}}{2\pi\sqrt{LC}} = \frac{3 \times 10^7}{2\pi\sqrt{LC}} \text{ where } \begin{cases} \text{L is measured in mics.} \\ \text{C is measured in jars.} \end{cases}$$

$$\text{or } \boldsymbol{\omega} = \frac{3 \times 10^7}{\sqrt{LC}}.$$

If an approximate value of 6·28 be taken for 2π, then the above formula becomes

$$f = \frac{4\cdot774 \times 10^6}{\sqrt{LC}} = \frac{4\cdot8 \times 10^6}{\sqrt{LC}} \text{ *approximately, where } \begin{cases} f \text{ is in cycles per second,} \\ L \text{ is in mics,} \\ C \text{ is in jars.} \end{cases}$$

---

* It must be remembered that the expression $f = \dfrac{4\cdot8 \times 10^6}{\sqrt{LC}}$ is only a very rough approximation, and should not be used if **an accurate answer is required.**

Example 35.

(i) Find the correct resonant frequency for the circuit given in Example 34.

(ii) If an alternating voltage V = 50 volts at this frequency be applied to the circuit, find the answer to (a), (b), (c) and (d) as before.

(i) $f = \dfrac{3 \times 10^7}{2\pi\sqrt{LC}} = \dfrac{3 \times 10^7}{2\pi\sqrt{900}} = \dfrac{3 \times 10^7}{2\pi \times 30} = \dfrac{10^6}{2\pi} = 159,200$ cycles per second.

(ii) (a) $\omega = \dfrac{3 \times 10^7}{\sqrt{LC}} = \dfrac{3 \times 10^7}{\sqrt{900}} = \dfrac{3 \times 10^7}{30} = 10^6.$

$\begin{cases} X_L = \omega L = 10^6 \times \dfrac{900}{10^6} = 900 \text{ ohms.} \\[2mm] X_C = \dfrac{1}{\omega C} = \dfrac{1}{10^6} \times \dfrac{9 \times 10^8}{1} = 900 \text{ ohms.} \end{cases}$

$X_L - X_C = 0.$ $\quad I = \dfrac{V}{R} = \dfrac{50}{10} = 5$ amperes.

(b) $\tan\phi = \dfrac{X_L - X_C}{R} = \dfrac{0}{10} = 0$, hence $\phi = 0°.$

(c) $\omega LI = X_L I = 900 \times 5 = 4,500$ volts.

(d) $\dfrac{I}{\omega C} = X_C I = 900 \times 5 = 4,500$ volts.

Notice particularly that the voltages across the inductance and capacity are very much greater than the applied voltage.

This occurs when the reactance of the inductance or of the capacity is great compared with the resistance of the circuit ; advantage is continually taken of this fact in W/T circuits.

Example 36.

Find how much inductance is required in series with a condenser of 2 jars capacity to make the circuit an acceptor for a frequency of 500 kilocycles per second.

$$f = \dfrac{3 \times 10}{2\pi\sqrt{LC}} \quad \text{(L in mics, C in jars.)}$$

$$500 \times 10^3 = \dfrac{3 \times 10^7}{2\pi\sqrt{LC}} = \dfrac{3 \times 10^7}{2\pi\sqrt{2L}}.$$

$$10\pi\sqrt{2L} = 300, \ \pi\sqrt{2L} = 30.$$

$$2L = \left(\dfrac{30}{\pi}\right)^2 = \dfrac{900}{\pi^2} = \dfrac{900}{9 \cdot 870} = 91 \cdot 16.$$

$$\therefore \ L = 45 \cdot 58 \text{ mics.}$$

299. Resonance in Daily Life.—The fact that very big voltages build up across the inductance and capacity of a circuit if, **and only if,** it is tuned to be in resonance, or nearly so, with the frequency of the current applied to it, is continually made use of in W/T. In fact, W/T would be quite impossible if the phenomenon of resonance did not exist.

Resonance may be defined as the transference of energy from one system to another in a series of periodic impulses or waves timed exactly to coincide with the natural rate of vibration of the second system (but see paragraph 391).

Numerous cases of this phenomenon occur in daily life. Watch, for instance, one child swinging another in a swing ; how carefully it gives each little push exactly as the swing has reached its limit and begins to go forward, and how the energy of each push is added to that of the moving swing so that very soon it would knock over a man who stepped in its way.

Walk across a room carrying a cup of tea, and note how quickly it slops over if your step is in time with its natural swing, and how, by walking with short irregular steps, it is much easier to avoid spilling it.

A good demonstration of resonance can also be given with a sponge in a bath. Just swing it to and fro in time with the wave it produces, and in a very few moments you will find the water is also swinging from end to end of the bath with rapidly increasing energy ; here also you will find that exact timing of the impulses is the sole condition of success.

300. **Currents at Resonance and Non-resonance.**—In any circuit containing R, L and C in series, the current is given by the quotient of the applied voltage by the impedance.

At resonance, as we saw above, the impedance consists of resistance only, and $I = \dfrac{V}{R}$.

If, however, the frequency of the applied voltage is increased above or decreased below the resonant frequency, the equality of ωL and $\dfrac{1}{\omega C}$ does not hold, and the impedance increases, reducing the current flowing.

Various results follow from these statements :—

(1) **Phasing.**—If the frequency is **increased** above the resonant frequency, ωL becomes greater and $\dfrac{1}{\omega C}$ becomes smaller, and the resultant reactance will be inductive, so that the current will lag behind the applied voltage.

Conversely, if the frequency is **decreased** below the resonant frequency, ωL becomes smaller and $\dfrac{1}{\omega C}$ greater, so that the resultant reactance is capacitive, and the current will lead on the applied voltage.

(2) **Effect of amount of departure from resonance.**—The more the frequency of the applied voltage differs from the resonant value, the greater will be the value of the expression $\left(\omega L \sim \dfrac{1}{\omega C} \right)$ which is the resultant reactance, and hence the greater will be the impedance, and the less the current.

Take the case of an increase of frequency above the resonant frequency. The greater the divergence from resonance, the greater ωL becomes, and the less $\dfrac{1}{\omega C}$ becomes, hence the greater is their difference.

For a decrease below resonant frequency, the greater the divergence from resonance, the greater $\dfrac{1}{\omega C}$ becomes and the less ωL becomes, hence the greater is their difference.

(3) **Effect of the proportion of inductance to capacity.**—If the LC value and the resistance R of a circuit are kept constant, but the ratio $\dfrac{L}{C}$ is altered, the current at resonance is constant, but the current at non-resonance is decreased as this ratio increases.

In the expression for impedance $\sqrt{R^2 + \left(\omega L \sim \dfrac{1}{\omega C} \right)^2}$, for a given ω, which does not correspond to resonance, an increase in the ratio $\dfrac{L}{C}$ means that ωL and $\dfrac{1}{\omega C}$ are both increased

If L is increased n times, n being greater than 1, C must be divided by n to keep the product LC the same.

ωL then becomes $n \times \omega$L, and $\dfrac{1}{\omega C}$ then becomes $\dfrac{1}{\omega \times \dfrac{C}{n}} = \dfrac{n}{\omega C}$,

both results for the different reactances having n times their previous value.

Hence the difference between them is n times what it was before, the impedance is increased, the current is less, and the " tuning " is " stiffer " or " sharper."

(4) **Effect of resistance.**—As the resistance R of the circuit is increased, the current at the resonant frequency $\left(= \dfrac{V}{R} \right)$ is decreased. This effect is independent of the ratio of inductance to capacity in the circuit, except in so far as alteration of this ratio also alters the resistance.

The ratio of the current at non-resonant frequencies to the current at resonance is also affected by the resistance. In a circuit of constant L/C ratio, the current at non-resonant frequencies is increased relatively to the current at resonance when the resistance is increased. The ratio of the current at resonance to the current for a value of ω corresponding to a non-resonant frequency is given by

$$\frac{Z}{R} = \sqrt{1 + \frac{1}{R^2}\left(\omega L - \frac{1}{\omega C} \right)^2}.$$

For given values of ω, L and C this expression decreases as R is increased, *i.e.*, the tuning becomes " flatter."

These points will be illustrated by examples.

Example 37.

(*a*) In a series circuit consisting of an inductance of 10 mics, a capacity of 10 jars and a resistance of 10 ohms, let an R.M.S. voltage of 100 volts be applied.
Find the R.M.S. current

(1) if the frequency of the applied voltage is the resonant frequency ;
(2) if it is 90 per cent. of the resonant frequency ;
(3) if it is 70 per cent. of the resonant frequency.

(*b*) Find the same three values of current if the resistance of the circuit remains 10 ohms, while the inductance is increased to 20 mics and the capacity reduced to 5 jars (same LC value = 100 as before).

(*c*) Find the same three values of current when the inductance is 20 mics, the capacity is 5 jars, and the resistance is increased to 20 ohms.

(*a*) The resonant frequency is f such that $2\pi f = \omega = \dfrac{3 \times 10^7}{\sqrt{LC}}$

$$\therefore \ \omega = \frac{3 \times 10^7}{\sqrt{100}} = 3 \times 10^6$$

(1) At resonance, current $I = \dfrac{V}{R} = \dfrac{100}{10} =$ **10 amperes.**

X_L and X_C are equal and cancel out, their value being

$$\omega L = 3 \times 10^6 \times \frac{10}{10^6} = 30 \text{ ohms.}$$

(2) In this case $\omega' = 90$ per cent. of the resonant ω
$$= 2 \cdot 7 \times 10^6.$$

$$X_L = \omega' L = 2 \cdot 7 \times 10^6 \times \frac{10}{10^6} = 27 \text{ ohms.}$$

$$X_C = \frac{1}{\omega'\,C} = \frac{9 \times 10^8}{2 \cdot 7 \times 10^6 \times 10} = \frac{90}{2 \cdot 7} = \frac{30}{0 \cdot 9} = \frac{10}{0 \cdot 3} = 33\tfrac{1}{3} \text{ ohms.}$$

$$X_C - X_L = 6\tfrac{1}{3} \text{ ohms.}$$

$$Z = \sqrt{R^2 + (X_C - X_L)^2} = \sqrt{100 + (6\tfrac{1}{3})^2} = \sqrt{140 \cdot 11} = 11 \cdot 83 \text{ ohms.}$$

$$\therefore \text{ Current } I = \frac{100}{11 \cdot 83} = 8 \cdot 45 \text{ amperes.}$$

It will be noticed, as mentioned in paragraph 300 (1), that with the frequency decreased below resonance the capacitive reactance X_C is **greater** than the inductive reactance X_L and so the current **leads** on the voltage.

(3) In this case $\omega' = 70$ per cent. of the resonant ω
$$= 2 \cdot 1 \times 10^6.$$

$$X_L = \omega'\,L = 2 \cdot 1 \times 10^6 \times \frac{10}{10^6} = 21 \text{ ohms.}$$

$$X_C = \frac{1}{\omega'C} = \frac{9 \times 10^8}{2 \cdot 1 \times 10^6 \times 10} = \frac{90}{2 \cdot 1} = \frac{30}{0 \cdot 7} = 42 \cdot 86 \text{ ohms.}$$

$$X_C - X_L = 21 \cdot 86 \text{ ohms.}$$

$$Z = \sqrt{10^2 + (21 \cdot 86)^2} = \sqrt{577 \cdot 9} = 24 \cdot 04 \text{ ohms.}$$

$$\text{Current } I = \frac{100}{24 \cdot 04} = 4 \cdot 16 \text{ amperes.}$$

This shows that the current is cut down more, the further from resonance is the frequency of the applied voltage (paragraph 300 (2)).

(b)—(1) At resonance, with the same LC value and the same R, the current is still **10 amperes.**

(2) With $\omega' = 2 \cdot 7 \times 10^6$, $X_L = \omega'\,L = 2 \cdot 7 \times 10^6 \times \frac{20}{10^6} = 54 \text{ ohms.}$

$$X_C = \frac{1}{\omega'\,C} = \frac{1}{2 \cdot 7 \times 10^6} \times \frac{9 \times 10^8}{5} = 66 \cdot 67 \text{ ohms.}$$

$$Z = \sqrt{100 + (12 \cdot 67)^2} = \sqrt{260 \cdot 4} = 16 \cdot 14 \text{ ohms.}$$

$$\text{Current } I = \frac{100}{16 \cdot 14} = 6 \cdot 2 \text{ amperes.}$$

which is less than the value in case (a) (2) above, justifying the result of paragraph 300 (3), that the current at non-resonance is decreased as the ratio L/C increases.

(3) With $\omega' = 2 \cdot 1 \times 10^6$, $X_L = \omega'\,L = 2 \cdot 1 \times 10^6 \times \frac{20}{10^6} = 42 \text{ ohms.}$

$$X_C = \frac{1}{\omega'\,C} = \frac{1}{2 \cdot 1 \times 10^6} \times \frac{9 \times 10^8}{5} = 85 \cdot 71 \text{ ohms.}$$

$$X_C - X_L = 43 \cdot 71 \text{ ohms.}$$

$$Z = \sqrt{R^2 + (X_C - X_L)^2} = \sqrt{100 + (43 \cdot 71)^2} = \sqrt{2011} = 44 \cdot 84 \text{ ohms.}$$

$$I = \frac{100}{44 \cdot 84} = 2 \cdot 33 \text{ amperes,} \text{ again less than the corresponding result in (a) (3).}$$

(c)—(1) At resonance, $I = \dfrac{V}{R} = \dfrac{100}{20} = 5$ **amperes.**

(2) With $\omega' = 2 \cdot 7 \times 10^6$, $X_C - X_L = 12 \cdot 67$ ohms, as in (b) (2).

$$Z = \sqrt{20^2 + 12 \cdot 67^2} = \sqrt{560 \cdot 4} = 23 \cdot 67 \text{ ohms.}$$

$$I = \frac{100}{23 \cdot 67} = 4 \cdot 23 \text{ amperes.}$$

(3) With $\omega' = 2 \cdot 1 \times 10^6$, $X_C - X_L = 43 \cdot 71$ ohms, as in (b) (3).

$$Z = \sqrt{20^2 + 43 \cdot 71^2} = \sqrt{2311} = 48 \cdot 07 \text{ ohms.}$$

$$I = \frac{100}{48 \cdot 07} = 2 \cdot 08 \text{ amperes.}$$

It will be seen that in each of these cases the current is exactly half of the corresponding current in (a). In other words, the ratio of resonant to non-resonant current for the same departure from resonance, which was increased by doubling the L/C ratio, has been restored by doubling the resistance.

301. Resonance Curves and Selectivity.—The currents flowing when an E.M.F. of constant amplitude is applied to a circuit consisting of inductance, capacity and resistance in series, at the resonant frequency, and at various percentage frequency departures from resonance, may be graphed against percentage frequency above and below resonance. The resulting curve is known as the **resonance** or **response curve** of the circuit.

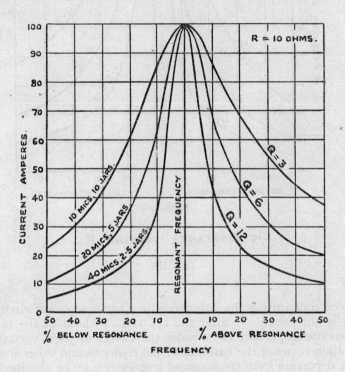

R CONSTANT; L/C VARYING.

FIG. 137.

In Fig. 137 are shown three very flat resonance curves for circuits of the same resistance and LC value, but with different ratios of inductance to capacity ; the results of Example 37 (a) and (b) correspond to points on two of these curves.

Each curve has a peak value at the resonant frequency, and the greater the ratio of inductance to capacity, the more sharply does the curve fall on either side of the peak. The curves are not symmetrical about the resonant frequency, and fall more sharply in the direction of decreasing frequency.

Resonance curves for circuits of the same LC value and L/C ratio, but of varying resistance, are shown in Fig. 138.

In this case the current at resonance varies inversely as the resistance, and so a better basis of comparison is obtained by plotting the percentage of the resonant current flowing at various percentage departures from the resonant frequency. The curves are similar to those of Fig. 137; the smaller the resistance the sharper is the resonance peak. Thus decreasing the resistance has the same effect as increasing the L/C ratio.

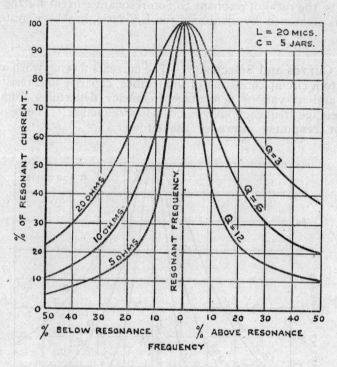

L/C CONSTANT; VARYING R.

FIG. 138.

In practice the coil constituting the inductance in a series resonant circuit must possess some resistance, so that it is not possible to alter the L/C ratio without at the same time altering the resistance. It is therefore important to consider the effects of joint variation of L/C ratio and resistance on the relation between the currents at the resonant and other frequencies. The effect at a given percentage departure from the resonant frequency may be obtained as follows :—

Let ω_0 correspond to the resonant frequency, ω_1 to the non-resonant frequency, and α to the fractional deviation of the frequency from resonance, such that $\omega_1 = \omega_0 (1 + \alpha)$. The value of α is positive or negative according as the actual frequency is greater or less than the resonant one ; t therefore varies from zero to ± 1.

The impedance at resonance is given by $Z_0 = R_0$. The impedance at the frequency $\omega_1/2\pi$ is

$$Z_1 = \sqrt{R_1{}^2 + \left(\omega_1 L - \frac{1}{\omega_1 C}\right)^2} = \sqrt{R_1{}^2 + \omega_1{}^2 L^2 \left(1 - \frac{1}{\omega_1{}^2 LC}\right)^2}$$

$$= \sqrt{R_1{}^2 + \omega_0{}^2 L^2 (1 + \alpha)^2 \left(1 - \frac{1}{\omega_0{}^2 (1 + \alpha)^2 LC}\right)^2}$$

Now $\omega_0{}^2 = \dfrac{1}{LC}$

$$\therefore \quad Z_1 = \sqrt{R_1{}^2 + \frac{L}{C}(1 + \alpha)^2\left(1 - \frac{1}{(1 + \alpha)^2}\right)^2}$$

$$= \sqrt{R_1{}^2 + \frac{L}{C}\frac{\alpha^2(2 + \alpha)^2}{(1 + \alpha)^2}}$$

$$\therefore \quad \frac{\text{Current at non-resonant frequency}}{\text{Current at resonant frequency}} = \frac{I_1}{I_0} = \frac{Z_0}{Z_1} = \frac{R_0}{\sqrt{R_1{}^2 + \dfrac{L}{C}\dfrac{\alpha^2(2 + \alpha)^2}{(1 + \alpha)^2}}}$$

$$\therefore \quad \frac{I_1}{I_0} = \frac{1}{\sqrt{\dfrac{R_1{}^2}{R_0{}^2} + \dfrac{L}{CR^2}\dfrac{\alpha^2(2 + \alpha)^2}{(1 + \alpha)^2}}}$$

If $\dfrac{L}{CR^2}$ is constant, the R/F resistance varies with frequency and $\dfrac{R_1}{R_0} = \dfrac{\omega_1}{\omega_0} = 1 + \alpha$.

$$\therefore \quad \frac{I_1}{I_0} = \frac{1}{\sqrt{(1 + \alpha)^2 + \dfrac{L}{CR^2}\dfrac{\alpha^2(2 + \alpha)^2}{(1 + \alpha)^2}}} \quad \dots\dots\dots\dots\dots\dots\dots\dots\dots \quad (1)$$

Hence, for a given departure from resonance, the current at the non-resonant frequency becomes a smaller proportion of the resonant current as L/CR^2 is increased.

It can easily be seen from this result, and was shown for a particular case in Example 37, that with any given LC value, if the resistance of an inductive coil increases proportionately to its inductance, the value of L/CR^2 is unaltered ; if the resistance increases more slowly than the inductance, L/CR^2 is increased, and if the resistance increases faster than the inductance, L/CR^2 is diminished. It is usually the case in practice, that the ratio of the inductance to resistance in a coil increases as the inductance is increased, and so L/CR^2 is increased by increasing the L/C ratio. Care must, however, be exercised in applying this result in practical W/T circuits where resistances other than that of the coil itself will normally be present.

The square root of L/CR^2, viz., $\dfrac{1}{R}\sqrt{\dfrac{L}{C}}$ is taken as a criterion of the selectivity (Section D.40) of a series resonant circuit, i.e., its response at frequencies away from resonance compared with its response at the resonant frequency.

It will be seen later (paragraph 397) that $\dfrac{1}{R}\sqrt{\dfrac{L}{C}}$ is in inverse proportion to the expression derived for the logarithmic decrement of an oscillatory circuit, in which a free oscillation has been set up.

The characteristics of a series resonant circuit may be summed up as follows :—

(a) At the resonant frequency, the current is a maximum, is independent of the inductance and capacity, and depends solely on the resistance of the circuit.

(b) At any other frequency, the current depends on all three quantities, and is smaller the further the given frequency departs from resonance.

(c) Below the resonant frequency, the nett reactance of the circuit is capacitive, and the current leads the voltage ; above the resonant frequency, the nett reactance is inductive and the current lags on the voltage.

(d) For any given LC value, the ratio of the resonant current to the current at a given percentage departure from resonance depends on the value of $\dfrac{1}{R}\sqrt{\dfrac{L}{C}}$. The greater this value becomes, the sharper is the peak of the resonance curve.

302. " Q " and Selectivity.—We have—

$$\text{Selectivity} \; \alpha \; \frac{1}{R} \sqrt{\frac{L}{C}} = \frac{\omega L}{R} \quad \ldots \ldots \quad \left(\text{since } \omega^2 = \frac{1}{LC}\right).$$

The fraction $\omega L/R$, usually represented by the symbol Q, has become the popular criterion of selectivity (cf. D.40). Its value gives a much more comprehensive idea of selectivity in particular cases than any treatment involving a separate consideration of the effects of R, or the L/C ratio.

Q is the reciprocal of the " power factor " of the coil, and typical values (cf. Figs. 137 and 138) vary from (say) 1 to 700, more common values in receiving circuits ranging from about 100 to (say) 300 at the higher frequencies. The value tends to remain constant for the same coil over a wide range of frequencies, since the R/F resistance R is almost proportional to the frequency.

In any LCR circuit, with an applied voltage E, the current I at resonance is given by E/R, and we have

$$= E_L \doteqdot \omega L I = \frac{\omega L E}{R} = EQ$$

(neglecting the resistance of the inductance L).

The resonant rise of voltage across the inductance or condenser is thus approximately Q times the applied voltage.

In terms of Q, equation (1) of paragraph 301 now appears as

$$\frac{I_1}{I_0} = \frac{1}{\sqrt{(1+\alpha)^2 + Q^2 \dfrac{\alpha^2 (2+\alpha)^2}{(1+\alpha)^2}}}$$

Over a limited range of frequencies near resonance, it may be assumed that Q is constant. If α is expressed in terms of $1/Q$ certain useful simplifications are possible when Q is normally big.

Thus, if $\alpha = 1/Q$, it and its squares are small in comparison with unity and may be neglected. That gives

$$\frac{I_1}{I_0} \doteqdot \frac{1}{\sqrt{1+4}} = \frac{1}{\sqrt{5}} = \frac{1}{2\cdot24}$$

or $I_1 \doteqdot 45$ per cent. of I_0.

Similarly, if $\alpha = \dfrac{1}{2Q}$

$$\frac{I_1}{I_0} \doteqdot \frac{1}{\sqrt{1+1}} = \frac{1}{\sqrt{2}} = \frac{1}{1\cdot414}$$

or $I_1 \doteqdot 70$ per cent. of I_0.

For example, with a " Q " of 200, at 6,000 kc/s., the current would be reduced to 70 per cent. of its resonant value at $1/400 \times 6,000$, i.e., 15 kc/s. off resonance, and to 45 per cent. of the value at 30 kc/s. away.

These useful approximate rules are independent of the frequency and enable the **sharpness of resonance** quickly to be estimated.

Conversely, an estimate of the value of Q for a single circuit can be obtained from its resonance curve, by measuring the frequency departure from resonance necessary to give a " drop " in response of 30 per cent., i.e., 3 db. " down " (Appendix A).

Selectivity can only be fully expressed by complete resonance curves.

In the laboratory, the overall selectivity of a receiver is usually measured not by finding how much the overall response drops as the frequency moves away from resonance, but by measuring the magnitude of the input necessary to give the same output in all cases (cf. N.64).

In the case of a service W/T receiver of the superheterodyne type, certain tests showed that signals on the 150-1,500 kc/s. band were 1 signal strength down on the " R " scale at about $1\cdot1$ kc/s. from resonance. The signal input had to be increased 6 dbs., roughly twice as strong, in order to give the same audio output. This represents a high degree of " adjacent channel " selectivity (F.49), signals being about 30 per cent. down at $0\cdot5$ kc/s. from resonance.

303. Acceptor Circuits in Series.—It is often desirable to join two or more acceptor circuits in series.

The tuning of the whole circuit is not altered, but the ratio L/C is increased.

Suppose two circuits L_1C_1 and L_2C_2 are joined in series, and that each is tuned to the same LC value, *i.e.*, that $L_1C_1 = L_2C_2$.

If $L_1 C_1 = L_2 C_2$, then $L_1 = \dfrac{L_2 C_2}{C_1}$, and $L_2 = \dfrac{L_1 C_1}{C_2}$.

Hence $L_1 + L_2 = \dfrac{L_2 C_2}{C_1} + \dfrac{L_1 C_1}{C_2} = L_1 C_1 \left(\dfrac{1}{C_1} + \dfrac{1}{C_2}\right)$, since $L_1 C_1 = L_2 C_2$

$$= L_1 C_1 \left(\dfrac{C_1 + C_2}{C_1 \times C_2}\right) \quad \dots\dots\dots\dots\dots\dots\dots\dots (a)$$

The LC value of the two inductances and the two capacities in series will be :—

$$(L_1 + L_2)\left(\dfrac{C_1 \times C_2}{C_1 + C_2}\right),$$

which equals $L_1 C_1 \left(\dfrac{C_1 + C_2}{C_1 \times C_2}\right)\left(\dfrac{C_1 \times C_2}{C_1 + C_2}\right)$, $\quad \dots\dots\dots\dots\dots\dots$ from (a)

$$= L_1 C_1 = L_2 C_2.$$

Hence the LC value of the whole circuit is equal to that of either of the two combinations.

The selectivity of the combination depends upon the " Q " of each circuit, and it can be shown that **the nett value of Q is greater than the lesser of Q_1 and Q_2 and less than the greater.** We have

$$Q_1 = \dfrac{\omega L_1}{R_1}, \quad Q_2 = \dfrac{\omega L_2}{R_2}, \quad \text{and } Q = \dfrac{\omega(L_1 + L_2)}{R_1 + R_2}.$$

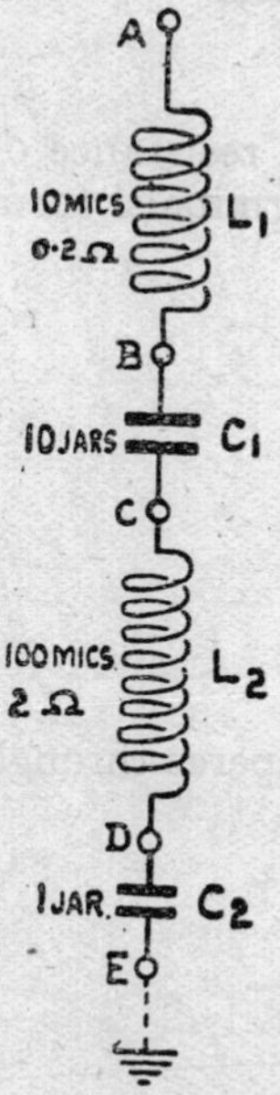

Let $\dfrac{L_1}{R_1} = k_1 \quad \dfrac{L_2}{R_2} = k_2$, where k_1 and k_2 are constants.

If $k_2 > k_1$, let $k_2 = nk_1$, where n is greater than 1.

Then $\dfrac{L_1 + L_2}{R_1 + R_2} = \dfrac{k_1 R_1 + k_2 R_2}{R_1 + R_2} = \dfrac{k_1 R_1 + nk_1 R_2}{R_1 + R_2}$

$$= \dfrac{k_1 (R_1 + nR_2)}{R_1 + R_2} > k_1$$

Also $\dfrac{L_1 + L_2}{R_1 + R_2} = \dfrac{\dfrac{k_2 R_1}{n} + k_2 R_2}{R_1 + R_2} = \dfrac{k_2 \left(\dfrac{R_1}{n} + R_2\right)}{R_1 + R_2}.$

$$< k_2$$

Hence $\dfrac{L_1 + L_2}{R_1 + R_2}$ $\left\{\begin{array}{l}\text{is greater than } \dfrac{L_1}{R_1} \\[2mm] \text{is less than } \dfrac{L_2}{R_2}\end{array}\right\}$ when $\dfrac{L_2}{R_2} > \dfrac{L_1}{R_1}.$

FIG. 139.

A
10 MICS
0·2 Ω L_1
B
10 JARS C_1
C
100 MICS
2 Ω L_2
D
1 JAR. C_2
E

Example 38.

The circuits A to C and C to E are each tuned separately to 100 mic.-jars or 478 kc/s.

Total inductance $= 10 + 100 = 110$ mics.

Total capacity $= \dfrac{10 \times 1}{10 + 1} = \dfrac{10}{11}$ jar.

The LC value of the circuit A to E is $110 \times \frac{10}{11} = 100$ mic.-jars

$$\omega = \frac{1}{\sqrt{LC}} = 10^6 \times 3$$

$$Q = 10^6 \times 3 \times \frac{110}{10^6} \times \frac{1}{2 \cdot 2} = 150.$$

and $Q_1 = Q_2 = 150.$

No increase in selectivity has been achieved.

304. Voltage across the Inductance or Capacity at Resonance.—The voltage across the inductance or condenser in a resonant circuit where the current is known may be found conveniently in the following manner, without working out the frequency (*cf.* 302) :—

The voltage across the inductance $= \omega LI$, which is equal to $\dfrac{I}{\omega C}$, the voltage across the condenser.

Hence $E_L = E_C = \omega LI$; but $\omega = \dfrac{1}{\sqrt{LC}}$.

Therefore $E_L = \dfrac{LI}{\sqrt{LC}} = I \sqrt{\dfrac{L}{C}}$, where $\begin{cases} L \text{ is in henries,} \\ C \text{ is in farads} \end{cases}$ .... (1)

Bringing henries to mics and farads to jars, we have

$$E_L = E_C = I \sqrt{\frac{L}{10^6} \times \frac{9 \times 10^8}{C}} = I \sqrt{\frac{900L}{C}} = 30 \ I \sqrt{\frac{L}{C}}, \text{ where} \begin{cases} L \text{ is in mics,} \\ C \text{ is in jars} \end{cases} .. (2)$$

This formula is useful in cases where the inductance and capacity of a circuit are both " concentrated," and not composed of several inductances and capacities in series or parallel.

Example 39.

In a circuit consisting of an inductance of 700 mics, a condenser of 1 jar, and a resistance of 30 ohms in series, find the voltage (*a*) across the condenser, (*b*) across the supply terminals, for a current $I = 10$ amperes at resonant frequency through the circuit.

(*a*) The voltage across the condenser

$$V_C = 30 \ I \sqrt{\frac{L}{C}} \text{ volts} = 30 \times 10 \sqrt{\frac{700}{1}} = 300 \sqrt{700}$$

$$= 300 \times 26 \cdot 5 = 7,950 \text{ volts.}$$

The maximum value of this voltage will be

$$\mathcal{V}_C = 7,950 \times \sqrt{2} = 7,950 \times 1 \cdot 414 = 11,240 \text{ volts.}$$

(*b*) The voltage required across the circuit to force the current of $I = 10$ amperes through the resistance of the circuit at resonant frequency will be

$$V = IR = 10 \times 30 = 300 \text{ volts.}$$

The maximum value of this voltage will be

$$\mathcal{V} = 300 \times \sqrt{2} = 300 \times 1 \cdot 414 = 424 \cdot 2 \text{ volts.}$$

305. It is interesting to note the distribution of voltage in the circuit of Example 38 above.

Assume that the resistance of L_1 is $0 \cdot 2$ ohm, that of L_2 is 2 ohms, and that a current of 1 ampere is flowing at the resonant frequency. Find the P.Ds. across the various portions of the circuit.

The voltage required to drive the current through the resistance of the acceptor circuit A to $C = IR = 1 \times 0 \cdot 2 = 0 \cdot 2$ volt.

Similarly, the voltage across the acceptor circuit C to E $= IR = 1 \times 2 = 2$ volts.

The total voltage required across the two acceptor circuits in series $= 2 \cdot 2$ volts. The voltages across intermediate points in the circuits are, however, much greater. Thus the voltage across AB is given by

$$I \sqrt{R^2 + \omega^2 L^2}.$$

Since the LC value of both acceptor circuits is 100 mic-jars, the reactance ωL_1 of L_1 is given by the product of

$$\omega = \frac{3 \times 10^7}{\sqrt{100}} = 3 \times 10^6, \text{ and } L_1 = 10 \text{ mics} = \frac{10}{10^6} \text{ henries};$$

$$\textit{i.e.,} \ \omega L_1 = 3 \times 10^6 \times \frac{10}{10^6} = 30 \text{ ohms.}$$

$\therefore$ Voltage across $AB = 1\sqrt{(0 \cdot 2)^2 + (30)^2} = 30$ volts approximately.

The resistance is really so small compared with the reactance that it can be neglected, and the formula of the last paragraph would give the same result.

$$\text{Voltage A to B} = 30 \ I \sqrt{\frac{L}{C}} = 30 \times 1 \times \sqrt{\frac{10}{10}} = 30 \text{ volts.}$$

This is also the voltage from B to C, across the condenser C_1.

Similarly, voltage C to D = voltage D to E = 300 volts. The voltages across the various portions of the circuit are therefore as follows :—

A—B = 30 volts (approximately).   C—D = 300 volts (approximately).
B—C = 30 volts.   D—E = 300 volts.
A—C = 0·2 volt.   C—E = 2 volts.

A to E = 2·2 volts.

The voltage A to C $= 0 \cdot 2$ volt is the vector sum of the voltages A to B and B to C ; A to B being just a little greater than B to C, and not in exact antiphase to it. The power required to maintain the current $= I^2 R = 2 \cdot 2$ watts.

This example will be found useful when dealing with receiving circuits later.

306. Potential Nodes and Loops.—In W/T great variations of potential are encountered between various portions of a circuit, an important point when considering the value of the insulation that must be provided.

The portions of a circuit where the potential does not vary much are often referred to as " nodes of potential," and the points undergoing large potential changes are termed " anti-nodes " or " loops " of potential.

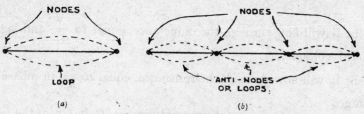

A vibrating violin string.

FIG. 140.

Take a taut violin string and pluck it ; it will vibrate as shown by the dotted lines, Fig. 140 (a). The two ends which are secured cannot move ; these two points are called " nodes " of vibration. The centre of the string will have a maximum of movement ; this point is called a " loop " or " anti-node " of vibration.

Now press the string lightly at a point one-third of its length from one end, Fig. 140 (b). This point and the two ends are held fixed. The remaining two-thirds will automatically divide itself into two equal vibrating portions, with the mid-point stationary. The string will vibrate and emit a note of three times the frequency of the fundamental note as given by the string in Fig. 140 (a).

This note is called the **third harmonic.**

As can be seen from the figure, we have in this second case four nodes and three anti-nodes of vibration.

Various interesting experiments of this nature may be tried by applying regularly-timed jerks to a taut signal halyard or stay.

Similar results apply to the wireless circuit we have just been discussing. Suppose we earth the point E. Then the point D will be oscillating at 300 volts above and below earth potential.

The potential of the point C will only vary 2 volts either way.

The point B will vary 30 volts, and A will vary 0·2 volt with respect to C.

Thus A, C and E may be spoken of as nodes of potential, and B and D as anti-nodes, or loops of potential.

D must have insulation from earth adequate to stand 300 volts, C to stand 2 volts, B to stand 30 volts, and A to stand 2·2 volts.

PARALLEL COMBINATIONS OF RESISTANCE, INDUCTANCE AND CAPACITY IN A.C. CIRCUITS.

307. Resistance and Inductance in Parallel.—In the treatment of various types of parallel circuit, vector diagram methods will be used.

If an inductance L and a resistance R are joined in parallel (as in Fig. 141 (a)), and an alternating voltage V is applied to the combination, currents of different value and different phase relationship will flow through the two parallel paths, and the current from the supply will be their vector sum.

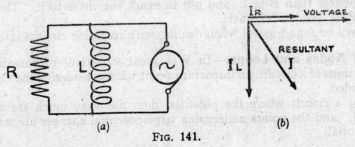

(a)   (b)

FIG. 141.

In this case,

(a) a current I_L will flow through the inductance, equal to $\dfrac{V}{\omega L}$ and lagging by 90° on the applied voltage ;

(b) a current I_R will flow through the resistance, equal to $\dfrac{V}{R}$, in phase with the applied voltage.

The resultant current from the alternating supply is seen to be, from the vector diagram (Fig. 141 (b)),

$$I = \sqrt{I_R^2 + I_L^2} = \sqrt{\left(\frac{V}{R}\right)^2 + \left(\frac{V}{\omega L}\right)^2} = V\sqrt{\frac{1}{R^2} + \frac{1}{\omega^2 L^2}}.$$

The angle of lag of current on voltage is given by ϕ, where $\tan \phi = \dfrac{\frac{1}{\omega L}}{\frac{1}{R}} = \dfrac{R}{\omega L}$.

As before, the **impedance** Z of the parallel circuit is given by the ratio of the maximum (or R.M.S.) value of the voltage to the maximum (or R.M.S.) value of the current.

$$\text{In this case } Z = \frac{V}{I} = \frac{1}{\sqrt{\left(\frac{1}{R}\right)^2 + \left(\frac{1}{\omega L}\right)^2}} = \frac{\omega LR}{\sqrt{R^2 + \omega^2 L^2}}$$

The ratio of current to voltage, $\sqrt{\left(\frac{1}{R}\right)^2 + \left(\frac{1}{\omega L}\right)^2}$, *i.e.*, the reciprocal of the impedance is called the **admittance** of the circuit.   It is denoted by the letter Y.

Example 40.

An alternating voltage of 100 volts at a frequency of 10,000 cycles per second is applied to a circuit consisting of a resistance of 20 ohms in parallel with an inductance of 300 mics.   Find (*a*) the current and (*b*) the angle of lag.

$$\omega = 2\pi \times 10{,}000 = 6 \cdot 28 \times 10^4.$$

$$X_L = \omega L = 6 \cdot 28 \times 10^4 \times \frac{300}{10^6} = 6 \cdot 28 \times 3 = 18 \cdot 84 \text{ ohms.}$$

$$I_L = \frac{V}{\omega L} = \frac{100}{18 \cdot 84} = 5 \cdot 31 \text{ amps.}$$

$$I_R = \frac{V}{R} = \frac{100}{20} = 5 \text{ amps.}$$

$$\text{Resultant current} = \sqrt{I_R^2 + I_L^2} = \sqrt{5^2 + 5 \cdot 31^2} = \sqrt{25 + 28 \cdot 17} = \sqrt{53 \cdot 17} = 7 \cdot 3 \text{ amps.}$$

$$\tan \phi = \frac{I_L}{I_R} = \frac{5 \cdot 31}{5} = 1 \cdot 06. \quad \phi = 46° \ 42'.$$

Hence the resultant current is one of $7 \cdot 3$ amperes lagging behind the applied voltage by an angle of 46° 42'.

308. From the above, the following general deduction may be made concerning the vectorial treatment of series and parallel circuits.

In series circuits—inductance, resistance, etc., in series—the current through each will be the same, and the voltage drop across each will be different. **Start by drawing the current line.** Lay off along it the voltage drop due to resistance, and at right angles to it the voltage drop due to reactance—inductive or capacitive or both. Completion of the vector diagram gives the necessary supply voltage for the given current.

In parallel circuits—inductance, resistance, etc., in parallel—the voltage applied to each will be the same and the current through each will be different. **Start by drawing the voltage line.** Lay off along it the current through the resistance, and at right angles to it the current through the inductance or capacity. Completion of the vector diagram gives the resultant current for the given supply voltage.

In parallel circuits, either or both arms of the circuit may contain combinations of resistance and inductance or capacity ; in which case the corresponding current vector will, as shown in paragraphs 307 and 309, be inclined to the voltage vector at an angle between 0° and 90°.

309. **Resistance and Capacity in Parallel.**—Suppose that a resistance R and a capacity C are in parallel, as in Fig. 142 (*a*).

An alternating voltage V is applied to the combination.

In this case,

(*a*) a current I_R flows through the resistance $= \dfrac{V}{R}$, in phase with the applied voltage

(*b*) a current I_C flows " through " *i.e.*, (charging up) the condenser, which leads the applied voltage by 90°, and is equal to V ωC.

The resultant current from the alternating supply is seen to be, from the vector diagram, Fig. 142 (b),

$$I = \sqrt{I^2_R + I^2_C} = V \sqrt{\frac{1}{R^2} + \omega^2 C^2}.$$

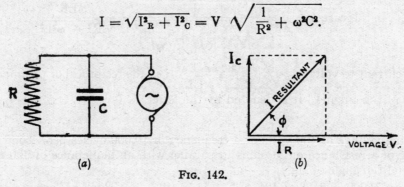

(a)   (b)

FIG. 142.

The angle ϕ, by which the current leads the voltage, is given by

$$\tan \phi = \frac{\omega C}{\dfrac{1}{R}} = \omega CR.$$

As in paragraph 307, $\sqrt{\dfrac{1}{R^2} + \omega^2 C^2}$, being the ratio of R.M.S. current to R.M.S. voltage, is termed the **admittance** of the parallel circuit, and its reciprocal,

$$\frac{1}{\sqrt{\dfrac{1}{R^2} + \omega^2 C^2}} = \frac{R}{\sqrt{1 + \omega^2 C^2 R^2}}$$

is the impedance of the circuit.

310. **Equivalent Capacity and Series Resistance.**—The case of a capacity in parallel with a resistance is important in practice, as it may represent a condenser with dielectric leakage, or leakage to earth from a high potential point in an aerial, or simply a condenser with an artificial resistance across it.

We propose to show that, for such a circuit an equivalent series circuit comprising capacity and resistance can be substituted, giving the same impedance and the same phase angle.

Let us assume that a circuit containing C_1 and R_1 in series is equivalent to C and R in parallel.

By equality of impedances, $\sqrt{R_1{}^2 + \dfrac{1}{\omega^2 C_1{}^2}} = \dfrac{R}{\sqrt{1 + \omega^2 C^2 R^2}}.$

By equality of phase angles, $\dfrac{1}{\omega C_1 R_1} = \omega CR.$

$$\therefore \frac{R}{\sqrt{1 + \omega^2 C^2 R^2}} = \sqrt{R_1{}^2 + \frac{1}{\omega^2 C_1{}^2}} = R_1 \sqrt{1 + \frac{1}{\omega^2 C_1{}^2 R_1{}^2}} = R_1 \sqrt{1 + \omega^2 C^2 R^2}$$

$$\therefore R_1 = \frac{R}{1 + \omega^2 C^2 R^2}$$

Also $C_1 = \dfrac{1}{\omega^2 CRR_i} = \dfrac{1 + \omega^2 C^2 R^2}{\omega^2 CR^2} = C\left(1 + \dfrac{1}{\omega^2 C^2 R^2}\right).$

In those practical cases where the resistance shunted across the condenser, e.g., the insulation resistance, is high compared with the capacitive reactance, $\dfrac{R^2}{\dfrac{1}{\omega^2 C^2}}$ or $\omega^2 C^2 R^2$ is large compared to unity.

Thus a good approximation to R_1 is $\dfrac{R}{\omega^2 C^2 R^2} = \dfrac{1}{\omega^2 C^2 R}$, and C_1 very nearly equals C.

Hence a parallel resistance R can be replaced by a series resistance $\dfrac{1}{\omega^2 C^2 R}$, a result which is very useful when considering power losses (cf D.23).

The higher the leak resistance the less power will be wasted.

It was shown, while dealing with condenser theory, that the various losses can all be represented by either resistances in series or parallel ; this paragraph shows that they can all be shown simply by an equivalent resistance in series.

311. Inductance and Capacity in Parallel (neglecting Resistance).—The investigation of a parallel circuit, in which one side of the circuit contains inductance only, and the other capacity only, will now be undertaken. It must be remembered that such conditions are impossible in practice, but the results obtained from the theoretical case lead up to those in the general case where resistance is included.

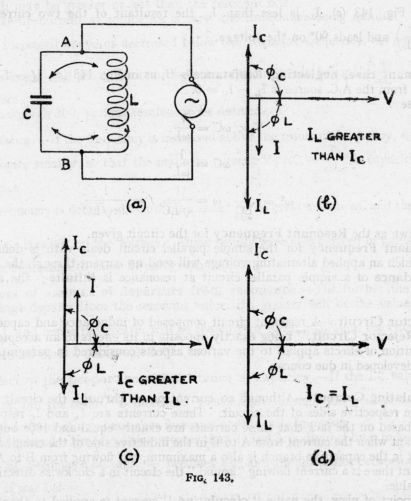

FIG. 143.

In this paragraph, and succeeding paragraphs up to and including paragraph 315, the existence of resistance is entirely neglected.

Hence the current $V\left(\dfrac{1}{\omega L} \sim \omega C\right)$ is increased n times. This result is the **same** as that in paragraph 300. In both cases, acceptor and rejector (taking the rejector circuit with **no** resistance), an increase in the ratio $\dfrac{L}{C}$ cuts down the current at a given non-resonant frequency, or increases the impedance of the circuit.

The rejector circuit is used to stop the flow of current at the resonant frequency through the circuit, and, by increasing C and diminishing L correspondingly, it can be made to allow large currents to pass through it at frequencies only slightly different from the resonant one.

In continuation of the results in (1) and (2) above, it is obvious that for frequencies very much greater or less than the resonant frequency, the rejector circuit is practically equivalent to a simple capacity C or a simple inductance L respectively.

Example 41.

If an alternating voltage of 1 volt be applied to a circuit consisting of an inductance of 4 mics in parallel with a condenser of 25 jars (a) at the resonant frequency, (b) at a frequency of 500,000 cycles per second, find the circulating current in the first case, and the current from the supply in the second case.

If the inductance is decreased to 1 mic and the capacity increased to 100 jars, find (c) the current from the supply corresponding to case (b) above.

(a) Circulating current $= \dfrac{V}{30}\sqrt{\dfrac{C}{L}} = \dfrac{1}{30}\sqrt{\dfrac{25}{4}} = \dfrac{1}{30}\times\dfrac{5}{2} = \dfrac{1}{12}$ amp. $= 83\cdot3$ milliamps.

(b) $\omega = 2\pi \times 5 \times 10^5 = \pi \times 10^6$ radians per sec.

$$I_C = \omega CV = \frac{3\cdot14 \times 10^6 \times 25 \times 1,000}{9 \times 10^8}\; mA = 87\cdot2\; mA.$$

$$I_L = \frac{V}{\omega L} = \frac{1}{3\cdot14 \times 10^6}\times\frac{10^6 \times 1,000}{4\cdot}\; mA = \frac{1,000}{12\cdot56} = 79\cdot6\; mA.$$

$$I_C - I_L = 7\cdot6 \text{ milliamps.}$$

The supply current is therefore one of $7\cdot6$ milliamps, leading by $90°$, since the condenser current is greater than the inductance current.

(c) $\omega = \pi \times 10^6$ radians per sec., as before.

$$I_C = \omega CV = \frac{3\cdot14 \times 10^6 \times 100 \times 1,000}{9 \times 10^8}\; mA = 349\; mA.$$

$$I_L = \frac{V}{\omega L} = \frac{10^6 \times 1,000}{3\cdot14 \times 10^6 \times 1}\; mA = 318\cdot3\; mA.$$

$$I_C - I_L = 30\cdot7 \text{ milliamps.}$$

The increase in the ratio $\dfrac{C}{L}$ has resulted in increasing the current at a given non-resonant frequency four times.

316. General case, including Resistance.—So far, we have been dealing with a circuit containing no resistance whatever.

In practice, such a state of affairs is not possible, although in an efficient circuit the resistances are small, especially in the condenser branch.

The general case, with resistance in each branch, will be considered first.

Owing to the presence of resistance, the current through the inductance branch will not now be equal to $\dfrac{V}{\omega L}$, but will be

$$I_L = \frac{V}{\sqrt{R_L^2 + (\omega L)^2}}$$

lagging on the applied voltage by an angle ϕ_L which is not 90°, but $\tan^{-1} \dfrac{\omega L}{R_L}$.

Similarly, the current through the condenser branch will be

$$I_C = \frac{V}{\sqrt{R_C^2 + \left(\dfrac{1}{\omega C}\right)^2}},$$

leading by an angle ϕ_C, whose tangent is $\dfrac{1}{\omega C R_C}$.

The resultant supply current I is the vector sum of these two currents I_L and I_C.

Let us resolve I_L and I_C into components in phase with the applied voltage, and components 90° out of phase with it.

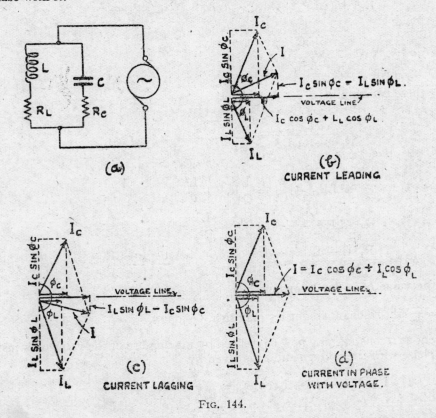

FIG. 144.

I_L is equivalent to $I_L \sin \phi_L$ lagging 90° behind the applied voltage, and $I_L \cos \phi_L$ in phase with it. Similarly, I_C is equivalent to $I_C \sin \phi_C$ leading 90° on the applied voltage, and $I_C \cos \phi_C$ in phase with it.

The supply current is then the vector sum of :—

(a) $I_L \sin \phi_L \sim I_C \sin \phi_C$, 90° out of phase with the applied voltage ; and

(b) $I_L \cos \phi_L + I_C \cos \phi_C$, in phase with the applied voltage (see Fig. 144 (b), (c), (d)).

Resonance occurs in a parallel circuit, in which resistance is taken into account, when the **supply current is in phase with the applied voltage.**

For this to be the case, the vertical components of I_L and I_C in the vector diagram must be equal and opposite, *i.e.*,

$$I_L \sin \phi_L = I_C \sin \phi_C.$$

There is then **no reactance** offered by the circuit, and its impedance is a pure resistance only.

At the resonant frequency the supply current flowing through the circuit is not necessarily a minimum, so that, while in the acceptor circuit resonance may be looked upon as meaning maximum current (minimum impedance), or zero reactance, in this case **zero reactance is the only correct definition of resonance.**

★**317. Resonant Frequency and Effective Resistance of a Resonant Parallel Circuit.—** At resonance $I_L \sin \phi_L = I_C \sin \phi_C$.

ϕ_L is an angle whose tangent is $\dfrac{\omega L}{R_L}$, and so $\sin \phi_L = \dfrac{\omega L}{\sqrt{R_L^2 + (\omega L)^2}}$.

$$\therefore\ I_L \sin \phi_L = \frac{V}{\sqrt{R_L^2 + (\omega L)^2}} \times \frac{\omega L}{\sqrt{R_L^2 + (\omega L)^2}} = \frac{V \cdot \omega L}{R_L^2 + (\omega L)^2}$$

Similarly, $I_C \sin \phi_C = \dfrac{V \cdot \dfrac{1}{\omega C}}{R_C^2 + \left(\dfrac{1}{\omega C}\right)^2}$

Equating these two results :—

$$\frac{\omega L}{R_L^2 + (\omega L)^2} = \frac{\dfrac{1}{\omega C}}{R_C^2 + \left(\dfrac{1}{\omega C}\right)^2}.$$

$$\omega^2 L R_C^2 + \frac{L}{C^2} = \frac{1}{C} R_L^2 + \frac{L^2}{C} \omega^2$$

$$\omega^2 \left(L R_C^2 - \frac{L^2}{C} \right) = \frac{R_L^2}{C} - \frac{L}{C^2}$$

$$\omega^2 = \frac{R_L^2 C - L}{L R_C^2 C^2 - C L^2} = \frac{L - R_L^2 C}{L^2 C - L R_C^2 C^2} = \frac{1}{LC} \left(\frac{L - C R_L^2}{L - C R_C^2} \right),$$

which gives the value of ω for resonance.

Since $f = \dfrac{\omega}{2\pi}$, the resonant frequency may then be found.

The current at resonance may now be derived by making use of the value of ω just found. The current is in phase with the voltage and so is given by

$$I = I_L \cos \phi_L + I_C \cos \phi_C, = \frac{V \cdot R_L}{R_L^2 + \omega^2 L^2} + \frac{V \cdot R_C}{R_C^2 + \dfrac{1}{\omega^2 C^2}},$$

by substitution for I_L, I_C, ϕ_L and ϕ_C.

$$\therefore \frac{I}{V} = \frac{R_L}{R_L^2 + \omega^2 L^2} + \frac{R_C}{R_C^2 + \dfrac{1}{\omega^2 C^2}}$$

But $\omega^2 L^2 = \dfrac{L}{C}\left(\dfrac{L - C R_L^2}{L - C R_C^2}\right)$, and $\dfrac{1}{\omega^2 C^2} = \dfrac{L}{C}\left(\dfrac{L - C R_C^2}{L - C R_L^2}\right)$.

$$\therefore \frac{I}{V} = \frac{CR_L (L - CR_C^2)}{L^2 - C^2 R_C^2 R_L^2} + \frac{CR_C (L - CR_L^2)}{L^2 - C^2 R_C^2 R_L^2} = \frac{C (R_L + R_C)(L - CR_L R_C)}{L^2 - C^2 R_C^2 R_L^2}$$

$$= \frac{C (R_L + R_C)}{L + CR_C R_L}.$$

Writing the total resistance $R_L + R_C$, as R, this gives

$$\frac{I}{V} = \frac{CR}{L\left(1 + \dfrac{C}{L} R_C R_L\right)}.$$

$\dfrac{I}{V}$ is the admittance, Y, of the parallel circuit.

The impedance (or effective resistance, since current and voltage are in phase) is given by

$$Z = \frac{1}{Y} = \frac{L\left(1 + \dfrac{C}{L} R_C R_L\right)}{CR}.$$

When R_L and R_C are small, as is generally the case in practice, **the approximate value of the effective resistance of the circuit is** $\dfrac{L}{CR}$, this result being in ohms, if L is in henries, C in farads, and R in ohms.

The supply current is $\dfrac{VRC}{L}$ amperes, V being in volts and the other quantities as above. The curious result must be noted that the supply current is **greater** and the impedance **less,** the **greater** the actual ohmic resistance included in the circuit.

Alternatively, if it is assumed that all the resistance of the circuit can be taken to be in the inductance branch, *i.e.*, $R_C = 0$, then

$$\omega^2 = \frac{1}{LC} - \frac{R_L^2}{L^2},$$

and the effective resistance of the circuit is given accurately by $\dfrac{L}{CR}$.

A similar result follows if all of the resistance is in the capacitive arm.

If we make the further approximation that R_L can be neglected, then $\omega = \dfrac{1}{\sqrt{LC}}$.

The statement made in paragraph 316 that resonance does not give a minimum value of supply current can be easily proved by finding the value of the supply current for the frequency corresponding to $\omega = \dfrac{1}{\sqrt{LC}}$ in the case where $R_C = 0$, but R_L is not taken equal to zero; though not in phase with the voltage, it will be found to be less than the supply current for the correct resonant frequency given by

$$\omega = \sqrt{\frac{1}{LC} - \frac{R_L^2}{L^2}}.$$

The difference is very small, however, and **it is always assumed in practice that the impedance of a rejector circuit is** $\dfrac{L}{CR}$ for an applied frequency $= \dfrac{1}{2\pi\sqrt{LC}}$, and that this impedance can be regarded as a pure resistance, the supply current being practically in phase with the voltage.

The last approximate result can also be derived as follows :—

If R_L and R_C are considered to be very small, the currents I_L and I_C may be assumed equal and are given by $\dfrac{V}{\omega L}$ or $V\omega C$; either of which expressions, with $\omega = \dfrac{1}{\sqrt{LC}}$, equals $V\sqrt{\dfrac{C}{L}}$.

The power expended by these circulating currents is given by

$$I_L^2 R_L + I_c^2 R_c = V^2 \frac{C}{L}(R_L + R_c) = \frac{V^2 CR}{L}, \text{ where } R = R_L + R_c.$$

This power is supplied by the source of alternating voltage.
If V is the supply voltage and I the supply current,

$$VI = \frac{V^2 CR}{L}.$$

$$\therefore I = V\frac{CR}{L}$$

and the effective resistance of the rejector circuit $= \dfrac{V}{I} = \dfrac{L}{CR}.$

If C is in jars, and L in mics, the supply current $= VR\dfrac{C}{9 \times 10^8} \times \dfrac{10^6}{L} = \dfrac{VRC}{900L}.$

Example 42.

If an alternating voltage of 10 volts be applied to a circuit consisting of 100 jars in parallel with an inductance of 4 mics. at the correct resonant frequency, find (a) the supply current required, (b) the circulating current, if the resistance of the circuit is equal to 0·1 ohm.

(a) Supply current $= V\dfrac{RC}{900L}$ (paragraph 317)

$$= 10 \times \frac{0 \cdot 1 \times 100}{900 \times 4} = \frac{1}{36} = 0 \cdot 028 \text{ ampere.}$$

(b) Circulating current $= I = \dfrac{V}{30}\sqrt{\dfrac{C}{L}}$ (paragraph 314)

$$= \frac{10}{30}\sqrt{\frac{100}{4}} = \frac{5}{3} = 1 \cdot 67 \text{ amperes.}$$

318. Parallel Resonance with Resistance in the Inductive Arm only.—With reference to Fig. 144 (d), with no resistance in the capacitive arm, the vector I_c is drawn at right angles to the voltage line, and at resonance

$$I_L \sin \phi_L = I_c = V\omega C, \dotfill (1)$$

ϕ_L is an angle whose tangent is $\dfrac{\omega L}{R_L}$, hence

$$\sin \phi_L = \frac{\omega L}{\sqrt{R_L^2 + \omega^2 L^2}}. \quad \text{Also } I_L = \frac{V}{\sqrt{R_L^2 + \omega^2 L^2}}$$

From (1) $$\frac{V}{\sqrt{R_L^2 + \omega^2 L^2}} \times \frac{\omega L}{\sqrt{R_L^2 + \omega^2 L^2}} = V\omega C$$

$$\therefore \frac{L}{C} = R_L^2 + \omega^2 L^2 \text{ or } \omega^2 = \frac{1}{LC} - \frac{R_L^2}{L^2}, \dotfill (2)$$

i.e., at resonance $\omega^2 = \dfrac{1}{LC}$ when $R_L = 0$.

The supply current at resonance is given by $I_L \cos \phi_L$, and $\cos \phi_L = R_L/\sqrt{R_L^2 + \omega^2 L^2}.$

Hence $I_L \cos \phi_L = \dfrac{V}{\sqrt{R_L^2 + \omega^2 L^2}} \times \dfrac{R_L}{\sqrt{R_L^2 + \omega^2 L^2}} = \dfrac{VR_L}{R_L^2 + \omega^2 L^2}.$

$\therefore$ Impedance at resonance $= Z = \dfrac{V}{I_L \cos \phi} = \dfrac{R_L^2 + \omega^2 L^2}{R_L}.$

Substituting for ω^2

$$Z = \frac{R_L{}^2 + \left(\dfrac{1}{LC} - \dfrac{R_L{}^2}{L^2}\right) L^2}{R_L} = \frac{L}{CR_L} \quad \text{accurately.}$$

319. Non-Resonant Case, including Resistance.—When the vertical components of I_L and I_C are not equal, the supply current is the vector sum of $(I_L \sin \phi_L \sim I_C \sin \phi_C)$ and $(I_L \cos \phi_L + I_C \cos \phi_C)$, these being at right angles to each other vectorially (paragraph 316).

(1) **Phasing.**—If the applied frequency is greater than the resonant one, the current I_C through

the condenser branch will be increased, and its vertical component $I_C \sin \phi_C = \dfrac{V \cdot \dfrac{1}{\omega C}}{R_C{}^2 + \left(\dfrac{1}{\omega C}\right)^2}$

will be increased. (This result is strictly true only if $\dfrac{1}{\omega C} > R_C$, but this would hold in practice.) In the same way, for an increase in frequency above resonant frequency, the current I_L through the inductive branch is decreased, and its vertical component $I_L \sin \phi_L = \dfrac{V \omega L}{R_L{}^2 + (\omega L)^2}$ is decreased. The resultant of the out-of-phase components of current, being $(I_L \sin \phi_L \sim I_C \sin \phi_C)$, is therefore capacitive, and the supply current will lead on the applied voltage.

If the applied frequency is less than the resonant one, the supply current lags on the applied voltage (*cf.* results of paragraph 315 for the case of no resistance).

(2) **Effect of departure from resonance.**—For frequencies sensibly different from resonance, the greater the departure from resonant frequency the greater will the current become through one branch of the circuit, and the less the current through the other, so that their vector sum, which is the supply current, increases.

It is difficult to give a strict proof of this statement. It is, of course, proved for the case of zero resistance in paragraph 315.

(3) **Effect of alteration of ratio of capacity to inductance.**—An increase in the ratio $\dfrac{C}{L}$

not only affects the results at non-resonance, but, from the formula $I = \dfrac{VRC}{L}$, it increases the supply

current **at resonance.** In the acceptor circuit the ratio $\dfrac{L}{C}$ or $\dfrac{C}{L}$ does not affect current at resonance.

At non-resonance a strict proof on the lines of paragraph 315 cannot be given, owing to the complicated form of the vector diagram, but it may be assumed that the inclusion of resistance into the

problem does not alter the results of paragraph 315, and that an increase in the ratio $\dfrac{C}{L}$ increases the

current at non-resonance in the case where the circuit includes resistance. An example follows to illustrate these points.

Example 43.

(1) In a circuit consisting of 10 mics in parallel with 10 jars, the inductive branch having a resistance of 1 ohm and the capacitive branch no resistance, find (*a*) the current through the circuit for an applied voltage of 100 volts at the resonant frequency, (*b*) the correct resonant frequency, (*c*) the current at a frequency which is 70 per cent. of the resonant frequency.

(2) Repeat the calculation for a circuit of 5 mics and 20 jars, the resistance being as before.
In this example resistance has been introduced as being wholly in the inductance branch—the numerical calculation being much longer if it is included in both branches.

The properties of a rejector circuit may now be summed up :—

At the Resonant Frequency—

  (a) If the circuit has no resistance losses at all (R = 0), it allows no current to flow through it from the source of supply, although a large circulating current is set up in the circuit ; its **impedance** approaches infinity on either side of the resonant point— Fig. 145 (b).

  (b) If it has any resistance losses, a supply current can flow through it which is greater the greater the resistance losses and the smaller the ratio L/C.

  (c) If the circuit contains resistance, the resonant frequency (at which the supply current is in phase with the voltage) is not entirely independent of the resistance, as is the case with the acceptor circuit.

At Non-Resonant Frequencies—

  (a) For non-resonant frequencies, the supply current increases the further the non-resonant frequency is from resonance, the smaller the ratio L/C, and the greater the resistance in the circuit.

  (b) If the non-resonant frequency is greater than the resonant frequency the current leads on the applied voltage ; if less the current lags on the applied voltage.

In general, **the higher the impedance at resonance with reference to the impedance at a given fractional departure from it, the greater the selectivity of the rejector.** For this reason, impedance/frequency curves, such as Figs. 145 (b), are of more value than current/frequency curves, and have the additional advantage that parallel resonance curves then appear to be essentially similar to those of series resonance.

321. **Comparison between Acceptor and Rejector Circuits.**—The essential difference is that the acceptor circuit is an easy path for currents at the resonant frequency, and a more difficult one for all others, whereas the rejector is a difficult path for currents at the resonant frequency and an easier path for all others.

At resonance, current through the acceptor is inversely proportional to its resistance, while current through the rejector is directly proportional to the resistance.

At resonance, current in the acceptor circuit is independent of the ratio of inductance to capacity ; in the rejector this is not so.

The resonant frequency for the acceptor circuit is independent of the resistance ; in the rejector circuit this is not so, but for small resistances in the circuit, the divergence from the value $f = \dfrac{1}{2\pi\sqrt{LC}}$, which is correct for the acceptor, is not very great.

322. **Selectivity and Q for Parallel Circuits.**—With the usual approximations for a resonant parallel circuit we have

$$Z = \frac{L}{CR} = \frac{\omega L}{\omega CR} = (Q)\,\frac{1}{\omega C} = (Q)\,\omega L.$$

The impedance at resonance is thus Q times the reactance of one branch of the circuit. Applying this rule to example 43 (1) we have $Z \doteqdot 30^2 = 900$ ohms ; accurately $Z = \dfrac{V}{I} = \dfrac{100}{0\cdot11} = 909$ ohms.

This resonant rise of impedance is precisely similar to the resonant rise of current in the case of the acceptor circuit, and the same approximate rules may be applied in order quickly to estimate the shape of the impedance curve, on which the selectivity of the rejector depends. High values of Q give highly selective circuits, the parallel impedance falling to 70 per cent. of its resonant value for a fractional difference of 1/2Q off resonance.

In terms of Q, parallel circuits appear no more complicated than series ones. Simple approximate expressions for the "supply current" and "circulating current" also appear when $1/Q$ is small in comparison with unity. We have

$$V = IZ = IQ\omega L \quad \therefore \quad I = \frac{V}{Q\omega L}.$$

But $V/\omega L$ is approximately the circulating current (paragraph 314), hence

$$I \doteqdot \frac{\text{Circulating current}}{Q} \quad \text{or Circulating current} \doteqdot Q \times \text{supply current.}$$

In example 42 we have $Q = 60$, hence circulating current $\doteqdot 60 \times 0{\cdot}028 = 1{\cdot}68$ amps.

POWER IN ALTERNATING CURRENT CIRCUITS.

323. Comparison with D.C. Circuits.—In any **direct** current circuit, the expenditure of power is easily obtainable in any one of three ways :—

(a) If the current and applied voltage are known, in amps. and volts respectively, then the power expenditure (in watts) is equal to $V \times I$.

(b) If the resistance of the circuit is known in ohms, and the current flowing through the resistance is known in amps., then the power expenditure (in watts) $= VI = IR \times I = I^2 R$.

(c) If the resistance of the circuit and the applied voltage are known, then the power expenditure $= VI = V \times \dfrac{V}{R} = \dfrac{V^2}{R}$.

In alternating-current circuits these simple relations do not all hold ; owing to the fact that the value of the applied voltage, and the value of current flowing, are continuously changing, and that they are generally out of phase with each other, the power supplied to the circuit is itself a variable quantity, and formulæ have to be derived which will give the **mean** power expenditure over a complete cycle.

324. A.C. Circuits containing Resistance only.—In an alternating current circuit in which the reactance is zero—for instance, a circuit which contains only a resistance R—the values of current and applied voltage are related to one another by the formula $\mathcal{I} = \dfrac{\mathcal{V}}{R}$ or, using R.M.S. values, $I = \dfrac{V}{R}$.

From the definition of the R.M.S. value of an alternating current, given in paragraph 273, which states that it is the equivalent value of D.C. current which would give the same power expenditure in a resistance R as an alternating current amplitude $\mathcal{J}$, the power expenditure this case is $I^2 R$ or VI or $\dfrac{V^2}{R}$ when I and V are the R.M.S. values of current and voltage respectively.

The strict mathematical proof has already been given in paragraph 275 (a), which shows that the **mean** power expenditure over a cycle is $\dfrac{\mathcal{J}^2 R}{2}$ which, **by definition,** is $I^2 R$.

In an A.C. circuit containing resistance only, therefore, the power expenditure (in watts) is the product of V (volts) and I (amperes), as read by alternating current voltmeters and ammeters, which register R.M.S. values.

325. General Case of A.C. Circuits.—We now consider A.C. circuits which have reactance as well as resistance, and in which the current and the voltage are therefore not in phase. Let us take the simple circuit illustrated in Fig. 146, consisting of a resistance R and an inductance L.

An ammeter (A) reads the R.M.S. value of the current flowing, and a voltmeter (V) reads the R.M.S. value of the applied voltage.

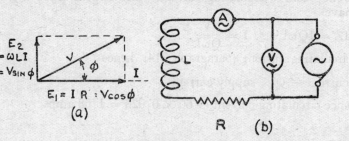

FIG. 146.

Then we know that the current will be lagging on the voltage by an angle ϕ, whose tangent is $\dfrac{\omega L}{R}$. The voltage V is performing two duties :—

(a) It is supplying a component $E_1 = IR$ to force the current through the resistance of the circuit. This voltage is in phase with the current, and is known as the **in-phase** component of the total voltage.

(b) It is supplying a component $E_2 = \omega LI$, to overcome the counter E.M.F. of the inductance. This component is 90° ahead of the current, and is known as the **wattless** component of the total voltage.

In the case of the inductance, the energy expended in creating a magnetic field round the inductance during a quarter of the cycle is completely restored to the circuit during the succeeding quarter cycle. In other words, the mean expenditure of energy, when the current and voltage are 90° out of phase with each other, is zero. Hence the component of the voltage E_2, or ωLI, does not, in conjunction with the current flowing, involve any power expenditure, and so arises the name " wattless " applied to it.

The only power required is that necessary to force the current through the resistance R. The voltage required to do this is E_1, and from paragraph 324 the power expenditure is E_1I.

(a) $E_1 = IR$.

∴ The power required $= E_1I = I^2R$.

(b) $\dfrac{E_1}{V} = \cos \phi$.

Hence $E_1 = V \cos \phi$, and the power required $= VI \cos \phi$.

In terms of maximum values it is $\dfrac{\mathcal{V}}{\sqrt{2}} \dfrac{\mathcal{J}}{\sqrt{2}} \cos \phi = \dfrac{\mathcal{V}\mathcal{J} \cos \phi}{2}$.

Similar considerations would apply to the case of a resistance in series with a condenser, or a resistance in series with both an inductance and a condenser. For the condenser, the component of voltage 90° out of phase with the current is also " wattless," since the energy associated with it and the current is alternately taken from and returned to the circuit with no losses, and the mean power expenditure over a whole cycle is zero.

★326. **Mathematical Proof of the General Case.**—We are assuming the general A.C. circuit, in which the current is not in phase with the voltage. The voltage can therefore be represented by $v = \mathcal{V} \sin \omega t$, and the current by $i = \mathcal{J} \sin (\omega t \pm \phi)$, according to whether it leads or lags.

At any moment the instantaneous power is the product of the instantaneous current and the instantaneous voltage, and is therefore

$$iv = \mathcal{J}\mathcal{V} \sin \omega t \sin (\omega t \pm \phi) \quad \dots \dots \dots \dots \dots (cf. \text{ paragraph 262})$$

$$= \frac{\mathcal{J}\mathcal{V}}{2}\{\cos (\pm\phi) - \cos (2\omega t \pm \phi)\} = \frac{\mathcal{J}\mathcal{V}}{2} \cos \phi - \frac{\mathcal{J}\mathcal{V}}{2} \cos (2\omega t \pm \phi)$$

Since $(2\omega t \pm \phi)$ can take all values from 0 to 360° for the different values of t in a complete cycle, the second term in this expression has a **mean** value of zero.

The mean value of *iv* over a complete cycle is therefore

$$\frac{\mathscr{I}\mathscr{V} \cos \phi}{2} = \frac{\mathscr{I}}{\sqrt{2}} \frac{\mathscr{V}}{\sqrt{2}} \cos \phi, \text{ or IV} \cos \phi,$$

which agrees with the result of paragraph 325.

$$I = \frac{V}{Z} \text{ and } \cos \phi = \frac{R}{Z}, \text{ hence IV} \cos \phi = I \times IZ \times \frac{R}{Z} = I^2 R.$$

327. Power Factor.—For the general A.C. circuit, with reactance and resistance, an A.C. voltmeter across the supply would read V, the R.M.S. voltage, and an A.C. ammeter in the circuit would read I, the R.M.S. current. The product of these readings VI is termed the " **apparent watts**," since this is the power that is **apparently** being expended on the circuit.

We have seen above that **true** mean power expenditure is VI cos ϕ, and this is known as the "**true watts**."

The ratio of the mean power supplied, VI cos ϕ, to the product of R.M.S. voltage and current, VI, is given by $\dfrac{\text{VI} \cos \phi}{\text{VI}}$, or cos ϕ, and this is defined as the **Power Factor.**

Hence, **True watts = Power Factor × R.M.S. voltage × R.M.S. current.**

$$\cos \phi = \frac{\text{True watts}}{\text{Apparent watts}} = \frac{\text{Resistance R}}{\text{Impedance Z}}.$$

True watts can be measured by a wattmeter.

$$\textbf{Power factor} = \cos \phi = \frac{\text{Wattmeter reading}}{\text{Ammeter reading} \times \text{Voltmeter reading}}.$$

The expression for Power, I²R (true watts), may be looked on as a method of determining the resistance of the circuit, which may be different under A.C. conditions from its D.C. value, due to hysteresis, eddy currents, etc.

We may thus define the effective resistance of an A.C. circuit as being

$$\frac{\text{True watts}}{(\text{R.M.S. current})^2},$$

the true watts expenditure being measured by a wattmeter and the current by an A.C. ammeter.

Example 44.

Find the Power Factor, true watts, and apparent watts for the circuit given in Example 34 above.

$$\text{True watts} = \text{I}^2 \text{ R} = 2 \cdot 97^2 \times 10 = 88 \cdot 21 \text{ watts.}$$
$$\text{Apparent watts} = \text{VI} = 50 \times 2 \cdot 97 = 148 \cdot 5 \text{ watts.}$$
$$\text{Power Factor} = \cos \phi = \frac{R}{Z} = \frac{10}{16 \cdot 83} = 0 \cdot 5941,$$
$$\text{or, True watts} = \text{VI} \cos \phi = 50 \times 2 \cdot 97 \times \cdot 5941 = 88 \cdot 21 \text{ (again),}$$
$$\text{or, Power Factor} = \frac{\text{True watts}}{\text{Apparent watts}} = \frac{88 \cdot 21}{148 \cdot 5} = 0 \cdot 5941.$$

328. If we have measuring instruments joined up to a motor alternator as illustrated in Fig. 147, then the ammeter and the voltmeter on the A.C. side will read the apparent watts, while the ammeter and the voltmeter on the D.C. side will give a measure of the true power being

expended on the circuit, together with the power required to overcome the frictional losses of the machine.

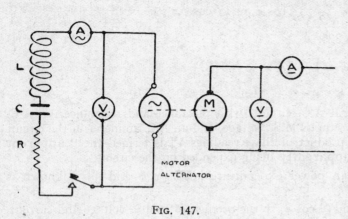

FIG. 147.

If a reading of the D.C. ammeter be taken with the machine running, but with the A.C. circuit broken, and another reading when the A.C. circuit is completed, the power factor can be calculated.

329. If the circuit contains nothing but resistance, or **if it is in resonance with the applied frequency,** then current and voltage are in phase, $\phi = 0$, $\cos\phi = 1$, and apparent watts = true watts.

On the other hand, if the circuit contains inductance and/or capacity only, and no resistance, current and voltage are 90° out of phase, $\phi = 90°$, $\cos \phi = 0$, and the true watts expenditure is zero.

330. Power Factor of a Condenser.—In the section on condensers in Chapter III, it was mentioned that various losses occur in practical condensers, which may be regarded as equivalent to resistances in series or parallel with the condenser. Again, it was shown in paragraph 310 that a parallel resistance can be replaced by an equivalent series resistance.

Let the total equivalent series resistance be R. For such a condenser, C, the current will not lead the voltage by 90°, but by an angle ϕ less than 90°, whose tangent is $\dfrac{1}{\omega CR}$. **The power absorbed by the resistance will be VI cos ϕ**, and cos ϕ is known as the Power Factor of the condenser.

In general, if the losses are small, the phase angle of the condenser will not differ much from 90°, and cos ϕ will be a small quantity, usually of the order 0·0001 or 0·001.

Now $\cos \phi = \dfrac{R}{Z} = \dfrac{R}{\sqrt{R^2 + \left(\dfrac{1}{\omega C}\right)^2}}$.

When R is very small compared with $\dfrac{1}{\omega C}$, R^2 may be neglected in the denominator, giving

Power Factor $= \cos \phi = \omega CR$.

The expression VI cos ϕ for the power absorbed by the equivalent series resistance is, of course, the power actually absorbed by the condenser owing to its various losses.

Also $\cos \phi = \sin (90° - \phi) = \left(\dfrac{\pi}{2} - \phi\right)$ in circular measure, as the angle $(90° - \phi)$ is small, so that the Power Factor may be taken as the angle which is the difference between 90° and the actual angle of lead of the current on the voltage (expressed in radians).

This angle is sometimes referred to as the " phase difference " of the condenser.

Example 45.

A condenser has a capacity of 1 jar and a phase difference of 1°. Find its equivalent series resistance, and the power absorbed by the condenser when an alternating voltage of 100 volts is applied to it at a frequency for which $\omega = 10^6$.

$$\omega C = \frac{10^6 \times 1}{9 \times 10^8} = \frac{1}{900} \; \therefore \; \frac{1}{\omega C} = 900 \text{ ohms.}$$

Since the phase difference is small, it is approximately equal to the power factor, and each may be taken equal to ωCR.

$$1° \text{ (in circular measure)} = \omega CR.$$

$$\frac{1 \times \pi}{180} = \omega CR.$$

$$\therefore R = \frac{\pi}{180} \times \frac{1}{\omega C} = \frac{\pi}{180} \times \frac{900}{1} = 5\pi = 15\cdot7 \text{ ohms.}$$

$$I = \frac{V}{Z} = V\omega C \text{ approximately (since R is small compared with } \frac{1}{\omega C}).$$

$$= \frac{100}{900} = \frac{1}{9} \text{ ampere} = 0\cdot11 \text{ ampere.}$$

$$\therefore \text{ Power consumed} = I^2 R = \left(\frac{1}{9}\right)^2 \times 15\cdot7 = \frac{15\cdot7}{81} = 0\cdot19 \text{ watts.}$$

$$\text{Power} = VI \cos \phi = VI \times \text{phase difference} = 100 \times \frac{1}{9} \times \frac{\pi}{180}$$

$$= \frac{\pi}{16\cdot2} = 0\cdot19 \text{ watts.}$$

331. Rating of Alternators.—Makers of alternating current machines rate their machines as being capable of delivering so many kilo-volt amperes (k.V.A.) and not as capable of delivering so many kilo-watts (kW.).

That is to say, they guarantee that the machine will generate a certain voltage if kept revolving at the correct speed, and that it will stand a certain current without overheating.

They cannot guarantee it as being capable of producing a certain power under all conditions, because they do not know the nature of the load the user is going to put on it.

For any circuit drawing a lagging or leading current we have

$$\text{True power} = I \ (V \cos \theta)\ldots\ldots\ldots\ldots\text{in watts,}$$

and, clearly, for the same power I will be least when θ = 0. When θ is large, I must relatively be very big for a given power.

For example, if a machine guaranteed to deliver 5 kW. at 200 volts were put on to a circuit having a power factor of 0·7, it would then have to supply an apparent power 5000/0·7 = 7143 watts, so that the true watts (5,000) should be equal to the apparent watts (7,143) multiplied by cos φ (0·7).

This would necessitate a current of 7,143/200 = 35·7 amps. instead of 5,000/200 = 25 amps. The increased heating effect would damage the machine.

A machine might be labelled—1½ kW., 0·8 P.F., 1·875 k.V.A., 60 volts—this means that with a P.F. of 1, the machine will supply 25 amps. at 60 volts. One is also told that the machine can give up to 1,875/60 = 31·2 amps. without overloading ; this corresponds to a P.F. of 0·8.

COUPLED CIRCUITS.

332. Methods of Coupling—Classification.—When two circuits are so arranged that energy can be transferred from one to the other, they are said to be coupled. Methods of coupling may be classified into **direct** and **mutual** coupling according to the nature of the path connecting the one circuit to the other ; in this way three distinct types are formed :—

(a) **Mutual** coupling has already been encountered when discussing mutual induction, where, owing to the proximity of two inductances, the changing magnetic field due to a changing current in one sets up voltages across the other. The two circuits are entirely disconnected (Fig. 148).

333. Free and Forced Oscillations in coupled circuits.—Two types of oscillatory action occurring in coupled circuits are of importance in W/T circuits :—

(a) **Free Oscillations.**—In this case two circuits are coupled together and one is set in oscillation, the energy being transferred to the other by means of the coupling. There is **no** continuously applied E.M.F. Since the theory of free oscillatory action in one circuit alone is not considered until Chapter VII, the more complicated theory of the frequencies at which two coupled circuits oscillate freely will be postponed till then.

(b) **Forced Oscillations.**—In this case a source of alternating E.M.F. is included in one of the two circuits which are coupled together. It is found that the degree of coupling has an effect on the frequency to which the circuits are **resonant.** If the coupling is small, and the two circuits are separately resonant to the same frequency, they will continue to be resonant to that frequency when coupled together ; but, if the coupling is increased, they will be resonant to **two frequencies** of numerical value dependent on the nature of the coupling.

The presence of the second circuit also affects the resistance and the reactance of the first circuit to an extent depending on the degree of coupling (paragraph 337).

These effects will now be considered in more detail.

334. Forced Oscillations, Equivalent Resistance and Reactance.—Let us take the case of **mutual inductive** coupling, and let the constants of the circuit be as shown in the following figure :—

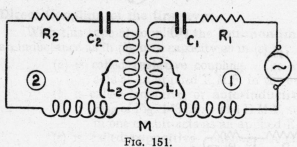

FIG. 151.

The currents flowing in the circuits (1) and (2) are I_1 and I_2. Let the frequency of the applied voltage be f, and let $2\pi f = \omega$.

The voltage induced in circuit (2) by a current I_1 in circuit (1) is $E_2 = \omega M I_1$.

The secondary current is $I_2 = \dfrac{\omega M I_1}{Z_2}$ which lags or leads on E_2 by an angle ϕ whose tangent is $\dfrac{X_2}{R_2}$.

This current may therefore be split up into two components, $I_2 \cos \phi$ in phase with E_2, and $I_2 \sin \phi$, which is 90° out of phase with E

Now $I_2 \cos \phi = I_2 \dfrac{R_2}{Z_2}$ and $I_2 \sin \phi = I_2 \dfrac{X_2}{Z_2}$.

Equivalent Resistance.—The component of current $I_2 \cos \phi$ gives an induced voltage in circuit (1) equal to $\omega M I_2 \cos \phi$ or $\omega M I_2 \dfrac{R_2}{Z_2}$, and lagging 90° on $I_2 \cos \phi$.

Since the voltage E_2, with which $I_2 \cos \phi$ is in phase, lags 90° on the current I_1, and the induced voltage in circuit (1) lags 90° on $I_2 \cos \phi$, this induced voltage in circuit (1) is 180° out of phase with the current I_1 in circuit (1).

It is therefore equivalent to an E.M.F. in circuit (1) acting in direct opposition to the component of the applied voltage E which is driving the current I_1 through the ohmic resistance of circuit (1), and so we can say that the in-phase component of the applied voltage less the induced E.M.F., $\omega M I_2 \dfrac{R_2}{Z_2}$, is equal to $I_1 R_1$.

For simplicity, write the in-phase component of E as E_R and the 90° out-of-phase component as E_X.

i.e. E_R is in phase with I_1, and

E_X is 90° out of phase with I_1.

Then $E_R - \omega M I_2 \dfrac{R_2}{Z_2} = I_1 R_1$, or $E_R = I_1 R_1 + \omega M I_2 \dfrac{R_2}{Z_2}$.

But $I_2 = \dfrac{\omega M I_1}{Z_2}$, $\therefore E_R = I_1 R_1 + \omega^2 M^2 I_1 \dfrac{R_2}{Z_2^2} = I_1 \left(R_1 + \dfrac{\omega^2 M^2 R_2}{Z_2^2} \right)$.

This is equivalent to saying that **the apparent resistance of circuit (1) is increased** from R_1 to $\left(R_1 + \dfrac{\omega^2 M^2 R_2}{Z_2^2} \right)$ because it is coupled to circuit (2).

Equivalent Reactance.—The reactance in both circuits will be assumed inductive, so that the currents lag on the voltages.

The component of the secondary current I_2 lagging 90° on the secondary E.M.F. E_2 is $I_2 \sin \phi$. This component gives rise to an induced E.M.F. in the primary circuit of value $\omega M I_2 \sin \phi$, or $\omega M I_2 \dfrac{X_2}{Z_2}$, lagging 90° on $I_2 \sin \phi$, and therefore lagging 180° on E_2. E_2 lags by 90° on the primary current I_1, and so $\omega M I_2 \dfrac{X_2}{Z_2}$ lags by 270° (*i.e.*, leads by 90°) on I_1.

Hence $\omega M I_2 \dfrac{X_2}{Z_2}$ is in phase with E_X.

Hence $E_X + \omega M I_2 \dfrac{X_2}{Z_2} = I_1 X_1$

$$E_X = I_1 \left(X_1 - \dfrac{\omega^2 M^2}{Z_2^2} X_2 \right).$$

This is equivalent to saying that **the apparent reactance of circuit (1) is decreased** from X_1 to $\left(X_1 - \dfrac{\omega^2 M^2}{Z_2^2} X_2 \right)$ because it is coupled to circuit (2).

As might be anticipated, the equivalent resistance and reactance are obtained in the case of **auto-inductive coupling** by substituting ωL_m, and in the case of capacitive coupling by substituting $\dfrac{1}{\omega C_m}$, for ωM in the above results.

The complete theory of **resistive coupling**, as in Fig. 149 (a), leads to a slightly different result, *viz.* that the equivalent resistance is decreased from R_1 to $R_1 - \dfrac{R_m^2}{Z_2^2} R_2$, while the equivalent reactance is increased from X_1 to $X_1 + \dfrac{R_m^2}{Z_2^2} X_2$.

Example 46.

Two circuits $L_1 R_1 C_1$ and $L_2 R_2 C_2$ are coupled mutually.
$L_1 = 200$ mics, $R_1 = 15$ ohms, $C_1 = 5$ jars.
$L_2 = 96$ mics, $R_2 = 8$ ohms, $C_2 = 10$ jars.
$M = 15$ mics.

An alternating voltage of 100 volts at a frequency $\dfrac{10^6}{2\pi}$ is applied to $L_1 R_1 C_1$. Find the equivalent resistance R_1', the equivalent reactance X_1' and the currents I_1 and I_2.

$$\omega = 2\pi \times \dfrac{10^6}{2\pi} = 10^6 \text{ radians per second.}$$

$$\omega L_1 = \dfrac{200}{10^6} \times 10^6 = 200 \text{ ohms, and } \dfrac{1}{\omega C_1} = \dfrac{9 \times 10^8}{5 \times 10^6} = 180 \text{ ohms.}$$

$$\therefore X_1 = 20 \text{ ohms, } R_1 = 15 \text{ ohms, } \therefore Z_1 = 25 \text{ ohms}$$

$$\omega L_2 = \dfrac{96}{10^6} \times 10^6 = 96 \text{ ohms, and } \dfrac{1}{\omega C_2} = \dfrac{9 \times 10^8}{10 \times 10^6} = 90 \text{ ohms.}$$

$\therefore X_2 = 6$ ohms.　$R_2 = 8$ ohms.　$\therefore Z_2 = 10$ ohms.

$$\omega M = 10^6 \times \frac{15}{10^6} = 15 \text{ ohms.}$$

Equivalent resistance $R_1' = R_1 + \left(\dfrac{\omega M}{Z_2}\right)^2 R_2 = 15 + \left(\dfrac{15}{10}\right)^2 \times 8 = 33$ ohms.

Equivalent reactance $X_1' = X_1 - \left(\dfrac{\omega M}{Z_2}\right)^2 X_2 = 20 - \left(\dfrac{15}{10}\right)^2 \times 6 = 6 \cdot 5$ ohms.

Current $I_1 = \dfrac{E}{Z_1} = \dfrac{100}{\sqrt{33^2 + 6 \cdot 5^2}} = \dfrac{100}{\sqrt{1089 + 42 \cdot 3}} = 2 \cdot 97$ amps.

Current $I_2 = \dfrac{\omega M I_1}{Z_2} = \dfrac{\omega M E}{Z_1' Z_2} = \dfrac{15 \times 100}{33 \cdot 63 \times 10} = 4 \cdot 46$ amps.

Since the total reactance in circuit (1) is inductive, the circuit may be said to be equivalent to a resistance $R_1 = 15$ ohms and a self-inductance L given by $\left(L_1 - \dfrac{1}{\omega^2 C_1}\right)$

$$= \left(\frac{200}{10^6} - \frac{9 \times 10^8}{5 \times 10^{12}}\right) \text{henries} = \left(\frac{200}{10^6} - \frac{900}{5 \times 10^6}\right) \text{henries} = (200 - 180) \text{ mics} = 20 \text{ mics.}$$

This result could also have been obtained by dividing the inductive reactance $\omega L = 20$ ohms by $\omega = 10^6$. When circuit (1) is coupled to circuit (2), however, its inductive reactance is only $6 \cdot 5$ ohms, so that its self-inductance is $6 \cdot 5$ mics. Therefore, coupling the circuit to another circuit has increased its resistance from 15 to 33 ohms and at the same time decreased its inductance from 20 to $6 \cdot 5$ mics.

An example is given below in which the primary current is known and it is desired to find the current in the secondary circuit. This corresponds to practical cases that occur in W/T, for example, the reading of an ammeter coupled to an oscillatory circuit by means of an ammeter transformer.

Example 47.　[Fig. 152.]

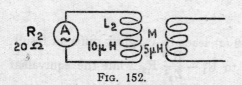

FIG. 152.

Let the primary current I_1 be 10 amps., the mutual inductance M be 5 mics, the secondary inductance L_2 be 10 mics, the resistance of the ammeter R_2 be 20 ohms, and let ω be equal to 10^6 radians per second.

Then $E_2 = \omega M I_1 = 10_6 \times \dfrac{5}{10^6} \times 10 = 50$ volts.

$X_2 = \omega L_2 = 10^6 \times \dfrac{10}{10^6} = 10$ ohms.

$Z_2 = \sqrt{R_2{}^2 + X_2{}^2} = \sqrt{20^2 + 10^2} = \sqrt{500} = 22 \cdot 37$ ohms.

$I_2 = \dfrac{E_2}{Z_2} = \dfrac{50}{22 \cdot 37} = 2 \cdot 237$ amps.

Hence the ammeter reading will be $2 \cdot 237$ amps., when the primary current is 10 amps.

335. Forced Oscillations.　Resonant Frequencies for Tight Couplings.—From the results of the last paragraph, the complete formulæ for I_1 and I_2 in the general case are :—

$$I_1 = \frac{E}{Z_1'} = \frac{E}{\sqrt{\left[R_1 + \left(\dfrac{\omega M}{Z_2}\right)^2 R_2\right]^2 + \left[X_1 - \left(\dfrac{\omega M}{Z_2}\right)^2 X_2\right]^2}}$$

$$I_2 = \frac{\omega M I_1}{Z_2} = \frac{\omega M E}{Z_1' Z_2} = \frac{\omega M E}{Z_2 \sqrt{\left[R_1 + \left(\dfrac{\omega M}{Z_2}\right)^2 R_2\right]^2 + \left[X_1 - \left(\dfrac{\omega M}{Z_2}\right)^2 X_2\right]^2}}.$$

If the reactance term is put equal to zero in the expression for the impedance given in the denominator above, I_1 will be in phase with the applied voltage and the solution of the equation

$$X_1^{'} - \frac{\omega^2 M^2}{Z_2^{2}} X_2 = 0.$$

will give the primary resonant frequency.

We shall first assume that the resonant frequency is not close to the frequency at which $X_2 = 0$, so that we may consider the resistance R_2 to be so small compared with X_2 that it can be neglected, and therefore $Z_2 = X_2$.

Hence $X_1 = \dfrac{\omega^2 M^2}{X_2^{2}} X_2 = \dfrac{\omega^2 M^2}{X_2}$,

$$\text{or } \omega^2 M^2 = X_1 X_2$$

$$\omega^2 M^2 = \left(\omega L_1 - \frac{1}{\omega C_1} \right)\left(\omega L_2 - \frac{1}{\omega C_2} \right) = \omega^2 L_1 L_2 \left(1 - \frac{1}{\omega^2 L_1 C_1} \right)\left(1 - \frac{1}{\omega^2 L_2 C_2} \right).$$

Let the two circuits be separately tuned to the same frequency $\dfrac{\omega_0}{2\pi}$.

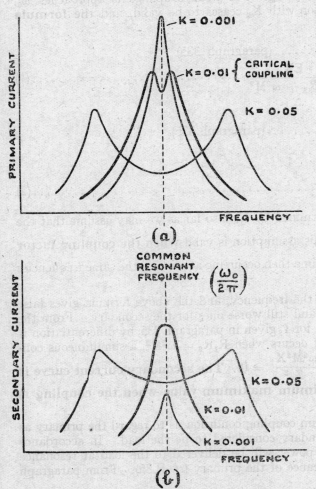

(a)

(b)

FIG. 153.

Then $(\omega_0)^2 = \dfrac{1}{L_1 C_1} = \dfrac{1}{L_2 C_2}$

$\therefore \ \omega^2 M^2 = \omega^2 L_1 L_2 \left(1 - \dfrac{(\omega_0)^2}{\omega^2} \right)\left(1 - \dfrac{(\omega_0)^2}{\omega^2} \right)$

$\dfrac{M^2}{L_1 L_2} = K^2 = \left(1 - \dfrac{(\omega_0)^2}{\omega^2} \right)^2$

$\therefore \ \pm K = 1 - \dfrac{(\omega_0)^2}{\omega^2}$

$\text{or } (\omega_0)^2 = \omega^2 (1 \pm K)$

$\omega_0 = \omega \sqrt{1 \pm K}$

Hence, $\omega = \dfrac{\omega_0}{\sqrt{1 \pm K}}$ or $f = \dfrac{f_0}{\sqrt{1 \pm K}}$.

Thus, under these conditions, there are **two frequencies of resonance in the primary response curve**, one higher and one lower than the individual equal resonant frequencies. This formula is true for resistanceless circuits, and gives satisfactory results whenever the two frequencies are appreciably separated. The coupling factor K varies from zero to 1 (or it may b expressed as a percentage), as the circuit vary from the uncoupled to the perfectly coupled state. When $K = 0$, there is only one resonant frequency; when $K = 1$ there is also only one $\left(\dfrac{\omega_0}{\sqrt{2}} \right)$, since the second is infinite in value.

In many cases K is relatively small, and the two resonant frequencies (f_1 and f_2) are then approximately equally spaced about $\omega_0/2\pi$, the separation between the current peaks being given by $f_1 - f_2 \doteqdot K f_0$ (cf. F.19). The bigger the value of K the more the peaks separate; Fig. 153 (a) gives a comparison between the resonance curve of a series resonant primary circuit, virtually by itself when K is small, and of the same circuit with a tighter mutual coupling to another similar one, the secondary circuit.

The two resonant frequencies may be physically accounted for by reference to the equation $X_1 - \dfrac{\omega^2 M^2 X_2}{Z_2^2} = 0$, from paragraph 335. Neglecting R_2 in comparison with X_2, we have $Z_2^2 = X_2^2$ and $X_1 - \dfrac{\omega^2 M^2}{X_2} = 0$.

At frequencies below the common resonant frequency, the series reactance (X_1) of the primary is capacitive, and the coupled-in reactance is rendered effectively inductive by the minus sign in the equation; resonance occurs when the two reactances balance. With a bigger mutual inductance (tighter coupling) the coupled-in reactance is bigger and the hump frequency has to move further from the common resonant one. At frequencies above the common resonant one X_1 is inductive, and resonance occurs when the coupled-in capacitance exactly balances it.

336. Weak Couplings and Optimum Coupling.—For weak couplings ω approaches ω_0, the assumption that R_2 is negligible in comparison with X_2 ceases to be valid, and **the formula $\omega = \omega_0/\sqrt{1 \pm K}$ gives erroneous results.**

We may now put $X_1 = X_2 = 0$, hence ....(paragraph 335)

$$I_1 \fallingdotseq \frac{E}{R_1 + \dfrac{\omega^2 M^2}{R_2}} = \frac{ER_2}{R_1 R_2 + \omega^2 M^2} \quad \dots\dots\dots\dots\dots\dots\dots(1)$$

and $I_2 = \dfrac{\omega M I_1}{Z_2} \fallingdotseq$

$$\frac{\omega M E}{Z_2 \sqrt{\left[R_1 + \dfrac{\omega^2 M^2}{Z_2^2} R_2 \right]^2}} \quad \dots\dots\dots(\text{paragraph 335})$$

$$\therefore \ I_2 \fallingdotseq \frac{\omega M E}{R_2 R_1 + \omega^2 M^2} \quad \dots\dots\dots\dots\dots\dots\dots\dots\dots(2)$$

In all cases the secondary current I_2 is determined by I_1, in so far as we may assume that the factor $\dfrac{\omega M}{Z_2}$ is independent of the frequency. This assumption is valid **when the coupling factor K is big,** the primary and secondary current maxima then occurring at sensibly the same frequencies given by $\omega = \omega_0/\sqrt{1 \pm K}$.

When K is small, $\omega M/Z_2$ is dependent on the frequency, and the above formula gives false results for the primary current resonance peaks, and still worse ones for the secondary. From the approximate formula (2), or the accurate formula for I_2 given in paragraph 335, by differentiation it may be shown that maximum secondary current occurs when $R_1 R_2 = \omega^2 M^2$, a simultaneous condition for this **optimum coupling** being $X_1 - \dfrac{\omega^2 M^2 X_2}{Z_2^2} = 0$. **The secondary current curve is always single humped, but reaches its maximum maximum value when the coupling is such that $R_1 R_2 = \omega^2 M^2$.**

An alternative way of arriving at the optimum coupling condition, is to regard the primary as a source of energy, like a battery, and the secondary considered to be the load. In accordance with well-known electrical principles, maximum power will be delivered to the load at resonance when the coupled resistance is equal to the resistance of the primary (*cf.* R.35). From paragraph 334 we have, therefore,

$$R_1 = \frac{\omega^2 M^2 R_2}{Z_2^2} = \frac{\omega^2 M^2}{R_2} \text{ at resonance.}$$

Hence $R_1 R_2 = \omega^2 M^2$ **for optimum coupling** .... (3)

Now $M = K \sqrt{L_1 L_2}$ $\therefore R_1 R_2 = \omega^2 K^2 L_1 L_2$

$$\therefore \frac{1}{K^2} = \left(\frac{\omega L_1}{R_1}\right)\left(\frac{\omega L_2}{R_2}\right) = Q_1 Q_2$$

Hence, **for optimum coupling**, $K = \dfrac{1}{\sqrt{Q_1 Q_2}}$ ....(*cf.* F.19).

This expression gives the "**optimum coupling**" for maximum transfer of energy from primary to secondary, and hence for maximum secondary current. When $Q_1 = Q_2 = Q$ we have $K = \dfrac{1}{Q}$; normal values of Q in receivers range from 100 to 200, the **critical value** of K for these circuits, therefore, ranging from 1 to $\frac{1}{2}$ per cent. For diagrammatic purposes in Fig. 153, $K = 0\cdot01$ is assumed to give optimum coupling.

When K is below optimum value there is *normally* only one hump in the primary response characteristic, as in the case of the curve for $K = 0\cdot001$ of Fig. 153 (a). The primary current curve is almost the same as though there were no attached secondary. The secondary current curve follows the general shape of the primary, the current being a maximum at the common resonant frequency, when the induced voltage has its maximum value, although not its *maximum maximum* value.

As K increases to the optimum value, each circuit begins to affect the other. The coupled-in impedance lowers the primary resonant current peak, and flattens the resonance curve. This, in turn, broadens the secondary current curve, since the induced voltage changes less with frequency. At the same time, the secondary induced voltage becomes greater and the secondary current larger ; the energy transferred to the secondary increases. Equations (1) and (2) show these changes clearly ; as $\omega^2 M^2$ increases the primary current I_1 decreases, and I_2 increases until $\omega^2 M^2 = R_1 R_2$.

When K reaches its optimum value there is still only one maximum in the secondary curve, given by (2) above, the secondary current peak occurring at the common resonant frequency. Under these conditions it can be shown that the primary current curve is *slightly* double humped. The actual optimum value of I_2 is given by substituting $\omega^2 M^2 = R_1 R_2$ in (2).

Thus—

$$I_2 = \frac{E\sqrt{R_1 R_2}}{2 R_1 R_2} = \frac{E}{2\sqrt{R_1 R_2}} = \frac{E}{2 R_1} \dots \text{if } R_1 = R_2.$$

It should be noted that the above value for I_2 is the same as that given for I_1, from equation (1) when $R_1 = R_2$.

For higher values of K the humps in both curves begin to be pronounced, being quite noticeable for a value K equal to twice the optimum coupling ; this corresponds to

$$\omega^2 M^2 = 2R_1 R_2 = 2R_1^2 \dots\dots\dots \text{if } R_1 = R_2.$$

In each curve the humps occur at about the same frequency, but the lower impedance of the secondary makes the current drop between the secondary humps relatively less than that in the primary.

The magnitude of the current peaks decreases as the coupling increases, slowly at first but more rapidly afterwards. For values of $\omega^2 M^2$ only slightly greater than $R_1 R_2$, the size of I_2 tends to remain constant. This follows from the general formula $I_2 = \omega M I_1 / Z_2$; the ratio $\dfrac{\omega M}{Z_2}$ only changes slowly for values of ωM not much in excess of that used for optimum coupling.

In W/T circuits, interest usually centres on the secondary current. The couplings employed vary from slightly below optimum coupling, in the case of stiffly tuned R/F amplifiers in purely telegraphic apparatus, to various degrees of overcoupling, when band-pass effects are desired.

From the point of view of the primary current, the mathematical treatment of weak couplings in the region of optimum coupling is subject to serious difficulties. For tight couplings, the equation (paragraph 335) $X_1 - \dfrac{\omega^2 M^2 X_2}{Z_2^2} = 0$, has two solutions ; Z_2^2 only changes slowly with the frequency,

The capacitive reactance of the circuit $C_a C_m R_1 L_1$ is given by $\dfrac{1}{\omega C_1} = \dfrac{1}{\omega C_a} + \dfrac{1}{\omega C_m} = \dfrac{1}{\omega} \dfrac{C_a + C_m}{C_a C_m}$, and a similar expression holds for the capacitive reactance of the other circuit.

$$K = \frac{\dfrac{1}{\omega C_m}}{\sqrt{\dfrac{1}{\omega} \times \dfrac{C_a + C_m}{C_a C_m} \times \dfrac{1}{\omega} \dfrac{C_b + C_m}{C_b C_m}}} = \sqrt{\frac{C_a C_b}{(C_a + C_m)(C_b + C_m)}}.$$

For the cases illustrated in Figs. 150 (b) and (c), where the direct coupling is by means of an inductance or capacity not included in either circuit, formulæ may be obtained as follows :—

Fig. 150 (b) : $K = \sqrt{\dfrac{L_1 L_2}{(L_1 + L_0)(L_2 + L_0)}}$,

Fig. 150 (c) : $K = \dfrac{C_0}{\sqrt{(C_1 + C_0)(C_2 + C_0)}}$.

Fig. 150 (c), with condenser C'_0 in the bottom line : $K = \dfrac{C'}{\sqrt{(C_2 + C')(C_1 + C')}}$, where $C' = \dfrac{C_0 C'_0}{C_0 + C'_0}$.

In these cases the " **mutual reactance** " can only be obtained by finding the voltage generated in the second circuit when a current of 1 ampere flows in the first. It is not proposed to carry out this investigation here, but the results are quoted for reference.

For the most common type of coupling, viz., mutual inductive, the coupling factor K may be increased in one of two ways :—

(a) By moving the coupled coils closer together.

(b) By increasing the inductances of the two coils, L_1 and L_2, which take part in the mutual inductive action, and decreasing the inductances of the two coils L_a and L_b, which do not so take part, in order to maintain resonance in both circuits.

For auto-inductive coupling, K may be increased by increasing the common inductance L_m and decreasing L_a and L_b to maintain resonance. For capacitive coupling, K may be increased by decreasing the value of the common capacity C_m and increasing C_a and C_b to maintain resonance. For capacitive coupling of the type illustrated in Fig. 150 (c) K is increased by increasing C_0.

338. Transient Conditions.—It must be remembered that the relationships between current and voltage developed throughout this chapter are those which pertain during " steady " conditions. When a switch is suddenly made in a circuit containing inductance or capacity, there is a period of transience, during which the current flowing is a combination of the forced oscillations we have considered and of " free " oscillations at the " natural " frequency of the circuit. The latter ultimately die away, leaving only the forced oscillations which continue until the switch is broken. The theory of free oscillations is considered in Chapter VII.

THE OPERATOR " J."

339. A short account of the use of the mathematical operator " j ", $(= \sqrt{-1})$, in solving alternating current problems will be given in the following paragraphs. This method is to be recommended for the simplification it introduces in writing down the equations necessary for the solution of any problem. It does not shorten the computation required to obtain a result in cases which can be treated as a combination of impedances in series and parallel, but its use, or that of some equivalent operator, is essential in analysing more complicated circuits such as alternating current bridge networks.

The idea of **number** was originally confined to the positive whole numbers or positive integers, and its first extension was to positive fractions or ratios of one positive integer to another. The next discovery was that it was not always possible to represent exactly the ratio of one length to another as a fraction whose numerator and denominator were integers. Two simple examples are the ratio of a diagonal of a square to its side ($\sqrt{2}$), and the ratio of the circumference of a circle to its diameter (π). Such numbers as $\sqrt{2}$ and π are called incommensurable. The introduction of the Arabic notation for numbers, in which the value of a digit is indicated by its position in a number, led to the use of zero as the number to which small numbers tend as a limit. For instance, in 123, 132, 312, the digit 3 represents successively three, thirty and three hundred. To represent thirty it is necessary to have another digit (0) following the digit 3, to indicate that 3 stands for 3 tens, and yet this other digit must not increase the size of the number as would be the case if 1, 2, etc., were used. Hence, arose the necessity for the symbol 0. A logical extension of the idea of large numbers to indefinite limits gives infinity (∞) as the other end from zero of the list of positive numbers.

The operation of subtraction led to the idea of negative numbers. The answer to the problem 7 minus 3 can be given purely by the use of positive numbers, the answer being 4. But if the converse problem 3 minus 7 is considered, no positive number can be found which represents the result. The answer is obviously exactly the opposite of the answer to 7 minus 3, and so we are led to the idea of the number -4, which represents the exact opposite of the number $+4$. The ideas of negative fractions, incommensurable numbers and $-\infty$ are now an easy extension.

All the numbers between $-\infty$ and $+\infty$ so far considered are called " **real** " numbers.

340. Operators.—Consider the problem $7 + 3$. The plus sign really stands for two separate things :—

(1) It indicates the positive number $+3$.

(2) It tells us that this number, $+3$, is to be added to 7. In other words, it indicates, the **operation** to be performed on $+3$.

Similarly, in the problem $7 - 3$, the minus sign can either be looked on as indicating the number -3, in which case the problem tells us to perform the **operation of addition** of -3 to 7 $[7 + (-3)]$, or it may be taken to mean the **operation of subtraction** of $+3$ from 7 $[7 - (+3)]$.

Thus, plus and minus signs, as well as being marks distinguishing numbers of opposite kinds, may also be considered as marks representing the **operations** of addition and subtraction.

341. Imaginary Numbers.—Even in quite elementary problems it is found that the answer cannot always be expressed as a real number. Consider the square root of a negative number, e.g., $\sqrt{-4}$. No real number can be found such that when it is multiplied by itself, the answer is -4. Suppose we proceed as far as possible in the solution :—

$$\sqrt{-4} = \sqrt{4 \times -1} = \sqrt{4} \times \sqrt{-1} = \pm 2\sqrt{-1}$$

since $\sqrt{4}$ is ± 2.

The problem of giving a meaning to the square root of any negative number thus reduces to that of finding a meaning for $\sqrt{-1}$. For convenience, $\sqrt{-1}$ is usually written as j.

Thus $\sqrt{-4} = \pm 2j$.

A number such as $2j$ is called an **imaginary** number. In other words, an imaginary number is any real multiple, positive or negative, of j. The name " imaginary number " should be looked on as a technical mathematical term, in the same way as is " real number." As regards their mathematical behaviour, it can be easily shown that all the ordinary mathematical operations such as addition, multiplication, etc., may be performed in exactly the same way for both real and imaginary numbers. The proof of this cannot be given here, but may be found in any textbook on Algebra.

Since $j = \sqrt{-1}$, it follows that $j^2 = -1$.

Similarly, $j^3 = j^2 \times j = -1 \times j = -j$,

$$j^4 = j^2 \times j^2 = -1 \times -1 = +1,$$

$$\frac{1}{j} = \frac{j}{j^2} = \frac{j}{-1} = -j, \text{ and so on.}$$

342. Complex Numbers.—These are numbers which contain both a real and an imaginary part, *e.g.*, $2 + 3j$, $5 - 4j$, etc.

Any complex number may thus be taken to be of the form $a + bj$, where a and b are real numbers.

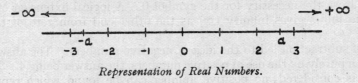

Representation of Real Numbers.

Fig. 154.

343. Graphical Representation of Numbers.—All real numbers may be represented as points on an infinitely long straight line, as indicated in Fig. 154. Zero is fixed at some point 0 in the line and the other real numbers filled in on any convenient scale. The line extends an infinite distance in both directions from the zero point, positive numbers being represented by points to the right of 0, negative numbers by points to the left of 0. It can further be shown that every point on the line corresponds to a real number. If we could magnify the line indefinitely after every real number had been given a place on it, no gaps between its points could be observed. It follows, therefore, that there is no possibility of representing the imaginary numbers on this line.

In obtaining a graphical representation for imaginary numbers, we turn to the interpretation of j as an **operator**. In deriving an imaginary number from a real number, the real number is multiplied by j.

Consider the simplest real number, unity.

$$1 \times j \times j = 1 \times j^2 = 1 \times -1 = -1.$$

The performance of the operation j twice over, (j^2), on $+1$ converts it into -1. Reference to the line representing the real numbers shows that we may arrive at the point -1, from the point $+1$, by turning the line 01 through 180°. This turning movement may be performed clockwise or counter-clockwise. We may thus interpret the operation of multiplying $+1$ by j^2 as equivalent to turning the line 01 through 180°. Multiplying by j^2 is the same as multiplying by j twice in succession. Thus multiplication by j may be interpreted as the operation which, performed twice in succession, gives a rotation of 180°. It follows that multiplication by j may be given the meaning of a rotation through $\frac{180°}{2} = 90°$.

Just as a positive number has two real square roots, *e.g.*, $\sqrt{4} = \pm 2$, so we saw that the operation $\sqrt{-4}$ gave formally two roots $+2j$ and $-2j$. The fact that the operation of turning through 180° above may be accomplished either in a clockwise or counter-clockwise direction enables us to give a meaning to this formal result. Thus, $\sqrt{-4}$ may be represented by turning the line 02 through 90° either counter-clockwise or clockwise. **Counter-clockwise rotation through 90° is taken as the operation of multiplying a number by $+j$: clockwise rotation through 90° as the operation of multiplying a number by $-j$.**

As $\frac{1}{j} = -j$, the operation of dividing by j may also be interpreted as a clockwise rotation through 90°, and so appears as the reverse of multiplying by j, as we should expect.

Imaginary numbers may thus be represented graphically by drawing a line through the point 0 at right angles to the line representing the real numbers. All real multiples of j are represented by points on this line, which extends an infinite distance in both directions. The graphical representation of real and imaginary numbers thus assumes the form of two axes at right angles as shown in Fig. 155 (*a*). It is called the **Argand Diagram.**

A complex number may be represented on the Argand Diagram by a combination of the operations which give the representation of real and imaginary numbers. Consider, for example, the number $2 + 3j$. The operations to be performed are :—

    (1) To traverse a distance of 2 units to the right of 0 along the axis of real numbers. This brings us to the point 2.

    (2) Having arrived at point 2, to turn through 90° counter-clockwise and traverse three units in this new direction. We thus arrive at a point (A) in the plane of the diagram which represents the number $2 + 3j$.

The complex number $2 + 3j$ may be considered to be represented either by the point A or by the line 0A, just as 2 is represented by the point 2 or the line 02.

It will be seen that to specify OA completely, not only its **length** must be given, but also its **direction** with respect to one of the axes.

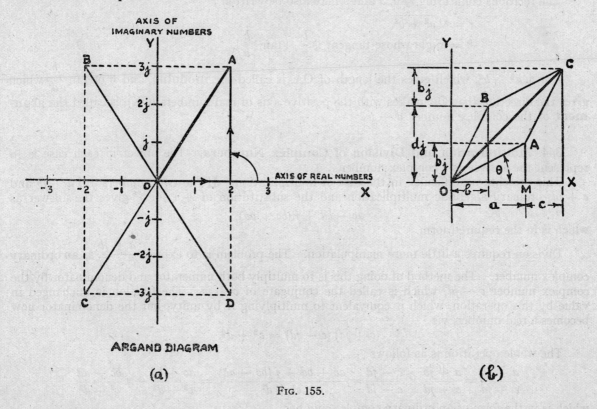

ARGAND DIAGRAM

(a)   (b)

FIG. 155.

The line OB, for instance, has the same length as OA, but has a different direction. It represents the number $-2 + 3j$. Similarly OC represents $-2 - 3j$ and OD represents $2 - 3j$.

The representation of complex numbers is thus a **vectorial representation. Complex numbers are equivalent to vectors on the Argand Diagram.** It is this result which furnishes their utility in alternating current problems.

The vector addition law, *i.e.*, the parallelogram law, can easily be seen to apply to complex numbers. We may represent two complex numbers by $a + jb$ and $c + jd$, where a, b, c and d are real numbers.

Addition by the ordinary rules of algebra gives their sum as

$$a + jb + c + jd = (a + c) + j (b + d),$$

i.e., their sum is another complex number.

$a + jb$ is represented by OA in Fig. 155 (*b*), and $c + jd$ by OB. The parallelogram OACB is completed. It is easily seen from the figure that OC, the diagonal of the parallelogram, represents the number $(a + c) + j (b + d)$.

The complex number $a + jb$ may also be expressed in a form which shows more obviously its vectorial nature.

Let the length of OA in Fig. 155 (*b*) be taken as *r* and the angle XOA, which it makes with the axis of real numbers, as θ.

Then in triangle OAM,

$$a = r \cos θ,$$
$$b = r \sin θ.$$

(The length of AM is obviously *b* units ; it is written *bj* merely to indicate its direction on the Argand Diagram.)

It follows that $a + jb = r \cos θ + jr \sin θ = r (\cos θ + j \sin θ)$.

The relations connecting *r*, θ, *a* and *b* may also be written

$$r = \sqrt{a^2 + b^2}.$$

$$θ = \text{angle whose tangent is } \frac{b}{a}, \; \left(\tan^{-1} \frac{b}{a}\right).$$

r or $\sqrt{a^2 + b^2}$, which gives the length of OA, is called the **modulus,** and θ or $\tan^{-1} \dfrac{b}{a}$, which gives the direction that OA makes with the positive axis of real numbers (OX), is called the **argument** of the complex number $a + jb$.

344. Multiplication and Division of Complex Numbers.—The object in each case is to represent the answer as a complex number.

This presents no difficulty in the case of multiplication. If the two numbers are $a + jb$ and $c + jd$, ordinary algebraic multiplication and the substitution of $- 1$ for j^2 gives the answer as

$$ac - bd + j (bc + ad),$$

which is in the required form.

Division requires a little more manipulation. The problem is to express $\dfrac{a + jb}{c + jd}$ as an ordinary complex number. The method of doing this is to multiply both numerator and denominator by the complex number $c - jd$, which is called the conjugate of $c + jd$. The fraction is unchanged in value by this operation, which is equivalent to multiplying it by unity, but the denominator now becomes a real number, viz.,

$$(c + jd) (c - jd) = c^2 + d^2.$$

The whole operation is as follows :—

$$\frac{a + jb}{c + jd} = \frac{a + jb}{c + jd} \times \frac{c - jd}{c - jd} = \frac{ac + bd + j (bc - ad)}{c^2 + d^2} = \frac{ac + bd}{c^2 + d^2} + j \frac{bc - ad}{c^2 + d^2}$$

which is in the form of an ordinary complex number.

The method rather than the results of these operations should be noted.

Example 48.

Express $\dfrac{1 + 2j}{2 + 3j}$ in the form $a + jb$

$$\frac{1 + 2j}{2 + 3j} = \frac{(1 + 2j)\,(2 - 3j)}{(2 + 3)j\,(2 - 3j)} = \frac{2 - 6j^2 + 4j - 3j}{4 - 9j^2} = \frac{8 + j}{13} = \frac{8}{13} + \frac{1}{13}j.$$

345. The significance of these operations is better realised if the two complex numbers are taken as

$$r (\cos \theta + j \sin \theta) \text{ and } r' (\cos \theta' + j \sin \theta').$$

Their product is

$$rr' (\cos \theta + j \sin \theta)(\cos \theta' + j \sin \theta')$$
$$= rr' [(\cos \theta \cos \theta' - \sin \theta \sin \theta') + j (\sin \theta \cos \theta' + \cos \theta \sin \theta')]$$
$$= rr' [\cos (\theta + \theta') + j \sin (\theta + \theta')].$$

In words, the **modulus** of the product of two complex numbers is the **product** of their moduli, and the **argument** of their product is the **sum** of their arguments.

The quotient is

$$\frac{r (\cos \theta + j \sin \theta)}{r' (\cos \theta' + j \sin \theta')} = \frac{r (\cos \theta + j \sin \theta)(\cos \theta' - j \sin \theta')}{r' (\cos \theta' + j \sin \theta')(\cos \theta' - j \sin \theta')}$$

$$= \frac{r (\cos \theta \cos \theta' + \sin \theta \sin \theta') + j (\sin \theta \cos \theta' - \cos \theta \sin \theta')}{r' (\cos^2 \theta' + \sin^2 \theta')}$$

$$= \frac{r}{r'} [\cos (\theta - \theta') + j \sin (\theta - \theta')].$$

In words, the **modulus** of the quotient of two complex numbers is the **quotient** of their moduli, and the **argument** of the quotient is the **difference** of their arguments.

These results correspond to the ordinary rules for vector multiplication and division.

346. Application to A.C. Problems.—The vector representation of alternating quantities has already been fully considered, and as complex numbers are equivalent to vectors they may also be used to exhibit the relations in amplitude (or R.M.S. value) and phase of alternating quantities. The method will be seen most easily by considering some simple examples.

(1) In a purely resistive circuit, the current I and E.M.F. E are in phase and connected by the relation $E = RI$.

The vector diagram in this case consists of two lines of the magnitude of E and I in the same direction. On the Argand Diagram they are thus most simply represented by two distances along the positive axis of real numbers.

(2) In a purely inductive circuit, the applied E.M.F. leads the current by 90° and their relative magnitudes are given by $E = \omega L I$.

Thus, if I is represented by a distance from O along the positive real axis, E is represented by a distance from O **along the positive imaginary axis** of magnitude $\omega L I$.

E is thus fully described with respect to I by the equation $E = j \omega L I$.

(3) In a purely capacitive circuit, $E = \dfrac{I}{\omega C}$ and lags on I by 90°. Under the same conditions as in (2) above, it may therefore be fully represented by

$$E = \frac{-jI}{\omega C} \text{ or since } -j = \frac{1}{j}, \text{ by } E = \frac{I}{j \omega C.}$$

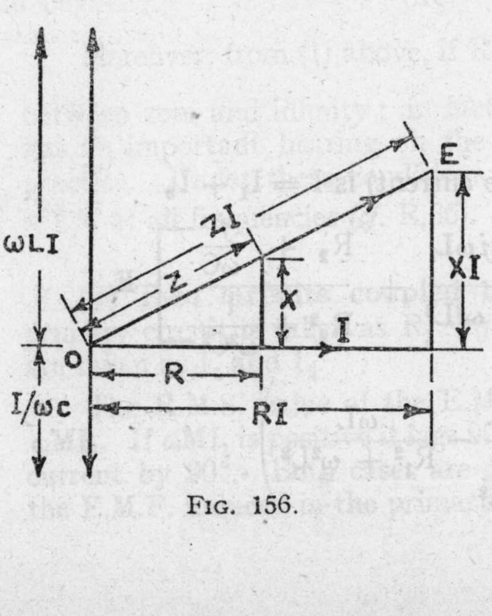

If we now consider any alternating current circuit, the relation between the magnitude of the current and the applied E.M.F. is given by $E = ZI = (\sqrt{R^2 + X^2})\, I$, and, if we take X to be inductive, E leads I by an angle ϕ whose tangent is $\dfrac{X}{R}$, $(\phi = \tan^{-1} \dfrac{X}{R})$.

Now the complex number $R + jX$ is such that its length on the Argand Diagram (modulus), is $\sqrt{R^2 + X^2}$,

FIG. 156.

Kirchhoff's Law applied to the two circuits then gives :—

(a) Primary $(R_1 + jX_1) I_1 = E - j\omega M I_2$

(b) Secondary $(R_2 + jX_2) I_2 = -j\omega M I_1$

$$\text{Hence } I_2 = \frac{-j\omega M I_1}{R_2 + jX_2}$$

Substituting this in the primary circuit equation gives

$$(R_1 + jX_1) I_1 = E + \frac{j^2 \omega^2 M^2 I_1}{R_2 + jX_2}$$

$$\therefore \quad E = \left[R_1 + jX_1 + \frac{\omega^2 M^2}{R_2 + jX_2} \right] I_1 \quad \dots \dots \dots \dots \dots (1).$$

The equivalent impedance of the two circuits is thus given by

$$Z = \frac{E}{I_1} = R_1 + jX_1 + \frac{\omega^2 M^2}{R_2 + jX_2} = R_1 + jX_1 + \frac{\omega^2 M^2 (R_2 - jX_2)}{R_2^2 + X_2^2}$$

$$= R_1 + \frac{\omega^2 M^2 R_2}{R_2^2 + X_2^2} + j\left(X_1 - \frac{\omega^2 M^2 X_2}{R_2^2 + X_2^2} \right).$$

The equivalent resistance is thus $R = R_1 + \dfrac{\omega^2 M^2 R_2}{R_2^2 + X_2^2}$, and the equivalent reactance is

$$X = X_1 - \frac{\omega^2 M^2 X_2}{R_2^2 + X_2^2}.$$

These results should be compared with those derived in paragraph 334.

It should be noted that this piece of work applies generally to all **transformer couplings.** In certain cases it may be simplified.

From line (1) above, the transformer coupling and secondary circuit acts like an equivalent impedance Z_e, where $E = [R_1 + Z_e] I_1$ and

$$Z_e = jX_1 + \frac{\omega^2 M^2}{R_2 + jX_2}.$$

Simplifying this to the case where $C_1 = C_2 = 0$, where L_1 and L_2 are both comprised within the transformer windings, and using $K = M/\sqrt{L_1 L_2}$, we have

$$Z_e = j\omega L_1 + \frac{\omega^2 K^2 L_1 L_2}{R_2 + j\omega L_2} = \frac{j\omega L_1 R_2 + \omega^2 L_1 L_2 (K^2 - 1)}{R_2 + j\omega L_2}.$$

Now the closer the coupling the smaller the factor $(K^2 - 1)$, and for a well designed **iron-cored transformer** we may assume no flux leakage and put $K = 1$.   Then

$$Z_e = \frac{j\omega L_1 R_2}{R_2 + j\omega L_2} \quad \dots \dots \dots \text{and using } \frac{L_1}{L_2} = \frac{1}{T^2}$$

(where T is the transformer ratio)

$$= \frac{j\omega L_1 R_2}{R_2 + j\omega L_1 T^2} = \frac{j\omega L_1 \left(\dfrac{R_2}{T^2} \right)}{j\omega L_1 + \dfrac{R_2}{T^2}} \quad \dots \dots \dots \dots \dots \dots (2)$$

Now (2) represents the effective impedance of a circuit consisting of the primary inductance L_1 in parallel with a resistance of value R_2/T^2, the "reflected secondary load."

Under these conditions, the simple **equivalent circuit** consists of the source of E.M.F. in series with R_1 and the above parallel circuit, as shown in Fig. 157.   This result should be compared with that of paragraph 369, and the application to a valve equivalent circuit in "F." 19 (f).

The primary of an ideal iron-cored transformer should have infinite reactance and take zero "magnetising current" when there is no secondary load (paragraph 351).   Infinite inductive reactance involves an *infinite* value of L_1, which in the small A/F transformers used in W/T circuit amounts, in practice, to 30 or 40 henries. When ωL_1, with no load on the transformer, is big in comparison with R_2/T^2, formula (2) simplifies to $Z_e = R_2/T^2$, the case of the ideally perfect transformer on load.

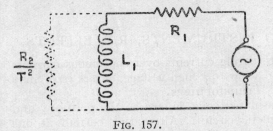

FIG. 157.

When the secondary is on " no-load," the value of R_2/T^2 is infinitely big, and formula (2) simplifies to $Z_e = j\omega L_1$.

The above two results are obvious when it is realised that either arm of the parallel circuit of Fig. 157 may be made infinite in value.

When the secondary load is an impedance, such as a telephone receiver or loud speaker, it acts as a series combination of R_2/T^2 and an equivalent reactance, in parallel across L_1. (*Cf.* paragraph 369.)

(c) **R, L and C in series.**

$$V = IZ = I(R + jX) = I\left[R + j\left(\omega L - \frac{1}{\omega C}\right)\right]$$

and the modulus is

$$|V| = I\sqrt{R^2 + \left(\omega L - \frac{1}{\omega C}\right)^2}$$

(d) **R and L in parallel ; impedances in parallel.**—By Kirchhoff's Law, the vector sum of the currents in each arm is equal to the supply current (*cf.* paragraph 307).

$$\therefore \quad I = I_1 + I_2 \quad \dots\dots\dots\dots\dots\dots \text{vectorially}$$

$$\therefore \quad \frac{V}{Z} = \frac{V}{Z_1} + \frac{V}{Z_2} \quad \dots\dots\dots\dots \begin{array}{l}\text{where } Z = R + jX \\ \text{where } Z_1 = R + jX_1, \text{ etc.}\end{array}$$

$$\text{or} \quad \frac{1}{Z} = \frac{1}{Z_1} + \frac{1}{Z_2} \quad \dots\dots\dots\dots\dots\dots \text{vectorially.}$$

The above formula may be extended to cover any number of circuits in parallel, and operates in a manner similar to that of resistances in parallel ; it **is of the greatest use in A.C. work.** In this case—

$$\frac{1}{Z} = \frac{1}{j\omega L} + \frac{1}{R} = \frac{R + j\omega L}{jR\omega L}$$

$$= \frac{\omega L - jR}{\omega LR}$$

$$\therefore \quad |Z| = \frac{\omega LR}{\sqrt{R^2 + \omega^2 L^2}}$$

A numerical example is seen in " F." 19 (*f*).

(e) **Impedances in series.**—Impedances may be split into resistive and reactive components, either by "*j*" methods or trigonometrically as in paragraph 316 ; in that case they may be added and, vectorially, we have

$$Z = Z_1 + Z_2 + \text{etc.}$$

where $Z = R + jX$, $Z_1 = R_1 + jX_1$, etc.

CHAPTER VI.

———

THE POWER TRANSFORMER, MEASURING INSTRUMENTS, R/F EFFECTS.

349. One of the most important advantages of alternating currents over continuous currents is the extreme ease with which the transformation from a low to a high voltage, or *vice versa*, may be accomplished. This process is effected by means of **Transformers.**

A power transformer consists essentially of two insulated coils, known as the **primary** and **secondary** windings, wound over a closed iron magnetic circuit. Alternating current at one voltage is supplied to the primary; from the secondary an alternating current is taken at a higher or lower voltage than that supplied to the primary. If the voltage is increased, the transformer is said to " step-up " the voltage; if decreased, the transformer is said to " step-down " the voltage.

Both types are used in wireless work; step-up transformers, for instance, to give voltages suitable for applying to the anode of a thermionic valve; step-down transformers, to give voltages suitable for the filament supply. It will be shown that this power conversion is effected with high efficiency.

350. **Construction of Typical Transformer.**—Two **iron cores** made of thin sheets of laminations of iron, averaging about 0·012-inch thick, are built up, each sheet being slightly japanned or oxidised. The ends of the iron cores are connected by two iron yokes constructed in the same manner.

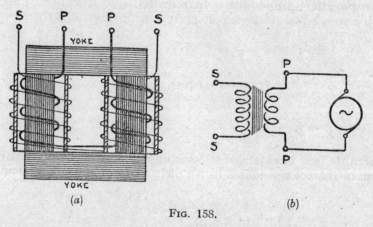

Fig. 158.

On each core is wound a coil of insulated copper wire, called the **Primary**; these two coils are connected in series, as illustrated in Fig. 158 (*a*).

The primary windings are covered with insulating sleeves, made of good insulating material—micanite, mica, or presspahn.

Over these again are wound the **Secondary** Coils, which have more turns than the Primary if the alternating voltage is to be increased.

The two secondary windings are joined in series, and their ends are brought to two terminals heavily insulated with ebonite or porcelain.

351. **Primary E.M.F.**—If an alternator is connected up to the primary terminals, and the secondary terminals are left disconnected or on " open circuit," as illustrated diagrammatically in Fig. 158 (*b*), then an alternating current will pass through the primary winding, and an alternating flux will be set up in the core.

Since the primary winding has a great many turns, and the magnetic path for the lines of force is a very good one, the inductance of the primary with the secondary on open circuit will have a very large value, of the order of several henries.

The applied voltage of the alternator has to perform two functions :—

(1) Cause the current to flow through the resistance of the primary winding.

(2) Balance the induced E.M.F. in the primary winding due to its self inductance.

It was seen in the preceding chapter that, in any circuit comprising inductance and resistance only,

$$I = \frac{V}{\sqrt{R^2 + (\omega L)^2}} \; ;$$

this formula applies here, where I is the magnetising current flowing from the alternator through the primary, V the voltage of the alternator, L the inductance, and R the resistance of the primary winding.

The inductance of the primary is, however, so great compared with its resistance that the latter may be neglected. Let L_1 denote the inductance of the primary winding, L_2 the inductance of the secondary winding, and I_m the magnetising current. The current I_m is then equal to $\frac{V}{\omega L_1}$, and the alternator voltage V is exactly balanced by the induced E.M.F. of the primary, *i.e.* $V = \omega L_1 I_m$ volts.

I_m, the magnetising current, will be lagging by 90° on the alternator E.M.F.

Hence, neglecting losses, these facts are expressed in the following vector diagram, Fig. 159.

The magnetising current will be an exceedingly small one, since the impedance of the transformer is so great.

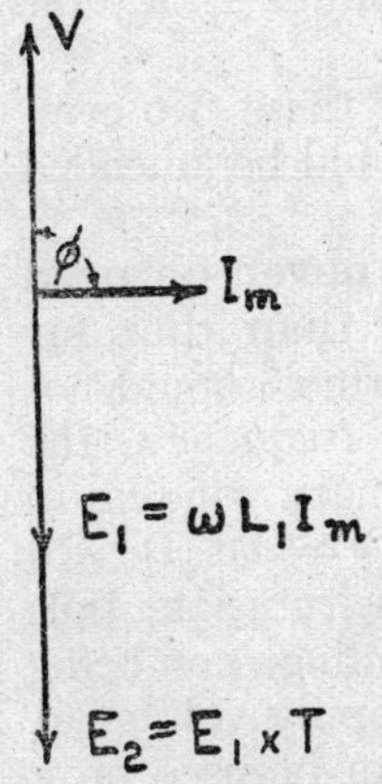

352. Secondary E.M.F. Secondary on open circuit.—In a well-designed transformer, practically all the flux ϕ due to the current flowing through the primary will cut every turn of the secondary winding also, as it expands and collapses round the primary winding.

From this it follows that the E.M.F. induced in *each turn* of the secondary is equal to that induced in each turn of the primary, since the flux through each changes at the same rate $\frac{d\phi}{dt}$; hence, the ratio of the total primary to the total secondary E.M.F. is equal to the **ratio of the number of primary turns to the number of secondary turns.** Thus

$$\frac{\text{Primary E.M.F.}}{\text{Secondary E.M.F.}} = \frac{\text{Primary Turns}}{\text{Secondary Turns}} = \frac{N_1}{N_2}$$

$$\text{or } \frac{E_1}{E_2} = \frac{N_1 \frac{d\phi}{dt}}{N_2 \frac{d\phi}{dt}} = \frac{N_1}{N_2} = \frac{1}{T}$$

FIG. 159.

The ratio of Secondary to Primary Turns is spoken of as the **Transformation Ratio,** and is denoted by the letter T.

If the transformation ratio is greater than 1, the transformer is a " step-up " one ; if less than 1, the transformer is a " step-down " one.

Since the secondary voltage of the transformer is the **induced** E.M.F. due to the alternating flux associated with the primary current I_m, the secondary voltage ($E_2 = E_1 \times T$) is in phase with the induced E.M.F. in the primary, and hence is 180° out of phase with the voltage applied to the transformer by the alternator, as shown in Fig. 159.

As an example, let us take a transformer with 100 primary turns, supplied by an alternator giving an alternating supply of 100 volts.

Leave the secondary on open circuit. Then the counter E.M.F. produced in the primary coil will be nearly as much as 100 volts—for the small magnetising current required to give this E.M.F. across the large primary inductance gives a negligible voltage drop across the primary resistance. Since the primary winding consists of 100 turns, the counter E.M.F. in each turn will be nearly 1 volt.

Again, each turn of the secondary winding will have the same voltage induced in it as each turn of the primary winding, for both are interlinked with the same magnetic flux. The voltage produced in any turn of the secondary winding will, therefore, be practically 1 volt.

If, for example, the secondary winding consists of 10 turns its voltage will be about 10 volts, if of 100 turns its voltage will be about 100 volts, if of 1,000 turns its voltage will be about 1,000 volts, etc.

353. Total Primary No-load Current, I_0.

—In the first vector diagram, Fig. 159, we assumed the current in the primary to be lagging exactly 90° behind the applied voltage. If losses, however, are considered, the primary current will lag by some angle less than 90°, and the current may be resolved into two components, one lagging by 90° on, and the other in phase with, the applied voltage. The component in phase with the applied voltage is necessary to account for the **power lost,** partly in the primary resistance, but mainly in hysteresis and eddy current losses in the core (these will be referred to more fully later).

This component may be termed the **iron-loss current,** and denoted by the symbol I_i.

The component which lags by 90° on the applied voltage is I_m, the magnetising current.

The total primary no-load current I_0 is the resultant of these two components, and hence the vector diagram given in Fig. 159 should be amended as in Fig. 160.

It must be pointed out that **a transformer should never be used with the same supply voltage at a frequency lower than that for which it was designed,** e.g., a 100-volt, 500-cycle transformer should not be used on a 100-volt, 50-cycle supply. The lower the frequency, the greater must be the magnetising current flowing in the primary winding to make the induced E.M.F. equal to the applied E.M.F. (since $V = \omega L_1 I$). In addition, this larger current will bring the core nearer to saturation, thus decreasing the effective value of L_1, and a still larger current will flow. The winding, not being designed to carry such large currents, will be burnt out immediately. The same supply voltage at a higher frequency can, however, be used, e.g., a 100-volt 50-cycle transformer can be used on a 100-volt 500-cycle supply, for in this case the current will be reduced.

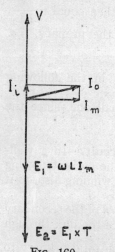

FIG. 160.

354. Effect of Load Applied to Secondary.

—So far the secondary has been taken to be on open circuit, i.e., no current has been flowing in it. Closing the secondary by an external circuit allows the secondary E.M.F. to give rise to a secondary current. This secondary current I_2 will set up an alternating magnetic flux proportional to itself and to the number of turns through which it flows, i.e., proportional to the secondary ampere-turns.

By Lenz's Law this secondary flux is in opposition to the cause which produces it, and hence in opposition to the primary flux already existing in the core. Thus part of the primary flux is cancelled, and the flux-linkage with the primary winding for a given primary current is decreased.

This is equivalent to saying that the primary inductance is decreased, and in consequence an increased current will flow through the primary to restore the state of equilibrium present under no-load conditions ; in other words, to restore the original value of the primary flux, and the approximate equality of applied voltage and counter E.M.F. of self-induction in the primary.

This additional current flowing through the primary must set up a flux, therefore, exactly equal and opposite to the demagnetising effect produced by the secondary ampere-turns ; hence the primary ampere-turns due to the additional primary current must be equal to the secondary ampere-turns, or $N_1 I_1 = N_2 I_2$.

This additional primary current is known as the **load** component of total primary current, and from the equality of ampere-turns just stated,

$$\frac{\text{Primary load current}}{\text{Secondary current}} = \frac{\text{secondary turns}}{\text{primary turns}} = T.$$

If we call the load component of primary current I_1, then

$$I_1 = I_2 \times T.$$

The total current flowing in the primary with the secondary on load is, therefore, the *vector sum* of the original no-load current and the additional, or load, current.

The greater the load on the secondary, the greater will be the primary load current, since $I_1 = I_2 \times T$. Therefore, with a very large current being taken from the secondary, the load current in the primary will be so much greater than the no-load current that it may be regarded as equal to the total primary current I_p. In this case, if we neglect the no-load current,

$$I_p = I_2 \times T.$$

Also, neglecting losses,

$$E_2 = E_1 \times T = V \times T.$$
$$\therefore I_p \times E_1 = E_2 \times I_2.$$

Therefore the energy input equals the energy output, and the device is 100 per cent. efficient.

This is to be expected, since losses have been neglected. In the practical case there are various losses which result in the transformer being less than 100 per cent. efficient. The complete theory can best be explained by the use of vector diagrams, and in the following paragraphs the vector diagrams will be drawn for purely resistive, inductive and capacitive loads, and also for the more practical case of a circuit possessing both resistance and reactance.

In drawing vector diagrams for voltage step-down transformers it is usual, in order to keep both sides of the diagram approximately the same size, to draw the voltages on the secondary side to a scale T times that of the voltage on the primary side, and the currents on the primary side to a scale T times that on the secondary side. For the same reason the scales are adjusted in exactly the opposite manner in the vector diagrams for voltage step-up transformers. This convention is employed in the vector diagrams in this chapter.

355. Purely Resistive Load.

Fig. 161 shows the vector diagram for a purely resistive load.

Neglecting the resistance and the leakage reactance of the two windings, the magnetising current I_m lags 90° on the applied voltage V. The flux Φ is in phase with the magnetising current. The total primary no-load current is given by I_o, the resultant of I_m and I_t, the iron-loss current.

The alternating flux Φ cutting the secondary winding sets up the alternating voltage E_2 across the terminals of the secondary, E_2 being equal to $E_1 \times T$, or $V \times T$.

The **secondary current I_2 is in phase with E_2, because the load is a pure resistance,** and is equal to $\dfrac{E_2}{R_2}$.

This current I_2 has a demagnetising effect on the core, and since E_1 **must remain equal to V** whether the transformer is on load or not, and E_1 depends on the value of the flux, **a primary load current I_1 must flow in antiphase to I_2 and of such magnitude that the ampere-turns due to it exactly balance the secondary ampere-turns.** Hence $I_1 = I_2 \times T$, and with our convention as regards scale it is shown as being the same length as the vector representing I_2.

The total alternator current, I_p, is the resultant of I_o and I_1, lagging on the applied voltage by an angle ϕ_p. The greater the secondary current I_2, the greater is I_1, and the more nearly are the primary current I_p and the primary voltage V in phase.

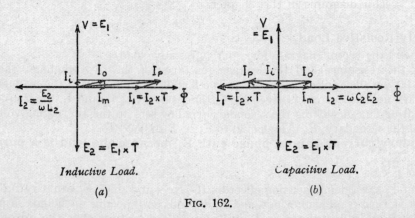

In other words, the greater the load on the secondary the nearer to unity is the power factor in the primary circuit, while the secondary power factor is exactly unity. The transformer on full-load behaves as if almost non-inductive, voltages and currents on both sides being practically in phase.

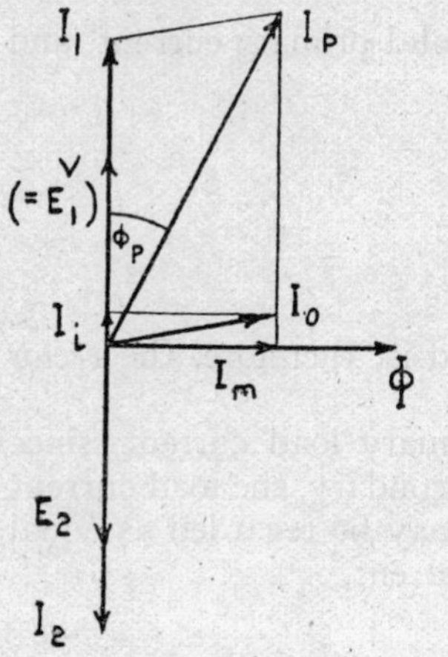

The essential anti-phase relationship between the primary current I_p and the secondary current I_2 may be demonstrated by a classical and most elegant experiment. It requires a long cylindrical open cored transformer, conveniently made by making a primary winding round a bundle of iron wires about 6 in. in length, and about 1 in. in diameter. The secondary circuit consists of a single turn of stout copper wire closed by a soldered joint, having a diameter slightly bigger than that of the cylindrical primary, so that it may fit easily over the latter. When the primary is connected to a suitable source of alternating E.M.F., the large anti-phase current flowing in the secondary turn gives rise to repulsion phenomena. If the primary coil is supported with its axis vertical, the mutual repulsion effects between the anti-phase current bearing conductors may be used to poise the secondary ring delicately in mid air ; if the ring is initially supported at any point above the mid point of the primary coil, an increase in the primary current will cause the secondary ring to be repelled still more strongly and ascend further up the primary.

FIG. 161.

356. Purely Inductive and Purely Capacitive Loads.—The corresponding vector diagrams for purely inductive and purely capacitive secondary loads are shown in Fig. 162 (a) and (b).

In the case of the inductive load the resistance R_2 of last paragraph is replaced by an inductance L_2. The secondary current I_2, therefore, lags 90° on the secondary voltage E_2, and is equal to $\dfrac{E_2}{\omega L_2}$.

To keep the value of flux the same as under no-load conditions, and maintain the equivalence of V and E_1, the alternator will have to supply a current I_1 in antiphase to I_2 and equal to $I_2 \times T$. I_1, with our scale convention, is shown equal in length to I_2. The total primary current I_p, is, as before, the vector sum of I_o and I_1.

Inductive Load.

(a)

Capacitive Load.

(b)

FIG. 162.

The secondary current lags by 90° on the secondary voltage, and the primary current I_p lags by nearly 90° on the applied voltage. The greater the load, the greater is I_1, and the more nearly does the angle of lag of the primary current I_p approach 90°.

The capacitive case is simply the reverse of the inductive case, and the diagram need not be explained.

357. General Case. Secondary Load both Resistive and Reactive.—The reactance in the secondary circuit will be taken to be inductive, so that the secondary current I_2 lags on the secondary voltage E_2 by an angle ϕ_2, whose cosine is the power factor of the secondary circuit.

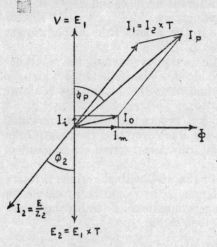

Fig. 163.

As before, the demagnetising effect of this secondary current must be counterbalanced by a current I_1 in the primary circuit, in antiphase to it and equal to $I_2 \times T$.

The total primary current is, as before, given by the resultant of I_o and I_1, and is I_p in the figure.

It will be seen from the figure that the angle of lag of the primary current I_p on the applied voltage, the angle ϕ_p, is greater than the angle of lag ϕ_2 of the secondary current on the secondary voltage, provided the secondary circuit is not so highly inductive that ϕ_2 exceeds the angle of lag of the primary no-load current I_o.

Also, as before, the greater the load on the secondary and in consequence the greater I_1, the more nearly equal do the angles of lag, ϕ_p and ϕ_2, become.

If a leading current were taken from the secondary, the angle of lead ϕ_p of the primary current would be slightly less than the angle of lead of the secondary current.

358. Transformer Losses.—The losses in a transformer may be considered under the following headings :—

(a) Magnetic Leakage, (b) Copper Losses, (c) Eddy Current Losses, (d) Hysteresis Losses. The last two are losses which occur in the iron core, and, in the simple vector diagrams already given, they have been allowed for by introducing the current I_i (iron-loss current) as a component of the total primary no-load current. These losses will be explained more fully in paragraphs 363 and 364.

The first two types of loss will now be considered, and a complete vector diagram drawn allowing for their effect.

359. Magnetic Leakage.—It is very nearly, but not quite, true that the whole of the magnetic flux passes through the iron core of the transformer and links with all the turns on both windings.

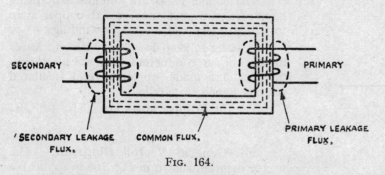

Fig. 164.

Some of the lines of flux produced by the primary current, instead of passing round the main iron magnetic circuit, will take shorter paths as illustrated in the figure above, mainly through air. Since they do not cut the secondary winding, they serve no useful pupose as regards generation of secondary voltage, and are known as the **primary leakage flux.**

Similarly, the current flowing in the secondary will produce some lines of flux which do not link with the primary. These constitute the **secondary leakage flux.**

The leakage flux from each winding is produced by the current in that particular winding, and is unaffected by the current in the other winding. This leakage flux is therefore in both cases in phase with, and proportional in amount to, the current in the particular winding which is producing it. Thus, both leakage fluxes increase with load, while the common flux remains practically constant.

The effect of the primary leakage flux is to add a certain amount of reactance to the primary winding, which uses up part of the primary applied voltage. Less of the applied voltage, therefore, has to be balanced by the counter E.M.F. due to the common alternating flux, and hence there is less common flux and less secondary voltage induced. The inductance " L " in series with the primary circuit which would give the same reactance as that due to the leakage field in the primary winding is known as the **primary leakage inductance**. ($N\phi = LI$.)

In the secondary circuit, some of the secondary voltage will be used in overcoming the reactance due to the leakage flux, so that the terminal voltage will be reduced. The inductance which, in series with the secondary circuit, would give the same effect is known as the **secondary leakage inductance.**

The effect of magnetic leakage upon the transformation ratio is to reduce the secondary terminal voltage for a given primary applied voltage. It is to diminish this voltage drop that the transformer coils are wound one upon the other, as previously described. By this construction the amount of leakage flux is reduced to a minimum.

If the coils are arranged in any other way, as, for instance, in Fig. 164, with the whole primary on one leg of the core and the secondary on the other, much larger paths would be available for the leakage flux and the falling-off of the secondary terminal voltage would be considerably increased.

A vector representation of the effect of magnetic leakage is given in Fig. 165.

360. Copper Losses.—The resistance of the primary and secondary windings must be taken into consideration. When the secondary is on open circuit, the primary no-load current I_0 is very small, and the voltage drop due to this current flowing through the resistance of the primary is negligible.

With the secondary on closed circuit, however, a very much larger current I_p flows in the primary and a considerable current I_2 in the secondary, and the losses due to these currents must be taken into account. The primary ohmic drop reduces the proportion of the applied voltage balanced by the counter E.M.F. due to the flux; the consequent decrease in flux decreases the secondary voltage.

In addition, there is an $I_2 R_2$ voltage drop in the secondary circuit, so that the secondary **terminal voltage** is further decreased below the value obtained by assuming the windings to have no resistance.

A vector diagram to illustrate this is given in Fig. 165.

The copper losses are minimised by using large section copper wire or flat copper strip for the primary and secondary windings.

In order to keep down eddy current losses in the copper conductors they are often subdivided and made up of several insulated strands joined in parallel.

The total copper losses are $I_p^2 R_1 + I_2^2 R_2$ watts.

361. General Vector Diagram.—The vector diagram shown in Fig. 165 is applicable to the general case of a secondary load, in which the current lags behind the voltage (cf. Fig. 163, paragraph 357), taking into account the resistances of the windings, and the reactances equivalent in effect to the magnetic leakage.

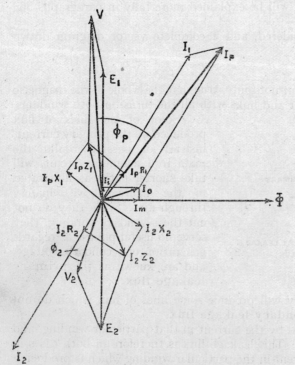

FIG. 165.

Superimposed on Fig. 163, paragraph 357, we have on the primary side the voltages $I_p R_1$ and $I_p X_1$, giving a resultant $I_p Z_1$.

These are respectively the resistance drop and the leakage reactance drop in the primary circuit, and hence the **primary applied voltage is given by V**, the resultant of E_1 and $I_p Z_1$. Actually this shows that E_1, the residual part of the primary applied voltage that is balanced by the counter E.M.F. of the flux, is less than V.

On the secondary side the resistance and leakage reactance drops combine to give $I_2 Z_2$, and hence V_2, **the secondary terminal voltage**, is less than the secondary induced voltage E_2, being given by the vector difference of E_2 and $I_2 Z_2$.

It is obvious from the diagram, that as the load is increased, both I_1 and I_2 increase, and **for a given applied voltage V**, which is the condition under which the transformer works, **V_2 falls for an increase of load.**

It has been convenient to use the diagram as shown, in continuation of previous diagrams, but it must be remembered that V is the constant factor, being the applied voltage, and so Φ, the flux, is smaller than when resistance and leakage reactance are neglected.

It may be noted that in this case, where the secondary load is inductive, the power factor in the primary is less than that in the secondary.

If the diagram is drawn for a capacitive load, it will be found that the power factor in the primary is greater than that in the secondary ; and also that is is possible under certain conditions for V_2 to be greater than E_2 ; that is, for the secondary terminal voltage to increase above its no-load value when load is applied.

362. **Regulation of a Transformer.**—The **Regulation** of a transformer is defined as the change in the terminal secondary voltage from no-load conditions to full-load conditions for a constant applied primary voltage, or $(E_2 - V_2)$.

It may also be defined as a percentage of the terminal secondary voltage on full load, thus :—

$$\text{Percentage regulation} = \frac{100 \, (E_2 - V_2)}{V_2}.$$

The regulation depends on the size of the transformer and the conditions of service. From the result quoted at the end of paragraph 361, with a capacitive load and a leading secondary current, the regulation may be a negative quantity (*cf.* " H." 11, 12).

363. **Core Losses.**—The two other types of loss mentioned in paragraph 358 will now be considered. They may be referred to by the common name of iron-losses or core-losses.

Eddy Current Losses.—If the core were solid throughout, large circulating currents would be set up in it in the same plane as the direction of the windings. This is indicated in Fig. 166 (*a*) which shows a cross section of one leg.

These currents are termed " **Eddy Currents.**" They represent an expenditure of energy which would heat up the core unduly, and damage the insulation of the winding.

They are kept down to a very small value by " laminating " the cores and yokes as indicated in Fig. 166 (*b*), *i.e.*, by making them up of a number of thin sheets of iron laid together and insulated from each other by varnish, shellac, or tissue paper.

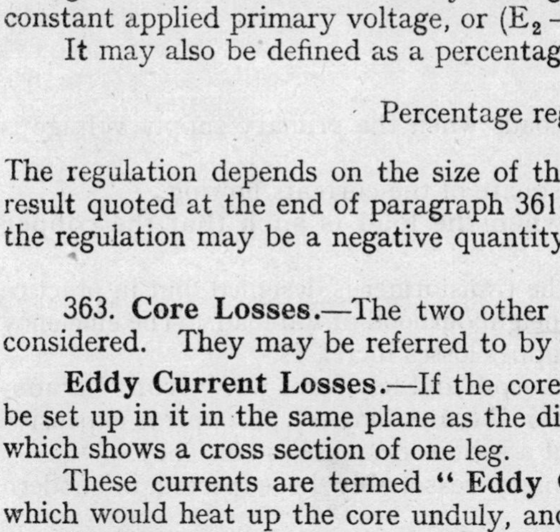

In this manner the eddy currents are forced to travel in very narrow high-resistance paths, and are kept down to such a small value that their effect is not serious.

The laminations are frequently " L "-shaped, being pushed inside the coils from alternate ends.

364. **Hysteresis Losses.**—During each alternating current cycle, the ferro-magnetic core is taken through a cycle of magnetisation.

(a)   (b)

FIG. 166.

Hence energy is lost due to hysteresis, (paragraph 89), and appears as heat in the core. The higher the frequency of the alternating current and the greater the flux density in the core the greater will be this loss.

Hard steel has a greater hysteresis loss than soft iron. Hence transformers have their cores constructed of soft iron, either pure or alloyed with a small percentage of silicon. The alloyed iron—known as " Stalloy "—is more expensive, but is found to cause considerably less hysteresis and eddy current loss. Other alloys used for cores are permalloy and μ-metal.

It will be remembered that a further effect of hysteresis is that flux changes lag behind the current changes producing them.

365. Efficiency of Transformers.—In a well-designed transformer, the expenditure of energy due to these various causes is not very great.

The efficiency of a transformer is expressed as a percentage.

The percentage efficiency is $\left(\dfrac{\text{output}}{\text{input}} \times 100\right)$ per cent.

The input, however, is equal to the output plus the losses.

Therefore, percentage efficiency may be written :—

Percentage efficiency

$$\eta = \frac{\text{output}}{\text{output} + \text{iron losses} + \text{copper losses}} \times 100$$

$$= \frac{I_2 V_2 \cos \phi_2}{I_2 V_2 \cos \phi_2 + \text{iron losses} + \text{copper losses}} \times 100$$

or, more simply, when the power factor is unity

$$\eta = \frac{I_2 V_2}{I_2 V_2 + A + I_2{}^2 R} \times 100.$$

The iron losses " A " remain practically constant at all loads when the primary supply voltage is constant.

The copper losses, $I_p{}^2 R_1 + I_2{}^2 R_2$ watts, vary as the square of the currents flowing.

It can be proved that **the efficiency is greatest when the load is such that the copper losses are equal to the (constant) iron losses.**

This need not necessarily be the full load for which the transformer is designed, but in practice it is arranged that the transformer is most efficient in the neighbourhood of full load. The efficiency only falls off slowly as the inequality between iron and copper losses increases.

The same transformer can be built with a large section core and few turns (an **" iron " transformer**) or a small section core and many turns (a **" copper " transformer**). Copper is expensive and economy can be exercised in the amount used without a serious decrease in efficiency.

The following table gives the efficiencies which might reasonably be expected in modern transformers :—

Output in kW.	1	5	10	20	50	100
Efficiency ..	94 per cent.	95 per cent.	95·5 per cent.	96 per cent.	96·5 per cent.	97 per cent.

It is evident that a transformer is an extremely efficient piece of apparatus.

366. Connections of Windings.—In transformers where the primary and secondary windings are arranged in two coils on the two legs of the core, the step-up varies according to whether the two primary and two secondary coils are joined in series or parallel.

For example, in a transformer with 100 secondary turns for every primary turn, with :—

(a) Primaries in series.   Secondaries in parallel,
    Step-up = 50 : 1.

(b) Primaries in series.   Secondaries in series,
    Step-up = 100 : 1.

(c) Primaries in parallel.   Secondaries in parallel,
      Step-up = 100 : 1.

(d) Primaries in parallel.   Secondaries in series,
      Step-up = 200 : 1.

In certain Service spark sets, arrangements (a) and (b) are used for convenience in charging the condenser. The condenser in the oscillatory circuit, which is charged up from the transformer, may have several different values, and, due to energy considerations (which will be referred to in Section " A "), it is necessary to have alternative values for the voltage obtainable from the secondary of the transformer. The primary windings are connected permanently in series, and the secondaries are changed over from series to parallel by means of a switch, as illustrated in Fig. 168.

367. Earth in Centre of Transformer.—The centre point of the two secondary windings is always earthed in large transformers, the reason being as follows :—

Suppose that a maximum voltage of 14,000 volts is being produced across the secondary of the transformer ; then each terminal will alternately reach a potential of 7,000 volts above and below " earth " potential or " zero."

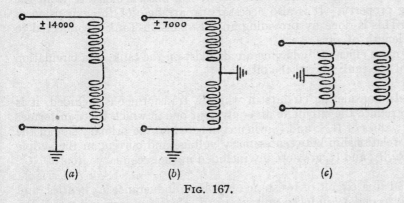

The thickness of the insulation on the secondary winding of the transformer is calculated so as to be sufficient, with a fair margin of safety, to stand this P.D.

If now an earth leak were to develop on one side of the transformer, the terminal on this side would automatically be fixed at earth potential. The same flux is still cutting the secondary. Hence as shown in Fig. 167 (a) the potential of the other end of the winding would be alternating between 14,000 volts above and below earth instead of 7,000 volts.

(a)   (b)   (c)

FIG. 167.

Since the casing and core of the transformer are connected to earth, it is evident that the insulation of the winding of the transformer secondary will be excessively strained at this point.

To obviate this, the centre point of the secondary winding is permanently connected to earth, as in Fig. 167 (b) ; or, if the secondaries are in parallel, as in Fig. 167 (c) ; the outer ends are thereby prevented from reaching a greater potential above earth than their normal 7,000 volts.

Under these conditions, should an earth develop at one terminal of the winding, that half will be put on short circuit, and the secondary voltage will be only half its proper value ; the short-circuited half of the secondary will call for a large primary current, and the A.C. cut-outs in the supply mains should blow.

Fig. 168 illustrates a Series-Parallel switch for earthing the centre point of the two windings when in the series position corresponding to Fig. 167 (b).

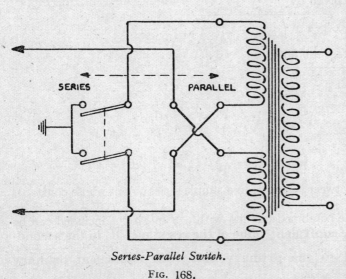

Series-Parallel Switch.

FIG. 168.

368. Cooling of Transformers.—It is necessary to make arrangements for radiating away the heat generated in the core and windings by the various losses referred to in paragraphs 360, 363 and 364, as otherwise the insulation of the windings will be impaired.

This is effected by means of air or oil cooling.

In small transformers, the windings are merely enclosed in a well ventilated iron case, and the heat is radiated away by convection through the air.

* Air cooling is cheap and clean, but the transformer must not be allowed to get damp, or the insulation of the high tension winding will suffer, nor must it be put away in a corner or covered up where no air will reach it or circulate round it.

Sometimes the case is filled with an insulating compound, in order to enable the clearance between the windings and casing to be decreased without fear of sparking over.

Air blast cooling may also be employed. Cold air is forced into the transformer by means of fans.

For oil cooling, the tank is filled with good insulating oil. The heat is then conveyed through the oil to the sides of the tank and radiated away from there. The oil protects the windings against damp, and the insulation of the windings is also materially assisted by its presence. It is necessary to make the lid of the tank perfectly air-tight; otherwise the oil will absorb moisture from the atmosphere and lose its insulating property. It is also necessary to arrange for the expansion of the oil when it becomes heated. This is done by providing an " Expansion Tank " connected to the transformer case by a short length of pipe.

Oil cooling may also be made more efficient by having an air blast on the tank, or a circulation of cold water in pipes at the top of the tank to cool the oil.

369. Equivalent Circuits.—In considering circuits in which a transformer is included, it is often convenient in calculations to reduce the circuit to an equivalent one in which the transformer is eliminated, that is, to find what values of R, L and C, when connected on the primary side of the transformer, would give the same relationship between primary voltage and current in the simple circuit as that which holds when R_2, L_2 and C_2 are actually included in the secondary circuit. (*Cf.* paragraph 348 (*b*).)

Let the secondary be connected to a circuit of resistance R_2 ohms, inductance L_2 henries, and capacity C_2 farads. Let E_2 be the secondary induced voltage and I_2 the secondary current, V the primary applied voltage and I_p the primary current.

Then, as in paragraph 354, **neglecting losses,**

$$V \times I_p = E_2 \times I_2.$$

The relationship between E_2 and I_2 is given by

$$E_2 = I_2 \sqrt{ R_2{}^2 + \left(\omega L_2 \sim \frac{1}{\omega C_2} \right)^2 }$$

Also $E_2 = V \times T$, and $I_p = I_2 \times T$ (paragraph **354**).

Therefore $V \times T = \dfrac{I_p}{T} \sqrt{ R_2{}^2 + \left(\omega L_2 \sim \dfrac{1}{\omega C_2} \right)^2 }$

$$V = \frac{I_p}{T^2} \sqrt{ R_2{}^2 + \left(\omega L_2 \sim \frac{1}{\omega C_2} \right)^2 } = I_p \sqrt{ \left(\frac{R_2}{T^2} \right)^2 + \left(\frac{\omega L_2}{T^2} \sim \frac{1}{\omega C_2 T^2} \right)^2 }$$

$$= I_p \sqrt{ R_1{}^2 + \left(\omega L_1 \sim \frac{1}{\omega C_1} \right)^2 }, \text{ where } R_1 = \frac{R_2}{T^2}; \ L_1 = \frac{L_2}{T^2}; \ C_1 = C_2 T^2.$$

But this is exactly the relationship found between V and I_p in a simple series circuit whose constants are R_1, L_1 and C_1.

Hence, for purposes of calculation, the combined circuits with a transformer included can be replaced by a single circuit, Fig. 169 (*b*), **the equivalent value of the resistance R_2 in the secondary being** $\dfrac{R_2}{T^2}$ **when it is transferred to the primary side; the equivalent primary** inductance corresponding to L_2 being $\frac{L_2}{T^2}$; and the equivalent primary capacity corresponding to C_2 being $C_2 \times T^2$ (cf. Fig. 157).

The equivalent impedance Z_1 corresponding to the secondary impedance Z_2 is $\frac{Z_2}{T^2}$.

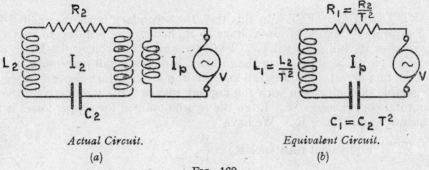

Actual Circuit.
(a)

Equivalent Circuit.
(b)

FIG. 169.

370. Transformer Testing.—Considerable insight into the behaviour of transformers may be obtained by a consideration of the practical tests to which they may be submitted. These are very numerous, and reference is only made to the following three simple ones :—

THE OPEN CIRCUIT TEST.—If the secondary is left on open circuit, the power taken by the primary will be equivalent to the power dissipated in **iron losses**, in addition to the very much smaller amount spent in $I^2 R$ losses, or copper losses. The latter is so small that it may be neglected, and the object of the experiment is to determine the total iron losses (paragraph 365) by direct measurement, using a **wattmeter** in the primary circuit. Fig. 170 (a) represents the general arrangement of the apparatus, showing voltmeters connected across the primary and secondary, and the current coil of the wattmeter connected in the way indicated. By this means the ammeter only reads the current in the primary, which is very small, and not also that in the voltage coil of the wattmeter. The wattmeter reading = power consumed + loss of power in current coils ; in this case the latter term is small and may be neglected.

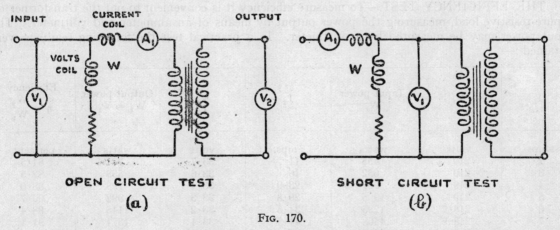

OPEN CIRCUIT TEST
(a)

SHORT CIRCUIT TEST
(b)

FIG. 170.

In a practical test on a 220 volt, 50 cycle, power transformer, the following readings were obtained :—

Primary volts $V_1 = 220$. Secondary volts $V_2 = 33 \cdot 7$
Primary current $I_1 = 0 \cdot 437$ amp. Wattmeter reading $= 67 \cdot 5$ watts

Hence **iron losses** $= 67 \cdot 5$ watts, for an input voltage of 220.

With a constant voltage supply, the iron losses should be constant for all loads. Incidentally, the above readings give the angle of lag of the primary no-load current, since

$$220 \times 0\cdot437 \times \cos \phi = 67\cdot5$$
$$\therefore \qquad\qquad \cos \phi = 0\cdot7$$
$$\therefore \qquad\qquad\qquad \phi = 45°.$$

The SHORT CIRCUIT TEST.—In this test, the secondary is short-circuited by a suitable conductor, and a carefully regulated low voltage is applied to the primary so that the current in the secondary reaches its full load value. Clearly, in order to achieve the latter condition, the voltage which will have to be supplied to the primary is only a small percentage of its full normal value. Hence, the flux density will be small and the iron losses, which depend on the flux density, will become negligible in comparison with the **copper losses** ; the wattmeter in the primary will then record the total copper losses W. From the figure obtained for copper losses it is convenient to derive an equivalent resistance R_0. We have

$$\text{Equivalent resistance } R_0 = \frac{W}{I_1{}^2}$$

$$\text{Equivalent impedance } Z_0 = \frac{V_1}{I_1}$$

$$\text{Equivalent reactance } X_0 = \sqrt{Z_0{}^2 - R_0{}^2}.$$

The wattmeter is connected as shown in Fig. 170 (b), so that the voltage coil records the actual volts across the primary ; the wattmeter records the power consumed, and this is large in comparison with the loss of power in the voltage coil, which may therefore be neglected.

In a practical test, the following readings were obtained :—

$$V_1 = 10\cdot4 \text{ volts.} \qquad I_1 = 10 \text{ amps.} \qquad W = 84 \text{ watts.}$$

Since the exciting voltage is small, 84 watts may be taken to represent the **total copper losses**. This is equivalent to a resistance R_0 given by $84/100 = 0\cdot84$ ohm.

In this test, either the primary or secondary may be short-circuited ; in this practical case and in the following efficiency tests, the transformer was arranged as a step-down transformer.

THE EFFICIENCY TEST.—To measure efficiency it is convenient to put the transformer on a pure resistive load, measuring the power output by means of an ammeter and voltmeter. The input power may be measured by a wattmeter. In a practical test the following readings were obtained :—

I_1	V_1	Input power W_1	I_2	V_2	Output power $W_2 = V_2 I_2$	Efficiency $\eta = \dfrac{W_2}{W_1}$
amps.	volts	watts	amps.	volts	watts	per cent.
2	219	455	11	33·7	371	81·5
3	219	652	16	33·6	538	82·5
4	219	907	23·9	33·4	798	88·0
5	219	1095	29·8	33·3	992	90·7
6	218·7	1295	34·5	33·2	1145	88·4
7	218·6	1508	41·5	33·1	1374	91·1
8	218·5	1710	48·0	33·0	1585	92·6
9	218·3	1913	54·5	32·8	1787	93·3

From the relation given in paragraph 365, it is also possible to arrive at a **pre-determination of efficiency under any load.** For example, with a primary load current of 9 amps., the copper losses would be given by $I_1{}^2R = 81 \times 0.84 = 68.1$. Taking the figure 67·5 watts for the iron losses, when the output load is 1,787 watts, the expected efficiency is given by

$$\eta = \frac{1787}{1787 + 67 \cdot 5 + 68 \cdot 1} \times 100 = 92 \cdot 7 \text{ per cent.}$$

This figure compares reasonably well with the figure obtained under practical conditions and given in the table above.

371. **Auto-transformer.**—This is a special type of transformer used for a small step-up or step-down of voltage.

It is a transformer with only one winding, as shown in Fig. 171 (*a*) and (*b*), and, having an iron-cored coil, possesses a large inductance.

To step-up the alternator voltage, tappings are taken as shown in Fig. 171 (*a*), $P_1 P_2$ being the primary terminals, and $S_1 S_2$ the secondary terminals.

If an alternator is joined to $P_1 P_2$ its voltage will be balanced by the counter E.M.F. of the turns N_1 between the terminals $P_1 P_2$. The flux due to the primary current will thread the whole coil of N_2 turns, and consequently the P.D. between the secondary terminals $S_1 S_2$ will be greater than the alternator voltage in the proportion of N_2/N_1, or the transformation ratio T. If a load is joined across the secondary terminals $S_1 S_2$, a current I_2 will flow in the secondary circuit.

As before, it must be counterbalanced by a current I_1 in the primary and $I_1 = I_2 \times T$. Neglecting losses, I_1 can be taken to be the whole primary current.

Also, I_1 and I_2 are in antiphase, so that, as shown in the figure, the current in the common portion of the winding is given by $I_1 - I_2 = I_3$.

To step the voltage down, the transformer would be used as shown in Fig. 171 (*b*).

It can be shown that there is a considerable saving in the amount of copper and in the copper losses with an auto-transformer as compared with a two-coil transformer, but this saving diminishes rapidly as the transformation ratio T increases. Hence, an auto-transformer is only suitable for a small step-up or step-down of voltage.

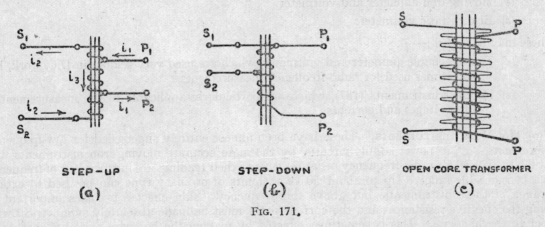

STEP-UP (a)   STEP-DOWN (b)   OPEN CORE TRANSFORMER (c)

FIG. 171.

Its great disadvantage is that there is direct electrical connection between primary and secondary. If a break occurs in the winding between $S_1 S_2$ in a step-down transformer, for instance, the higher primary voltage is applied to the low tension apparatus and leads. This is another reason for limiting the utility of the auto-transformer to cases where T is small. In addition, part of the winding has to be thick enough to stand the primary current, and the whole well enough insulated to stand the secondary voltage.

For these reasons an iron-cored auto-transformer is not used in wireless telegraphy for alternating currents, but the principle is an important one to understand, as it often comes in when considering, for example, how to join up aerial coils in oscillating circuits, and in many other cases.

372. Open-core Transformers.—By an " open-core " transformer is meant one where the **iron** magnetic circuit is not completely, as in the induction coil.

Fig. 171 (c) illustrates the primary and secondary windings of an induction coil.

Here the windings are wound over an iron core, but the return path for the magnetic lines of **force** consists of air, and magnetic leakage is much greater.

373. Air-cored R/F Transformers.—These include the various arrangements used for transferring energy at high frequency from one oscillatory circuit to another by means of a mutual inductive coupling. · Many examples will be found later in connection with transmitting and receiving circuits.

Usually these transformers have no iron core, and the inductances concerned are of the order of microhenries.

In an R/F transformer there is considerable leakage, and hence it cannot be assumed that the voltage across the secondary is T times that across the primary ; for this reason care must be taken in employing the term " transformer ratio " in connection with R/F transformers (*cf.* " F." 19).

A.C. MEASURING INSTRUMENTS.

374. Ammeters and Voltmeters.—It was pointed out in paragraph 273 that any instrument whose pointer deflection is proportional to the first power of the current is useless for A.C. measurements, as the mean deflection of the pointer is zero.   If, however, the pointer movement depends on the square of the current a mean deflection of a definite amount is produced, and an instrument operating on this principle, and calibrated for direct current, reads R.M.S. values of alternating current.   Of the instruments described in Chapter III, this eliminates the moving coil ammeter or voltmeter, leaving as measuring instruments suitable for A.C.,

(*a*) Hot-wire ammeter and voltmeter.

(*b*) Moving-iron ammeter and voltmeter.

(*c*) Electrostatic voltmeter.

To these may be added :—

(*d*) Thermo-couple ammeter and voltmeter, which are used **very seldom** in D.C. work, but sometimes used for radio-frequency measurements.

(*e*) Rectifier instruments (187), which are particularly applicable to the measurement of low voltages and currents.

(*a*) **Hot Wire Instruments.**—These have been almost entirely superseded for low-frequency measurements, *e.g.*, in power supply circuits, by the more accurate moving-iron instruments, but are still largely used for radio-frequency measurements as their readings are independent of frequency over a considerable range.   Up to about 50 kc/s. shunts of ordinary type can be used to extend the range of these instruments, but above this frequency " skin effect " becomes important in altering the effective resistances and the current paths must be made absolutely symmetrical with respect to the hot wire.   This is sometimes effected by making the hot wire one of a number of conductors in parallel, arranged in the form of a squirrel cage, but a better method is to step-down the current to a suitable value by a radio-frequency transformer, the primary winding carrying the current to be measured and the hot-wire being connected across the secondary.   The iron core of such a transformer must be very thoroughly laminated to prevent excessive power losses.   With such a transformer, currents of 1,000 amperes can be measured at any frequency up to at least 1,000 kc/s.

(*b*) **Moving Iron Instruments,**—As mentioned above, these instruments are used for low-frequency as opposed to radio-frequency measurements.   Within this range their readings are moderately independent of frequency, particularly in the case of the ammeter. The voltmeter, owing to its relatively high self-inductance, may be seriously affected, so that if calibrated at 50 cycles/sec. an error of as much as 40 per cent. may occur at 500 cycles/sec. The arrangement shown in Fig. 172 illustrates one method of compensating for this defect. W is the winding and R is the non-inductive series resistance. To compensate for frequency errors, R is shunted by a condenser C. The reactance of this condenser decreases as the frequency increases, and so the impedance of the C-R parallel circuit decreases sufficiently to compensate for the increase in reactance of the winding.

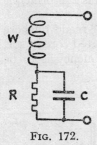

FIG. 172.

A well-designed attracted-iron instrument will give almost as accurate readings as a moving-coil instrument and is often employed in A.C. circuits where accuracy is necessary, e.g., in measuring the filament voltage of valves.

(c) **Electrostatic Voltmeter.**—It was shown in paragraph 189 that the pointer movement of this instrument was proportional to the square of the P.D. between the fixed and moving plates, so that when calibrated for D.C. voltage it reads R.M.S. alternating voltages. As it is unaffected by temperature changes, stray magnetic fields, changes of frequency or waveform, and wastes no power, it is a very suitable instrument for A.C. measurements.

(d) **Thermo-Couple Instruments.**—Thermo-electric effects are fully described in the Section on **wavemeters.** It is sufficient to state here that if two wires of different metals are connected to form a closed circuit, and one junction of the two wires is raised in temperature relatively to the other, an E.M.F. is set up between the hotter and colder junctions, proportional to their temperature difference. The E.M.F. is not affected by inserting a wire of a third material in some intermediate part of the circuit.

Fig. 173 shows the arrangement of an ammeter based on this effect. The thermo-junction C is attached to a heater wire AB, which carries the current to be measured. The heat developed in AB is proportional to the square of the current, and so the rise in temperature, and consequently the thermo-electric E.M.F. produced, is roughly proportional to the square of the current. The moving-coil milli-voltmeter V measures this E.M.F., so that its deflection is also roughly proportional to the square of the current through the heater, and it can be calibrated in R.M.S. values.

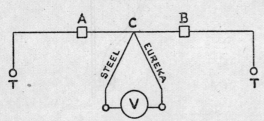

Thermo-couple Ammeter.

FIG. 173.

This instrument is largely used for radio-frequency measurements. For large currents (above 10 amps.), or high frequencies (above 1,000 kc/s.), errors due to "skin effect" are appreciable and special calibration is necessary. The radio-frequency current may also find its way into the thermo-couple circuit with consequent losses due to stray capacity. To prevent this, the heater is sometimes electrically insulated from the thermo-couple, while maintaining close thermal contact with it. This precaution is only effective up to medium radio-frequencies.

375. Frequency Meters.—The measurement of frequency is an important part of alternating current practice which has no parallel in direct-current work. Measurement of radio-frequencies is accomplished by wavemeters, which are described in Section "W." Here we are simply concerned with the instruments which measure frequencies from 50 to 1,400 cycles/sec., such as are often encountered in the circuits used for H.T. and filament supplies in transmitters.

376. The three types of frequency meter used in the Service are :—

(a) Reed type, (b) inductor type, (c) magneto-generator type.

(a) **Reed Type.**—It has been seen that in an electrical oscillatory circuit there is a definite frequency (the resonant frequency) at which an applied E.M.F. gives a maximum current. A mechanical oscillatory system behaves in a similar manner. The amplitude of vibration produced by an applied periodic force depends on the period, and is a maximum when the frequency of the applied force is the same as the resonant frequency of the oscillatory system. This is the principle of the reed type of frequency meter, a diagram of which is shown in Fig. 174.

A small piece of soft iron X is attached to one end of a thin steel blade R (the " reed "), whose other end is firmly held to the supporting structure. This structure carries a laminated core of soft iron, and wound on this is a coil W, through which flows the current whose frequency is to be

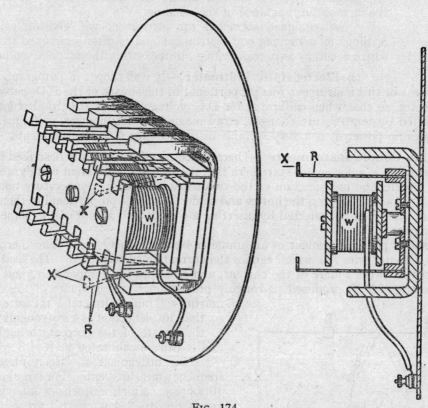

FIG. 174.

ascertained. The alternating flux due to the core magnetises X, and the resultant force between X and the core is proportional to the square of the current, as in a moving-iron ammeter. It is therefore always in the same direction and has two maxima per cycle of alternating current. The reed is thus acted on by a periodic force of twice the frequency of the alternator. If this force has the same frequency as the resonant frequency of the reed, large vibrations are set up in the reed, but as the reed is a highly-damped system, its amplitude of vibration is very small if the applied frequency has any other value.

A number of reeds of differing known frequencies are mounted in this fashion and only the one whose resonant frequency is twice the alternator frequency gives a notable response. The top of each reed is whitened or reddened and is visible through a slot in the cover of the instrument. When its amplitude of vibration is large it appears to the eye as a broad white or red band because of the persistency of the impression on the retina. Reeds of neighbouring frequencies show a slight broadening and the remainder are not appreciably affected. This is a very accurate and sensitive type of frequency meter.

(b) **Inductor Type.**—This is a simpler instrument designed to cover only a small range of frequencies around some standard frequency. The principle is shown in Fig. 175. Two field coils whose axes are at right angles act on a light freely-pivoted iron vane carrying a pointer. The direction in which the pointer sets itself depends on the direction of the resultant field of the two windings.   One end of each winding is common and the other ends are connected to an inductance

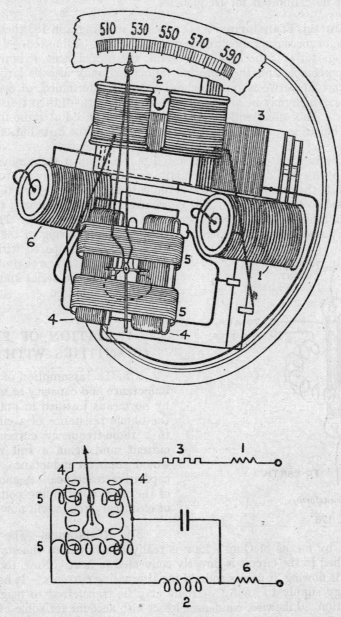

FIG. 175

and resistance respectively. The current through the resistive path is nearly independent of frequency, while that through the inductive path is inversely proportional to the frequency ($I = V/\omega L$).   The ratio of the currents and therefore the direction of the resultant field thus alters with the frequency, giving a different equilibrium position of the pointer at each frequency.

(c) **Magneto-Generator Type.**—In this instrument a small magneto-generator is driven off the shaft of the alternator whose frequency is required.   The E.M.F. of the generator is directly proportional to the speed of rotation of the armature and is read on a moving-coil voltmeter. The frequency of an alternator in cycles/sec. is given by the product of the speed in revs./sec. and the number of pairs of poles (paragraph 196). It is thus directly proportional to the reading of the voltmeter, which can be calibrated for frequencies.

377. **Aerial Ammeter Transformer.**—It was seen in paragraph 185 that, in order to increase the range of ammeters for measuring direct currents, they might be shunted. This procedure cannot be applied to ammeters for A.C. because, in general, the inductances of both the ammeter itself and the shunt are appreciable and their mutual inductance may also be large enough to matter. The distribution of current between ammeter and shunt is determined, of course, by the ratio of their total impedances, which may be very different from the ratio of their resistances and moreover varies with frequency. This effect will be particularly pronounced at radio-frequencies, when the the ratio of the inductances may often give a better criterion of the distribution of current than the resistance ratio.

A common Service method of measuring aerial current, when the ammeter has too small a maximum reading to be inserted directly in the aerial circuit, is to employ a " toroidal transformer," as illustrated in Fig. 176, the primary being the aerial wire and the secondary the toroidal coil whose terminals are connected to the ammeter. The concentration of the flux in a toroid inside the coil itself has already been referred to on several occasions (*cf.* paragraph 152). Thus the mutual flux-linkage of the primary and secondary is small and the current flowing in the coil is considerably stepped down compared with the aerial current. Further, the back reaction of the current flowing in the coil on the aerial and other neighbouring circuits is minimised.

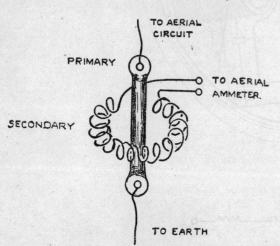

Toroidal Transformer.

FIG. 176.

VARIATION OF ELECTRICAL QUANTITIES WITH FREQUENCY.

378. The assumption of constant resistance, inductance and capacity at various frequencies is by no means justified in practice ; for instance, the ohmic resistance of a circuit is much larger to a radio-frequency current than to a direct current, and again a coil which at first sight would seem an inductance, may actually have capacitive reactance. A short account of some of the more outstanding points in the behaviour of electrical circuits will now be given.

379. **Resistance.**—The definition of the resistance of a circuit by means of Ohm's Law is really equivalent to the statement that all the electrical energy supplied to the circuit is directly converted to heat. Now, though this is the case when a direct current is flowing, it ceases to hold for alternating currents. It has already been seen that part of the energy supply to an A.C. circuit may be transferred to neighbouring circuits if there is mutual induction. Likewise, condenser losses also account for some of the energy. Eddy currents and hysteresis cause energy loss, and in high-frequency circuits, energy radiated as " wireless waves " may be a considerable fraction of the energy input. The idea of the resistance of a circuit as being merely the " ohmic " resistance of its conductors has, therefore, to be generalised. Resistance is directly connected with power dissipation by the formula $RI^2 = P$ (power), which has been seen to hold both for direct and alternating currents. It is therefore convenient (in fact it is forced on us by circumstances), to define the resistance of a circuit to alternating current as

$$R = \frac{P}{I^2}.$$

This amounts to finding an equivalent " ohmic " resistance for each source of energy dissipation, such that when the said resistance is multiplied by the square of the current it gives the energy dissipated per second. These resistances, however, no longer obey Ohm's Law and so the resistance as above defined will vary with current and frequency.

380. **Skin Effect.**—It is found that even the true " ohmic resistance " of a circuit to alternating current, e.g., the ratio of P.D. to current in a straight conductor, is not constant but increases with frequency. This is due to the fact that when an alternating current flows in a conductor, the distribution of the current over the cross section of the conductor is not uniform.

If a direct current of 2 amps:, for instance, were flowing through a conductor whose cross section is 0·02 sq. cms., we might split the conductor lengthwise into two conductors each of cross section 0·01 sq. cm., and it would be found that under the same conditions 1 amp. flowed in each part. The conclusion that the resistance of a conductor is inversely as its area was derived from such reasoning (paragraph 61). If the total resistance of the original conductor was 1 ohm., the resistance of each part would be 2 ohms, giving their equivalent resistance in parallel as 1 ohm. The total power dissipation RI^2 is 4 watts, whether it is calculated as $1\ \Omega \times (2 \text{ amps.})^2$ or $2 \times 2\ \Omega \times (1 \text{ amp.})^2$.

Suppose now that instead of the current distributing itself equally between the two parts, it could be arranged that 1·5 amp. flowed in one part and 0·5 amp. in the other. The power dissipation would then be given by

$$2\ \Omega \times (1\cdot5 \text{ amp})^2 + 2\ \Omega \times (0\cdot5 \text{ amp})^2 = 4\cdot50 + 0\cdot50 = 5 \text{ watts.}$$

and the equivalent resistance, as calculated from the power dissipation would be

$$R = \frac{P}{I^2} = \frac{5 \text{ watts}}{(2 \text{ amps})^2} = 1\cdot25\ \Omega$$

i.e., the equivalent resistance has increased by $0\cdot25\ \Omega$ owing to the non-uniform current distribution.

This uneven distribution of current across the cross section of a conductor actually occurs when an alternating current is flowing, owing to the E.M.Fs induced in the conductor. Consider the case of a straight conductor. The lines of flux are circles round the conductor. During one cycle, they start with zero number, rise to a maximum, fall again through zero to a minimum (or maximum value in the opposite direction) and rise to a zero value again. The number interlinking with the material of the conductor is thus continually altering and E.M.Fs are induced in the conductor. In the central part of the wire all the flux lines, in being produced or in disappearing, must cut the material of the conductor ; but towards the outer surface of the conductor this is not the case. The flux lines which were established in the central part of the conductor itself obviously do not cut the outer parts of the conductor in disappearing, and so make no contribution to the E.M.F. induced in these outer parts. The induced E.M.F. is thus not constant over the cross section of the wire, but increases in value from the surface to the centre. The result is that the current finds an easier path along the outer parts of the conductor, and a greater part of it proportionately flows there than in the central parts. This uneven distribution of current leads, as shown above, to the power dissipation in the conductor being increased, and so to an increase in its resistance.

This tendency of alternating currents to flow in the outer parts or " skin " of a conductor is called " skin effect."

We should expect it to increase with frequency (f) since the higher the frequency, the greater is the rate of change of flux ; and with increase in the area of cross-section of the conductor, which increases the disproportion between the flux cutting its outer and central parts. At radio frequencies it is very pronounced and practically no current flows except in the skin of a conductor. For this reason transmitting inductances are often made of copper tubing instead of solid copper. The effect also depends in amount on the permeability μ and resistivity ρ of the conductor. Expressed as a formula, this may be written

$$\frac{R_{A.C.}}{R_{D.C.}} \propto d. \sqrt{\frac{\mu f}{\rho}}$$

where d is the diameter of the conductor.

It is important to keep the resistance of leads, coils, etc., used in W/T circuits as low as possible to prevent power losses as heat, and this is generally achieved by the use of stranded " Litz " wire. If the strands are insulated from each other, and interwoven so that each strand has the same part of its total length on the surface of the resulting cable, and therefore the same proportion in the interior of the cable, as the others, a much more uniform distribution of current over the cable may be obtained and a corresponding decrease in skin effect. The skin effect in the individual strands themselves, however, is still pronounced at high frequencies. Another obvious precaution is never to use iron wire because of its high permeability. If, in aerials, for example, iron wire must be employed because copper wire is not strong enough, it should be galvanised. The galvanised outer skin will then carry all the high frequency current.

For use as aerial wire on board ship, insulated wire is inefficient as it collects a film of soot, etc., from funnel smoke, which gives it a high resistance skin. On the other hand, bare wire is corroded by sulphur fumes for the same reason, which also increases its skin resistance. Bare wire coated with anti-sulphuric enamel is therefore generally used.

When the conductor is wound as a coil or solenoid, the non-uniformity of distribution of current is still more marked than when it is straight. Owing to the arrangement of the flux lines in a coil (Fig. 19), the side of the wire further from the former is cut by more flux lines than the nearer side and so the current tends to flow on the inner side of the wire. Thus the increase of resistance with frequency is greater in a conductor wound as a solenoid than in a straight conductor. The greater the number of layers in the winding the more pronounced is the skin effect, as would be expected. Another factor tending to increase the apparent resistance of a coil is its self-capacity, which is considered below.

381. **Inductance.**—In winding a coil, the straightforward method is to wind the wire along the former in the bottom layer, as shown in various previous figures representing solenoids, then to wind another layer above the first one in the reverse direction until the starting point of the winding is again arrived at, and so on. The result is that adjacent turns in the winding may be at very different potentials. In a two-layer winding, for example, the first and last turns wound on would be adjacent, and their difference of potential would be the total P.D. across the winding. They are separated from each other by the insulation of the wire and so form in effect a condenser. It is obvious that the condenser is in parallel with the total winding. In a similar manner, every

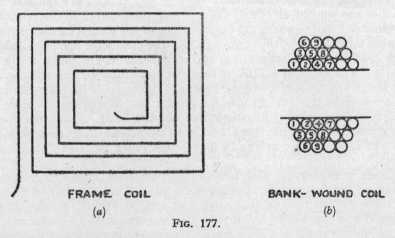

FRAME COIL   BANK- WOUND COIL
(a)   (b)

FIG. 177.

turn of the winding has a certain capacity to every other turn, and the combined effect of these capacities may be taken as a capacity in parallel with the inductance of the coil. The coil is thus really a parallel circuit of the type discussed in Chapter V, and instead of its reactance increasing steadily with frequency, it rises to a peak value at the frequency at which the self-capacity of the coil tunes with its inductance. At higher frequencies the reactance is capacitive. This is further discussed in Section " F."

It has already been explained that at its resonant frequency the " rejector circuit " behaves as a very large resistance and it will be obvious that even at frequencies removed from resonance, this tendency will be to some extent in evidence, *i.e.*, the effect of the self-capacity is to increase the component of the applied E.M.F. in phase with the current and so to increase the power loss in the coil. In other words, the A.C. resistance of the coil is increased.

The effect of self-capacity in a single layer coil is not nearly so large, as adjacent turns do not differ so much in potential. It can be decreased in a multilayer coil by winding the turns on top of each other in the same plane as in the ordinary frame coil winding, Fig. 177 (*a*), or by arranging the layers in a banked winding, as in Fig. 177 (*b*), where the order in which the turns are wound on is shown by the numbers. Another method is to adjust the thickness of the air spacing between turns and layers. A spacing approximately equal to the diameter of the wire gives minimum self-capacity effect. The object in each case is to reduce the P.D. between adjacent turns.

382. Tapped Inductances.—It often happens in wireless sets that tuning adjustments are obtained by varying the amount of inductance in a circuit. This may be effected by having a variable contact on a coil, which according to its position alters the number of turns in circuit ; alternatively, several coils of different inductance may be separately wound on the same former and the inductance altered by varying the number of such windings included in the circuit. These methods are illustrated in Fig. 178 (*a*) and (*b*). The unused turns or windings are supposed to be

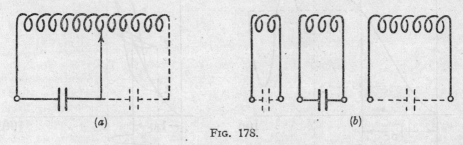

(*a*)   (*b*)

FIG. 178.

" dead," *i.e.*, to have no effect on the rest of the circuit, but actually, owing to their self-capacity, it will be seen that they are in reality closed oscillatory circuits, which are closely coupled by auto-inductive or mutual coupling to the circuit aimed at. If these unwanted circuits happen to tune at a frequency not greatly different from that being employed, they may absorb a large amount of energy from the main circuit, and increase its apparent resistance considerably (paragraph 334). In addition, they alter its resonant frequency and may even produce a noticeable double frequency effect. It may often be found advisable to short-circuit the unused turns, as the impedance of their inductance by itself may be much greater than the impedance of the turns in conjunction with their self-capacity : a much smaller current will then flow in the unused turns. The question of the best procedure depends on the number of unused turns. A large number should be short-circuited ; a small number should be left open.

383. Cores for Inductances.—The advantages of ferromagnetic cores in increasing and concentrating the flux-linkage with a coil for a given current have already been discussed. The difficulties found in their use with radio frequency currents arise principally from the loss of energy due to eddy currents in the core ; comparatively speaking, the hysteresis loss can be neglected. Even with well-laminated iron cores the losses at radio-frequencies due to eddy currents render their use prohibitive. Two effects are produced :—

(1) Owing to the power losses, the apparent resistance of the coil is greatly increased.

(2) The flux produced by the eddy currents is in the opposite direction to that produced by the magnetising current in the coil. The result is that the resultant flux in the core is much smaller than with a direct current of the same strength, *i.e.*, the permeability of the core appears to be considerably lower.

The eddy current losses increase with frequency and so the inductance of the coil decreases as the frequency increases. This may be so pronounced that the inductive reactance of an iron-cored coil remains nearly constant over a large range of frequencies or even falls as the frequency increases. In general iron-cored coils are used only in the audio-frequency stages of wireless sets.

The copper losses in such coils are generally negligible compared with the iron losses, and little advantage is gained by using wire of large diameter.

Many endeavours have been made to reduce the iron losses at high frequencies, and special iron and steel alloys, such as permalloy (an alloy of steel and nickel), have been developed, possessing especially large permeabilities for small magnetising currents (cf. " F." 20). Another method is to reduce the size of the laminations by using iron dust for the core, the dust particles being coated with insulating cement. The eddy current loss is thus considerably reduced, but in the earlier cores of this type it was found that the permeability was also very much less. It was later discovered that, by subjecting the coated dust particles to high pressures in moulds, they could be made to bind together, and a material of low eddy current loss and yet of high permeability could be obtained.

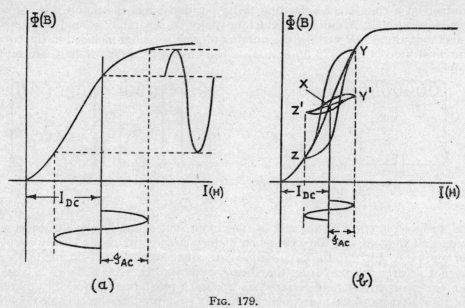

FIG. 179.

It is usually the case that when coils are being used for wireless purposes, a direct current is flowing through them, and the high-frequency alternating current, often of smaller amount, is superimposed on this. The result in an iron-cored coil is that the iron is already magnetised to a degree corresponding to the point on the permeability curve for the direct current flowing. Care must therefore be taken, when the alternating current is superimposed, that the maximum current values do not bring the iron to a saturated condition. The effect of this is shown in Fig. 179 (a). It produces a distortion of the alternating flux wave from the sinusoidal form and therefore a similar distortion in the wave form of the induced E.M.F. The permeability is also less the nearer the direct flux is to saturation point, and so the value of the induced E M F. is decreased. It may quite often occur that an air gap in the iron core will produce an increase in the A.C. inductance of the coil, by bringing down the working point on the permeability curve, owing to the increased reluctance of the core.

Even on the steep part of the permeability curve the apparent permeability for alternating current is less than would be found for direct current. This is shown in Fig. 179 (b). The loop described in a cycle of magnetisation corresponding to a cycle of the alternating current is not the YZ loop, as might be expected, but the loop Y'Z'. The averag slope of Y'Z' is less than that of YZ, i.e., the A.C. permeability is decreased.

384. **Transformers.**—The remarks above on ferromagnetic cores also apply to transformers. The limitations which prevent high transformation ratios will be better appreciated, when the conditions under which transformers operate in wireless circuits have been considered. It may be pointed out at this stage, however, that the self-capacity of the windings means that at high frequencies the transformer secondary is closed through a circuit of comparatively low reactance. In addition, the coupling between the primary and secondary coils at radio-frequencies may be as much capacitive as inductive, owing to the self-capacity between the windings, and caution must be exercised in applying the results derived earlier in this chapter for power transformers.

A simple example of this is to be found in the variometer. If the magnetic coupling between the fixed and moving coils is alone considered, the mutual inductance is zero when the coils are at right angles, and no E.M.F. should be produced in either coil by changes of the current flowing in the other. At high frequencies it is found that the capacitive coupling produces an E.M.F. in this position and zero E.M.F. is actually obtained at some other angle where the mutual inductive and capacitive couplings are equal and opposite.

385. **Capacity.**—The effect of dielectric losses, etc., in increasing the resistance of a capacitive circuit have already been discussed. Perhaps the most important point to grasp about capacities at high frequencies is the low reactance of even minute capacities and the easy shunt paths they provide, with consequent loss of H/F current where it is required. This may best be realised by giving a comparative table of the reactances of a capacity of 1 jar and an inductance of 100 microhenries at various frequencies.

$f.$	1 jar $\left(X_c = \dfrac{9 \times 10^8}{2\pi f} \right)$	100 mics $(X_L = 2\pi f \times 10^{-4})$
100 cycles/sec.	14·3 megohms.	0·0063 ohm.
1 kc/s.	143,000 ohms.	0·63 ohm.
1 Mc./s.	143 ohms.	630 ohms.
100 Mc./s.	1·43 ohms.	63,000 ohms.

In wireless sets for high frequencies it is often found that the inductive reactance of a proposed earth lead is high enough to provide an appreciable obstacle to H/F currents, and a large condenser is inserted in the lead to reduce the reactance to a negligible amount (H/F earth). By-pass condensers are also frequently used to conduct H/F currents to earth by the shortest possible path in order to prevent unwanted coupling between the various stages of a wireless receiving circuit. Examples of this will be found in later chapters.

SCREENING OF W/T APPARATUS.

386. **Electromagnetic and Electrostatic Screening.**—Most especially in the case of receivers, it is frequently necessary to provide electrical isolation for certain stages, or for the inductances and condensers composing them, or for the receiver itself. This is necessary in order to prevent unwanted inter-coupling between units or components, and to stop external fields from producing unwanted interference.

The spreading of electrostatic or electromagnetic fields can only be prevented by confining them within shields, the nature of which may vary with the frequency, and depends on whether electromagnetic screening, or electrostatic, or both is intended.

In modern receiver construction, it will be observed that the screening of units is effected by placing them in separate metal enclosures, within which certain tuning coils or condensers may be further screened by covering them with metal shields or cans. The metals employed are usually copper or aluminium, and in certain cases ferro-magnetic materials, all screening cases being earthed.

ELECTROSTATIC SHIELDING.—The principle of E.S. shielding was referred to in paragraph 104. It is necessary whenever there is a large difference of potential between parts of a circuit which are close to each other in the assembly. The interposition of an earthed metal shield provides a terminal on which lines of force may end, and thereby acts as a screen. Where more complete E.S. shielding is required, each individual component must be enclosed within a metal conductor, the latter forming a Faraday cage which effectually provides electrical isolation for anything that is in it.

E.M. AND E.S. SHIELDING AT L/F.—In this case, use is made of the high permeability of ferro-magnetic materials. As shown in Fig. 180 (*a*), lines of force from the north pole of the bar magnet crowd into a sheet of iron in preference to following a high reluctance path in air. If the sheet of iron is thick enough it may provide effective screening of apparatus beyond it. Fig. 180 (*b*)

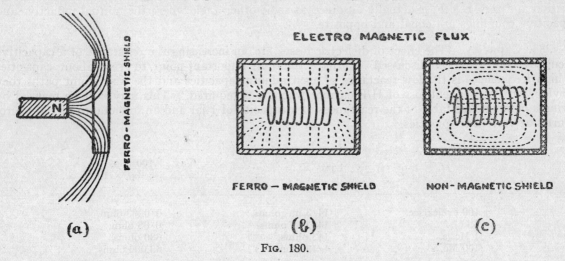

Fig. 180.

represents a coil carrying a current, the whole completely enclosed in a ferro-magnetic shielding box. Lines of force from the coil take the shortest path to the shield and travel through it, the latter acting as a magnetic short circuit preventing the E.M. flux from spreading outside the screening box. This method of screening is commonly seen in the A/F stages of receivers, and elsewhere when the frequency is below (say) 15 kc/s.

E.M. AND E.S. SHIELDING AT R/F.—At R/F it is found that more effective shielding is provided by employing a different electrical principle. The ferro-magnetic screening box is replaced by a non-magnetic metal of high conductivity, and shielding is achieved by eddy current action. When E.M. flux cuts the material of the screening box, eddy currents are set up which produce magnetic fields of their own in opposition to the original field. The action of these opposing fields makes the field outside the shielding box negligibly small, an effect which may be represented as in Fig. 180 (*c*).

This shielding action increases with frequency and with increase in conductivity of the screening material; the induced voltage which gives rise to eddy currents is proportional to the *rate of change* of flux, for which reason at radio-frequencies effective screening can be given by the use of lighter non-magnetic materials.

Aluminium and copper are metals commonly employed for shielding purposes. For efficient shielding, the resistance offered to eddy currents must be small; all joints in the screened compartments must be electrically perfect.

ELECTROSTATIC SHIELDING WITHOUT MAGNETIC SHIELDING.—In some cases this is necessary, a Service example occurring in Direction Finding (T.11). In that case, the coil to be screened was surrounded with an earthed metal conductor in which steps were deliberately taken to provide a high resistance path to eddy currents in certain directions. In general, this effect may be accomplished by arranging a metal conductor so that its surface is approximately *parallel to the magnetic field* ; under those conditions, the magnetic flux does not cut the screen, and no eddy currents, with their opposing magnetic fields, will be generated. "T" 10 gives another Service example.

EFFECTS OF SHIELDING.—Screening by eddy current action naturally involves certain losses, the effect of which renders the design of screened inductances a matter of considerable difficulty. Very often, the maximum dimensions of the screening box are fixed from considerations of the space available, and the problem for the designer is to choose the size and form of coil of given inductance which will have the highest efficiency when enclosed in the given screened compartment.

If the coil is made too large, its efficiency in air may be good, but, owing to its proximity to the screening box, the losses in the latter may be increased out of all proportion ; on the other hand, if the coil is made too small, its own resistance may become unreasonably high.

The efficiency of a tuning inductance may be measured by its " log dec.," or in other ways (" D." 40 ; " W." 9). The log dec. (δ) is given by $\delta = R/2fL$ (paragraph 397), where R is the H/F resistance in ohms at frequency f, and L is the inductance in henries. The value of δ is not constant, but its variation with frequency is much less than that of R or R/L. Moreover, log decrements can be used to obtain a comparison between coils of entirely different inductance values at widely varying frequencies.

When an inductance is enclosed in a metal shield the value of δ alters, since the apparent H/F resistance (R) is increased and the apparent inductance (L) is decreased ; these two factors contribute towards increasing the effective log dec. of the coil. The increase in effective H/F resistance is due to the loss of power in eddy currents. The decrease in inductance is due to the restriction of the magnetic flux within the shielding box ; the reluctance of the magnetic circuit is increased, the flux is decreased, and the effective inductance is therefore made smaller.

In general, losses are not excessive providing high conductivity screening material is used, and the latter is not too close to the coil ; a rough rule is to space the coil from the walls of the screen by a distance about equal to the coil radius.

inductance L, and the lower spark plug.   Between the condenser plates the electrons in the dielectric will be strained to one side, and similarly for the electrons in the spark gap.   The potential difference across the condenser will be

$$V = \frac{Q}{C} \text{ volts.}$$

The energy stored in the condenser will be

$$\tfrac{1}{2}CV^2 \text{ joules.}$$

(b) Assume that the spark gap G has been set to such a width that, when the charge put into the condenser has risen to its maximum value, the voltage across the gap is sufficient to break down the insulation of the air.   The spark gap now becomes effectively a resistance included in the circuit, of value less than 1 ohm, and usually about 0·01 ohm, or slightly above.   There will be a drift of electrons in a counter-clockwise direction, or an electric current from the right-hand plate across the gap, through L, to the left-hand plate.

A conductive bridge is set up between the spark plugs, composed of positive and negative ions of air, and small particles of copper driven off from the spark plugs.   This constitutes a convection current.

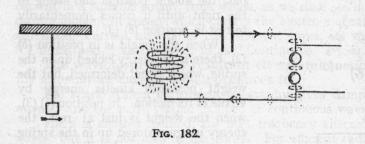

FIG. 182.

As the current gradually rises from zero it builds up a magnetic field, and when it has reached its maximum value I, the energy stored in the magnetic field is $\tfrac{1}{2}LI^2$.   At the same time, the potential difference across the condenser is zero, so that all the energy in the system is now in the magnetic field, instead of being in the electric field, as at the beginning of the current flow. Assuming no resistance losses,

$$\tfrac{1}{2}LI^2 = \tfrac{1}{2}CV^2.$$

In the mechanical analogy, at the corresponding point in the cycle, the energy is all kinetic and situated in the moving weight, while at the beginning it was all potential and stored in the spring.

(c) When the P.D. across the condenser is zero, there is no voltage left to keep the current flowing.

It will not, however, stop instantaneously, but will continue flowing for some time while the magnetic field dies down.   By Lenz's law, the collapsing magnetic field sets up an E.M.F. in the inductance opposing the cause of its collapse, i.e., the reduction of the P.D. and the current to zero, and hence it tends to maintain the current flowing in the same direction.   When the magnetic field has entirely died away, the condenser is charged up again, but now positively on the left-hand plate, and negatively on the right-hand plate.

At this stage of the operation, the energy in the system is again in the form $\tfrac{1}{2}CV^2$.

In the mechanical case, the energy was at this stage concentrated

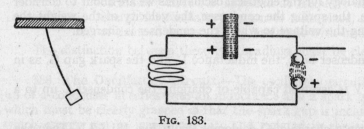

FIG. 183.

once again in the spring, the latter being in position (3) in Fig. 181 (b).

The conductive bridge between the spark plugs is not broken down at this moment, because the P.D. across the condenser immediately sets up an increasing current in the opposite direction.

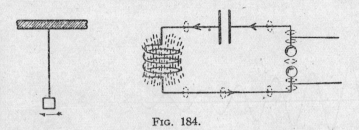

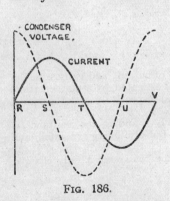

FIG. 184.

(*d*) As before, after an interval of time, the current rises to a maximum value I and the P.D. across the condenser falls to zero, the whole of the energy being again in the form $\frac{1}{2}LI^2$.

(*e*) Once again the magnetic field round the inductance dies away, and the current continues to flow in a clockwise direction, until it charges up the condenser in the same manner as that in which it was originally charged. We have thus traced out one complete cycle of the oscillatory action, corresponding to a complete movement of the weight from position 1 back to position 1 in the mechanical analogy.

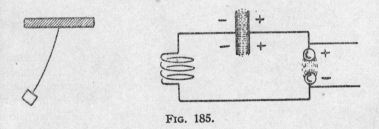

FIG. 185.

389. Relative Phases of Current and Voltage.—In the foregoing, nothing has been said about the ohmic and other losses, which are responsible in practice for a steady diminution in the energy stored in the circuit.

If these are neglected for the moment, graphs can be drawn showing the relationship between the values of instantaneous current flowing and P.D. across the condenser at different points in the cycle.

FIG. 186.

The moment "R" in Fig. 186 corresponds with Fig. 181 (*c*). The condenser is fully charged and no current is flowing out of it. Between "R" and "S" the P.D. across the condenser is falling and the current round the circuit is rising, energy being present during this stage both in the electric and in the magnetic field. At moment "S" (*see* Fig. 182) the condenser is completely discharged, and the current has risen to its maximum value. Between "S" and "T" the condenser is becoming charged in the opposite direction, and the current into it gradually decreases because the increasing charge in the condenser sets up a stronger back E.M.F.

Moment "T" corresponds to Fig. 183, moment "U" to Fig. 184, moment "V" to Fig. 185, and so on. From an inspection of Fig. 186, we therefore see that in the oscillatory circuit, condenser voltage and current flowing are 90° out of phase. This is only true if resistance is neglected, under which conditions, of course, the voltage and current curves will have the same amplitudes during succeeding cycles as during the first.

If resistance losses are taken into account the successive amplitudes of both the voltage and the current curves decrease in value, and the oscillatory action is said to be **damped**. The action will go on until the energy left in the circuit is insufficient to maintain the ionisation of the spark gap. The complete series of cycles of current or voltage variation which occurs during the oscillatory discharge of a condenser is termed a "Train of Waves" or a "Wave Train." The correct representation of the voltage to which the condenser is charged during a wave train is given in Fig. 187, and a similar curve for the current flowing is given in Fig. 188.

It may be remarked that the current and voltage curves in this case are not exactly 90° out of phase with each other.

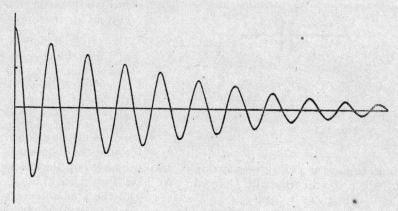

FIG. 187.

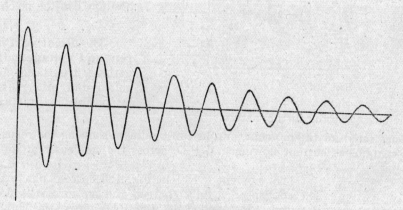

FIG. 188.

★390. **Mathematical Treatment.**—The complete theory of the wave forms of current and voltage in the oscillatory circuit, and the frequency at which the action occurs, can only be investigated by a mathematical treatment on the lines of that already given in paragraphs 158 and 174, which deal respectively with the case of resistance and inductance, and resistance and capacity, in the same circuit.

As regards mathematical treatment, the circuit can be taken as consisting of L, C and R, the resistance R representing not only the ohmic losses in the leads and the conductive spark gap, but also energy radiated, etc. A detailed account of the various damping losses is given later.

We shall deal with the case already considered in paragraph 388, in which the condenser is fully charged and the current zero at time $t = 0$.

Let V be the voltage across the condenser when fully charged.
   Q be the charge on the condenser at voltage V.
   v be the voltage across the condenser at time t.
   q be the charge on the condenser at time t.
   i be the instantaneous value of current at time t after the condenser begins to discharge.

Then we have the following relationships :—

$$q = Cv. \qquad Q = CV.$$

Also the current i is the rate at which the charge on the condenser is decreasing, so that

$$i = -\frac{dq}{dt} = -C\frac{dv}{dt}.$$

At time t, the voltage v is maintaining a current i through the resistance R and also overcoming the counter E.M.F. of the inductance L.

The equation representing the relationship between voltage and current in the circuit is therefore

$$v - L\frac{di}{dt} = iR \quad \text{or} \quad v - L\frac{di}{dt} - iR = 0.$$

Now $i = -C\frac{dv}{dt}$, so that $\frac{di}{dt} = -C\frac{d^2v}{dt^2}$.

$$\therefore \quad v + LC\frac{d^2v}{dt^2} + RC\frac{dv}{dt} = 0 \quad \text{or} \quad \frac{d^2v}{dt^2} + \frac{R}{L}\cdot\frac{dv}{dt} + \frac{v}{LC} = 0.$$

A similar differential equation can be derived in terms of i or q, with the same coefficients as in this case.

The solution of a differential equation of this nature is known to be of the form $v = Ae^{\lambda t}$. If we assume this answer, differentiate to find $\frac{dv}{dt}$ and $\frac{d^2v}{dt^2}$, and substitute in the differential equation, the latter becomes

$$Ae^{\lambda t}\left(\lambda^2 + \frac{R}{L}\lambda + \frac{1}{LC}\right) = 0.$$

Equating $\lambda^2 + \frac{R}{L}\lambda + \frac{1}{LC}$ to zero, it is found that there are two roots of the equation, given by

$$\lambda_1 = -\frac{R}{2L} + \sqrt{\frac{R^2}{4L^2} - \frac{1}{LC}}, \text{ and } \lambda_2 = -\frac{R}{2L} - \sqrt{\frac{R^2}{4L^2} - \frac{1}{LC}} \text{ respectively.}$$

There are therefore two independent solutions of the form $e^{\lambda t}$, and the general solution is obtained by multiplying them respectively by different constants, and adding the results.

Hence the complete solution of the differential equation is given by $v = Ae^{\lambda_1 t} + Be^{\lambda_2 t}$.

Before discussing the significance of the arbitrary constants, the values of λ_1 and λ_2 will be inspected. These values may be real and unequal, real and equal, or imaginary and unequal, according as the quantity under the square root $\left(\frac{R^2}{4L^2} - \frac{1}{LC}\right)$, is positive, zero or negative, *i.e.*, according as R is greater than, equal to, or less than $2\sqrt{\frac{L}{C}}$

The first two cases are examples of non-oscillatory, or unidirectional discharge, in which the resistance is so great that the current, starting at zero, rises to a maximum and dies away again to zero without reversing its direction ; in other words, the resistance losses are so high that all the energy in the circuit is wasted in these before the first half cycle is completed. The current graph is similar to that in paragraph 174, where no inductance was present in the circuit. The other case, $R < 2\sqrt{\frac{L}{C}}$, gives the case of oscillatory discharge, in which we are interested.

The two arbitrary constants, A and B, can be determined in any given case by considering the initial conditions at $t = 0$. In our case these are—

    (1) that $i = o$ at $t = o$.

    (2) that $v = V = \frac{Q}{C}$ at $t = o$.

The complete solution will not be worked out, but the result will be quoted.

It is found that, with these initial conditions, the value v of the condenser voltage at any time t is given by

$$v = Ve^{-at}\sqrt{1 + \frac{\alpha^2}{\omega^2}}\cos(\omega t - \phi), \tag{A}$$

$$\text{where } \phi = \tan^{-1}\left(\frac{\alpha}{\omega}\right).$$

" α " and " ω " are recognised symbols for the quantities $\frac{R}{2L}$ and $\sqrt{\frac{1}{LC} - \frac{R^2}{4L^2}}$ respectively.

The value i of current at time t is $-C\frac{dv}{dt}$, and so by differentiation of the expression for v above,

$$i = \frac{V}{\omega L}e^{-at}\sin\omega t \tag{B}.$$

The last equation (B) represents an oscillatory current whose frequency is $\frac{\omega}{2\pi}$ and whose amplitude is $\frac{V}{\omega L}e^{-at}$ and therefore decreases as the time increases ; in other words the oscillations are damped.

The equation (A) represents the instantaneous value of the voltage across the condenser. It is periodic with the same frequency as the current, and its amplitude $Ve^{-at}\sqrt{1 + \frac{\alpha^2}{\omega^2}}$ also decreases with time.

The frequency $\frac{\omega}{2\pi}$ at which the oscillatory action takes place is given (written in full) by $f = \frac{1}{2\pi} \sqrt{\frac{1}{LC} - \frac{R^2}{4L^2}}$ and is known as the **Natural Frequency** of the circuit. This frequency, and various results arising from it, will be discussed in the next few paragraphs, and after that the question of damping.

391. Natural Frequency.

—This frequency $f_N = \frac{1}{2\pi} \sqrt{\frac{1}{LC} - \frac{R^2}{4L^2}}$, called the **Natural Frequency,** must be carefully distinguished from the frequency $f_R = \frac{1}{2\pi} \sqrt{\frac{1}{LC}}$, which was found in Chapter V to be the **resonant frequency** of a circuit comprising inductance, capacity and resistance in series.

The natural frequency is the frequency of free oscillations, *i.e.*, the frequency at which the ircuit will oscillate if left to do so ; while the resonant frequency is the frequency at which **an applied voltage** will give **the biggest current,** *i.e.*, at which **forced** oscillations have a maximum amplitude.

The theoretical grounds from which these formulæ are derived are entirely different ; but it so happens that they give practically the same result, and **the simple formula** $f = \frac{1}{2\pi} \sqrt{\frac{1}{LC}}$ is **generally used for the natural frequency.** This is quite legitimate as long as it is understood that it is a close approximation to the truth, and arises from different considerations from those dealt with under resonance.

If the resonant frequency is denoted by f_R and the natural frequency by f_N, the exact relationship between them is given by

$$(2\pi f_N)^2 = (2\pi f_R)^2 - \alpha^2$$

and so the natural frequency is always smaller than the resonant frequency.

Even if R is small enough to justify the approximations above, it must be remembered that in a circuit at its **resonant** frequency, the current is $\frac{V}{R}$, where V is the applied voltage, and that the resistance, however small, is the only quantity limiting the size of the current under resonant conditions.

In the usual wireless circuits, the resistance R is so small that the term $\frac{R^2}{4L^2}$ is negligible compared with $\frac{1}{LC}$; that is, R is very much less than $2\sqrt{\frac{L}{C}}$, and so the assumption that Natural Frequency $(f_N) = \frac{1}{2\pi\sqrt{LC}}$ is justified.

In this formula L is measured in **henries,** and C in **farads.**

If L is in **mics,** and C in **jars,** the formula becomes

$$f = \frac{3 \times 10^7}{2\pi\sqrt{LC}} \text{ cycles per second} = \frac{3. \times 10^4}{2\pi\sqrt{LC}} \text{ kilocycles per second, or kc/s.}$$

Example 49.

Find the correct natural frequency of free oscillations in a circuit in which C = 50 jars, L = 2 mics, and R is 1 ohm. Also find the approximation to the natural frequency, using the formula for resonant frequency, and the minimum value of R which would make the discharge of the condenser unidirectional.

Natural frequency $= \dfrac{1}{2\pi} \sqrt{\dfrac{1}{LC} - \dfrac{R^2}{4L^2}}$

$$= \dfrac{1}{2\pi} \sqrt{\dfrac{1}{\dfrac{2}{10^6} \times \dfrac{50}{9 \times 10^8}} - \dfrac{1}{4 \times \dfrac{2}{10^6} \times \dfrac{2}{10^6}}} = \dfrac{1}{2\pi} \sqrt{\dfrac{9 \times 10^{14}}{100} - \dfrac{10^{12}}{16}}$$

$$= \dfrac{1}{2\pi} \sqrt{9 \times 10^{12} - \dfrac{10^{12}}{16}} = \dfrac{10^6}{2\pi} \sqrt{9 - \dfrac{1}{16}} = \dfrac{10^6}{2\pi} \sqrt{8 \cdot 9375} = \dfrac{10^6 \times 2 \cdot 9895}{2\pi}$$

$$= 475{,}700 \text{ cycles/sec.} = 475 \cdot 7 \text{ kc/s.}$$

Resonant frequency $= \dfrac{1}{2\pi} \sqrt{\dfrac{1}{LC}}$ or, using mics and jars,

$$= \dfrac{3 \times 10^7}{2\pi\sqrt{LC}} = \dfrac{3 \times 10^7}{2\pi\sqrt{100}} = \dfrac{3 \times 10^6}{2\pi}$$

$$= 477{,}400 \text{ cycles per second} = 477 \cdot 4 \text{ kc./s.}$$

These results are very nearly equal.

To make the discharge non-oscillatory, R must be at least equal to $2\sqrt{\dfrac{L}{C}}$.

$$R = 2\sqrt{\dfrac{L}{C}} = 2\sqrt{\dfrac{\dfrac{2}{10^6}}{\dfrac{50}{9 \times 10^8}}} = 2\sqrt{\dfrac{900 \times 2}{50}} = 2\sqrt{36} = 12\,\Omega$$

so that with the resistance equal to 12 ohms or more the circuit would not oscillate freely. The term " aperiodic " is sometimes used to denote the type of discharge in this case.

392. **Oscillation Constant.**—The quantity LC is called the **oscillation constant** of the circuit. Provided this product remains the same, no matter what changes are made in the individual values of L and C, the resonant frequency, and, to all intents and purposes, the natural frequency remain constant.

393. **Period.**—If the circuit oscillates at the rate of f cycles per second, then one cycle will last for a period of $1/f$ of a second.

Natural period $= \dfrac{1}{\dfrac{1}{2\pi\sqrt{LC}}} = 2\pi\sqrt{LC}$ seconds, where L is in henries and C in farads.

Natural period $= \dfrac{1}{\dfrac{3 \times 10^7}{2\pi\sqrt{LC}}} = \dfrac{2\pi\sqrt{LC}}{3 \times 10^7}$ seconds, where L is in mics and C in jars.

Example 50.

Find the natural period of the circuit given in Example 49.

$$\text{Period} = \dfrac{2\pi\sqrt{100}}{3 \times 10^7} = \dfrac{2\pi}{3 \times 10^6} = 2 \cdot 1 \times 10^{-6} \text{ seconds} = 2 \cdot 1 \text{ micro-seconds.}$$

394. **Wavelength.**—So far we have only discussed high-frequency oscillatory currents in a circuit. If the circuit in which these currents are flowing is an efficient radiator (paragraph 408), energy is sent out in the form of electro-magnetic waves. The wave form, frequency, and damping of the electro-magnetic wave are the same as those of the oscillatory current which produces it. It is a well-established fact that all electro-magnetic waves (light being a well-known example)

The decrement is thus constant throughout the wave train, and is given by $e^{\frac{2\pi a}{\omega}}$

The persistency is, of course, $e^{-\frac{2\pi a}{\omega}}$.

397. Logarithmic Decrement.

—Instead of using the persistency, or the decrement, to measure the rate at which the amplitude decreases, the Naperian Logarithm of the decrement is generally used. This is simply the logarithm of the decrement to the base e (not base 10), and is, from the formula above, equal to $\frac{2\pi a}{\omega}$.

Note.—Numerically the Naperian Logarithm of a quantity is derived from the Common Logarithm (to the base 10) by multiplying the Common Log by 2·3026.

The expression Logarithmic Decrement is generally referred to by the contraction " Log. Dec.," and written δ (delta).

$$\text{Log. Dec.} = \frac{2\pi a}{\omega} = \frac{a}{f}.$$

Now $a = \dfrac{R}{2L}$ and $\omega = \sqrt{\dfrac{1}{LC} - \dfrac{R^2}{4L^2}}$,

which, if R is small, is very nearly $\dfrac{1}{\sqrt{LC}}$

$\therefore$ Log. Dec. $\delta = \dfrac{2\pi a}{\omega} = \dfrac{\pi R}{\omega L} = \dfrac{R}{2fL} = \pi R \omega C = \pi R \sqrt{\dfrac{C}{L}}.$ .... (*Cf.* D 40).

All these equivalent forms can be used to give the log. dec. of a circuit, according to the constants which are known.

R, L and C are, of course, in ohms, henries and farads respectively.

If L is in mics and C in jars,

$$\delta = \pi R \sqrt{\frac{\dfrac{C}{9 \times 10^8}}{\dfrac{L}{10^6}}} = \pi R \sqrt{\frac{C}{900L}} = \frac{\pi R}{30} \sqrt{\frac{C}{L}} = \frac{R}{9·6} \sqrt{\frac{C}{L}}$$

Similar formulæ in terms of mics and jars can be obtained for all the equivalent forms above.

398. Number of Oscillations in a Wave-train.

—Although, in theory, the oscillations take an infinite time to reach zero value, they actually become of negligible size after a certain time.

It is customary to consider that the wave train is effectively ended when the amplitude of current has fallen to 1 per cent. of its initial value. This is, of course, quite an arbitrary value to choose.

Let the number of effective oscillations, on this assumption, be N.

Let the amplitude of the Nth oscillation be written I_N.

Then $I_N = I_1 e^{-(N-1)\delta}$ or $\dfrac{I_1}{I_N} = e^{(N-1)\delta}$.

But we are taking $\dfrac{I_1}{I_N}$ to be equal to 100.

$$\therefore 100 = e^{(N-1)\delta}, \text{ or, } \log_e 100 = (N-1)\delta$$

$$\therefore N - 1 = \frac{\log_e 100}{\delta}, \text{ or } N = 1 + \frac{\log_e 100}{\delta}.$$

The logarithm of 100 to the base e is $4 \cdot 605$.

$$\therefore N = 1 + \frac{4 \cdot 605}{\delta}.$$

Thus, if the log. dec. of a circuit is $0 \cdot 1$, there will be $1 + \frac{4 \cdot 605}{0 \cdot 1} = 1 + 46 = 47$ oscillations, before the current amplitude is reduced to 1 per cent. of its initial value.

399. Duration of a Wave-train.—As we have now derived formulæ for the period of free oscillation in an oscillatory circuit, and for the number of oscillations which may be considered effective, a practical example can be worked out to give the duration of a wave-train.

Example 51.

Let R be 1 ohm, C = 5 jars, L = 5 mics,

$$Period = \frac{2\pi\sqrt{LC}}{3 \times 10^7} \text{ seconds (para. 393).}$$

$$= \frac{2\pi\sqrt{25}}{3 \times 10^7} \text{ seconds} = \frac{10\,\pi}{3 \times 10^7} \text{ seconds} = \frac{\pi}{3} \times 10^{-6} \text{ seconds} = 1 \cdot 047 \text{ micro-seconds.}$$

" δ ", for this circuit, $= \frac{R}{9 \cdot 6}\sqrt{\frac{C}{L}} = \frac{1}{9 \cdot 6}\sqrt{\frac{5}{5}} = \frac{1}{9 \cdot 6} = 0 \cdot 104.$

Therefore the number of effective oscillations is

$$1 + \frac{4 \cdot 6}{0 \cdot 104} = 1 + 44 = 45,$$

and the duration of the wave train is

$$(1 \cdot 047 \times 45) \text{ micro-seconds} = 47 \text{ micro-seconds} = 0 \cdot 000047 \text{ second.}$$

400. Damping Losses in the Practical Circuit.—The mathematical investigation in the paragraphs above has been concerned with the purely theoretical circuit containing resistance, inductance, and capacity, and the damping, or dying away of the oscillations, has been determined in terms of these quantities. The practical circuit we started with at the beginning of the chapter will now be considered, and the various losses, which can all be covered by the term damping losses, investigated in turn. It will be found that ohmic resistance is by no means the only way in which energy is dissipated, but other forms of loss can be considered as adding a certain amount of equivalent resistance to the circuit, so that the theoretical results hold good if the resistance term in them is replaced by a total equivalent, or effective, resistance.

This subject will also be referred to in Section " R." The damping losses may be classed under the following headings :—

(a) Damping due to ohmic resistance.
(b) Damping due to spark gap resistance.
(c) Damping due to eddy currents induced in neighbouring conductors.
(d) Damping due to condenser losses.
(e) Damping due to dielectric losses in surrounding dielectrics.
(f) Damping due to energy radiated away into the surrounding ether.

401. Ohmic Resistance.—Since $\delta = \frac{R}{9 \cdot 6}\sqrt{\frac{C}{L}}$, the greater the ohmic resistance the more quickly will the wave be damped out. It is necessary to take account of the increase in resistance produced in the conductors by " skin effect " at these high frequencies.

As was explained in paragraph 380, in a cylindrical conductor a high frequency current tends to flow on the outer surface layers and there is practically no current in the centre of the conductor, whereas a direct current takes advantage of the whole cross sectional area of the conductor.

(*a*) **Inductive.**—The component electric and magnetic fields are in space quadrature (at right angles to each other) and in time quadrature (90° out of phase with each other) and the effect is simply to cause a transference of energy from one to the other in the neighbourhood of the circuit without any energy being detached. The inductive field at any point varies inversely as the square of the distance from the oscillator to the point.

(*b*) **Radiative.**—The electric and magnetic fields of radiation are in space quadrature and time phase, and therefore represent a motion of energy at right angles to both in space. This radiated energy is, of course, equivalent to the energy which would be dissipated in the fictitious equivalent radiation resistance. The greater the space occupied by both fields the more energy is radiated. A circuit specially designed to give good radiation, like the circuit of this paragraph, in which the condenser plates are widely separated, is known as an **open oscillator.** The stronger the total electric and magnetic fields the greater the energy radiated, hence high voltages and large currents are necessary to give good radiation. The radiation field varies inversely as the first power of the distance from the oscillator. It thus decreases much more slowly with increasing distance than the induction field, and, at the distances over which wireless communication is practised, only the radiation field is effective. Its magnitude is also directly proportional to the frequency, hence the use of radio-frequencies in wireless telegraphy.

A fuller account of wireless radiation is given in Section " R " (1).

409. The Aerial Circuit.—The first type of open oscillator consisted of two metal plates joined by a wire, the inductance being in the wire and the capacity that between the plates.

It was found later that the earth could be used as one of the plates of the condenser, and the higher the other plate the more efficiently did the oscillator radiate. The spark gap was in series with the circuit.

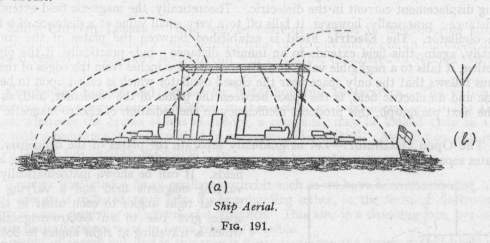

(*a*)

Ship Aerial.

FIG. 191.

The normal transmitting antenna is of this type, though the use of the spark gap in the aerial circuit itself is now prohibited. In the well-known " Roof " type of aerial, as fitted in ships and ashore, the overhead wires form one plate of the condenser, and the earth itself forms the other plate. The dielectric consists of the intervening layer of air. •

An aerial is conventionally represented as in Fig. 191 (*b*).

410. Natural Capacity of an Aerial.—The higher we make the overhead, or " roof " part of an aerial, the better it radiates energy.

Since the capacity of a condenser varies inversely with the thickness of the dielectric—in this case the distance between the aerial and earth—the capacity of the aerial will be small.

Again, the capacity varies directly as the area of dielectric charged, that is, of the opposed plates.

The earth is big, but the overhead portion of an aerial is very limited, especially in a ship. Consequently, this factor also goes to keep the condenser capacity small. In fact, the capacity of the aerial feeder wire to the trunk along which it is led from the transmitter and which is in parallel with the aerial capacity proper, forms an appreciable part of the total capacity.

We therefore expect the capacity of a ship aerial to be small, and in practice it varies from about 0·3 jar in a submarine to about 2 jars in a big ship. (Shore station aerials may have larger capacities than these.)

The natural capacity of an aerial is denoted in the Service by the letter " σ " (sigma) to distinguish it from other capacities. (*Cf.* " R." 23.)

411. Natural Inductance of an Aerial.—An aerial will likewise have a certain natural inductance, made up of the inductance of the wires composing the " roof," and of the " feeders " (or wires from the W/T Office to the roof).

As these wires are in parallel with one another, their total inductance will not be very great and generally lies between 10 and 70 mics. for ship aerials.

412. Primary and Aerial Circuits.—The oscillation is generated in a closed circuit, generally termed the primary circuit. To give efficient radiation, we must transfer the oscillation to an open oscillator, in practice the aerial circuit.

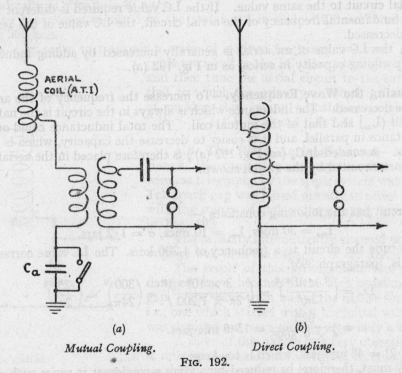

AERIAL	
COIL (A.T.I)	

C_a

(a)   (b)

Mutual Coupling.   *Direct Coupling.*

FIG. 192.

The theory of the interaction of coupled circuits, when one of the circuits is set freely oscillating, will be given in paragraph 421.

The type of coupling employed is either mutual or direct as illustrated in Fig. 192 (a) and (b). The direct coupling in this case is auto-inductive.

413. Mutual Coupling (Fig. 192 (a)).—Here a coil of wire (known as the " Mutual Coil ") in series with the aerial, is placed close to the primary inductance.

system, the decrement is less, because the spark gap resistance is not present in the aerial circuit. The frequency transmitted is, however, dependent on the coupling factor between the two circuits, and we shall proceed in paragraph 421 to consider the physical and mathematical treatment of free oscillations in coupled circuits.

419. Tight and Loose Coupling.

—It was stated in paragraph 413 that the oscillation set up in the primary circuit is transferred to the aerial circuit by mutual induction between the primary and mutual coils.

Since our object is to induce the maximum energy possible into the aerial, it might appear at first sight that the closer the mutual coil is to the primary the better.

This is not the case, for the following reasons :—

Consider the oscillation in the primary circuit ; each time the magnetic field rises and falls round the primary inductance a certain amount of energy is transferred to the aerial via the mutual coil, until eventually all the energy originally available in the primary circuit has been transferred to the aerial circuit.

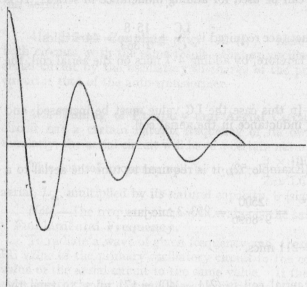

Fig. 194.

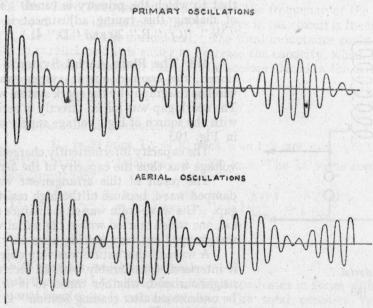

PRIMARY OSCILLATIONS

AERIAL OSCILLATIONS

Tight Coupling.

Fig. 195.

Similarly, when the aerial circuit is oscillating, it will gradually transfer its energy back to the primary, until eventually, all the energy has been handed back to the primary circuit, ignoring I^2R losses and the amount radiated.

This transfer and re-transfer of energy between primary and aerial continues until all the energy originally available has been expended in overcoming the various losses in the two circuits.

Every time the primary is set in oscillation, a great deal of energy will be expended in damping losses in the spark gap, while in the aerial the chief expenditure of energy is by radiation ; the latter expenditure is very desirable, but the former is not.

If the mutual coil is placed close up to the primary, the energy is transferred very rapidly backwards and forwards, as in Fig. 195.

This is known as " Tight Coupling."   The effect will be as follows :—

It will be seen from the above that the oscillations in both primary and aerial die away and rise again several times in a series of " beats " before the wave train is entirely damped out.

Each time the oscillations are transferred to the primary, the damping effect of the spark gap is experienced, with consequent loss of energy, which might otherwise have been available for radiation into space.

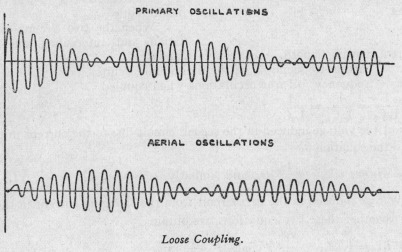

PRIMARY OSCILLATIONS

AERIAL OSCILLATIONS

Loose Coupling.

FIG. 196.

If the mutual coil be moved further away from the primary, the energy will be transferred more slowly between the two circuits, as in Fig. 196.   The primary circuit is not set in oscillation so often before the wave train finally dies away and the primary damping losses are decreased.   This is known as " Loose Coupling."

The advantages of loose coupling in lessening interference are discussed below.   All damped wave transmission, however, is liable to cause " shock " excitation of receiving aerials whether tuned to it or not, and so to produce interference.

420. Brushing or " Corona Discharge."—If the aerial voltage is excessive the insulation of the air between the aerial and neighbouring earthed conductors breaks down, and a violet-blue discharge occurs.   This represents a waste of energy, and also discloses the position of the ship at night.   High aerial voltages are produced in sharply tuned circuits, *i.e.*, circuits with a large $\frac{L}{C}$ ratio.   On the other hand, if the $\frac{L}{C}$ ratio is decreased so as to flatten the tuning, the band of frequencies on which energy is radiated is widened and the possibility of interference is again increased. (*Cf.* "R." 23.)

421. Radiation of Two Wave-Frequencies.—The question of the resonant frequencies of two coupled circuits with forced oscillations due to a source of alternating E.M.F. in one has already been considered in Chapter V.

It is proposed to investigate here the other type of oscillations, viz., free oscillations (*see* paragraph 333). Free oscillations occur when one circuit is set oscillating, as in the case of the primary circuit of a spark transmitter, the energy being transferred and re-transferred by means of the coupling from one circuit to another until it is all consumed in damping losses. There is **no** continuously applied source of E.M.F. in either circuit.

It will be found that, although both circuits have the same LC value and therefore equal natural frequencies, there are two frequencies of free oscillation of the combination, both differing from the natural frequency of the independent circuits.

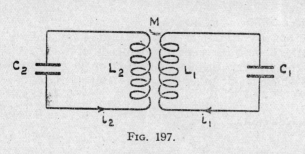

FIG. 197.

Let the two circuits be L_1C_1 and L_2C_2 as in the figure, where $L_1C_1 = L_2C_2 = L_0C_0$.

Let the mutual inductance be M.

The resistances of the circuits will be neglected.

When the two circuits are both in oscillation and interacting one on the other, there will be currents flowing in both. Let these be i_1 and i_2.

Let $\Omega = 2\pi \times$ natural frequency F of the individual circuits.

Let $\omega = 2\pi \times$ frequency f of free oscillations when coupled.

Then $\Omega^2 = \dfrac{1}{L_0C_0} = \dfrac{1}{L_1C_1} = \dfrac{1}{L_2C_2}$

At any instant the voltage induced in the second circuit due to the current in the first is $\omega M i_1$. This leads to the equation :—

$$\omega M i_1 = \left(\omega L_2 \sim \frac{1}{\omega C_2} \right) i_2, \text{ and similarly, } \omega M i_2 = \left(\omega L_1 \sim \frac{1}{\omega C_1} \right) i_1,$$

$\omega M i_2$ being the voltage induced in the first circuit from the changing current in the second.

Multiplying together these two equations, we obtain

$$\omega^2 M^2 \, i_1 i_2 = \left(\omega L_1 \sim \frac{1}{\omega C_1} \right) \left(\omega L_2 \sim \frac{1}{\omega C_2} \right) i_1 i_2$$

$$\text{or } \omega^2 M^2 = \left(\omega L_1 \sim \frac{1}{\omega C_1} \right) \left(\omega L_2 \sim \frac{1}{\omega C_2} \right)$$

$$= \omega^2 L_1 L_2 \left(1 - \frac{1}{\omega^2 L_1 C_1} \right) \left(1 - \frac{1}{\omega^2 L_2 C_2} \right) = \omega^2 L_1 L_2 \left(1 - \frac{\Omega^2}{\omega^2} \right)^2$$

$$\therefore \frac{M^2}{L_1 L_2} = K^2 = \left(1 - \frac{\Omega^2}{\omega^2} \right)^2$$

$$\therefore \ 1 - \frac{\Omega^2}{\omega^2} = \pm K \quad \therefore \ \frac{\Omega^2}{\omega^2} = 1 \pm K$$

$$\therefore \ \omega^2 = \frac{\Omega^2}{1 \pm K} \text{ or } \omega = \frac{\Omega}{\sqrt{1 \pm K}}.$$

There are thus two values for ω, one greater and one less than Ω.

Since $\Omega = 2\pi F$ and $\omega = 2\pi f$,

$$f = \frac{F}{\sqrt{1 \pm K}}.$$

Thus, the frequency of oscillation of the two coupled circuits has two values, which may be written f_1 and f_2,

$$f_1 = \frac{F}{\sqrt{1 + K}} \text{ and } f_2 = \frac{F}{\sqrt{1 - K}}.$$

It will be noticed that these two frequencies are exactly the same as the two frequencies of resonance obtained in paragraph 335 for forced oscillations in coupled circuits. This result holds generally, provided the resistances of the circuits are small, so that any complex arrangement of circuits will oscillate freely at the same frequencies as those for which the reactance is zero when an alternating E.M.F. is introduced somewhere in the arrangement.

In the practical case of a spark primary and aerial circuit, the two frequencies of free oscillation, and consequently of radiation, will correspond to two different wave lengths, λ_1 and λ_2, which will be sent out by the transmitter.

Since wavelength is inversely proportional to frequency, $\lambda_1 = \lambda\sqrt{1 + K}$, and $\lambda_2 = \lambda\sqrt{1 - K}$, where λ is the wavelength corresponding to the natural frequency of each circuit separately. Also, since F is the frequency whose LC value is L_0C_0, the frequencies f_1 and f_2 are those which correspond to $L_0C_0 (1 + K)$ and $L_0C_0 (1 - K)$.

Each of the circuits has therefore apparently two LC values, neither of which is equal to their individual LC value, L_0C_0.

The difference between the wave frequencies radiated by the aerial depends on the degree of coupling K between the two circuits.

Example 54.

In a spark transmitting circuit tuned to 500 kc/s., the primary condenser is 40 jars, the aerial capacity is $1 \cdot 5$ jars, and the mutual inductance between primary and aerial circuits is 2 mics. Find the two wave frequencies radiated, and the percentage coupling.

The LC value of each circuit will be

$$\left(\frac{3 \times 10^4}{2\pi \times 500}\right) = \left(\frac{30}{\pi}\right)^2 = 91 \cdot 2 \text{ mic-jars.}$$

$$L_1 = \frac{91 \cdot 2}{40} = 2 \cdot 28 \text{ mics} \; ; \; L_2 = \frac{91 \cdot 2}{1 \cdot 5} = 60 \cdot 8 \text{ mics.}$$

$$K = \frac{M}{\sqrt{L_1 L_2}} = \frac{2}{\sqrt{2 \cdot 28 \times 60 \cdot 8}} = 0 \cdot 17.$$

$$f_1 = \frac{500}{\sqrt{1 + K}} \text{ kc/s.} = \frac{500}{\sqrt{1 \cdot 17}} \text{ kc/s.} = \frac{500}{1 \cdot 082} = 462 \cdot 1 \text{ kc/s.}$$

$$f_2 = \frac{500}{\sqrt{1 - K}} \text{ kc/s.} = \frac{500}{\sqrt{0 \cdot 83}} \text{ kc/s.} = \frac{500}{0 \cdot 911} = 548 \cdot 9 \text{ kc/s.}$$

The percentage coupling = K $\times$ 100 = 17 per cent.

422. We seem here to have two conflicting statements. It was stated in paragraph 419 that the energy in the aerial is in the form of beats, as shown in Figs. 195 and 196, and in paragraph 421 that two waves, differing in frequency, are set up in the aerial.

The truth of both these statements can be reconciled by drawing these two waves occurring simultaneously. In Fig. 198, curve A shows f_2, the higher frequency set up in the aerial, and curve B shows f_1, the lower frequency.

As these frequencies are different, it follows that if they start in step they will work out of step, then in step, then out of step and so on, just as two men walking side by side and taking a different length of stride, get in and out of step in turn. When the two waves are in step, it means that the currents due to the two waves are flowing in the same direction, and when out of step, in opposite directions.

The **total** current at any moment can be found by adding the heights of these curves together, at each moment. The result is shown in curve C, which corresponds to the lower curve of Fig. 195 or 196.

From this we see that the current in the aerial rises and falls in a series of beats, being a maximum when the waves are exactly in phase, and a minimum when the two waves are exactly out of phase. Similarly, the instantaneous voltage in the aerial can be found by drawing two voltage curves for the two frequencies and adding them together.

Hence, the total voltage and current in the aerial rises and falls in a series of beats, and these beats are due to the two waves oscillating simultaneously at the two different frequencies, f_1 and f_2.

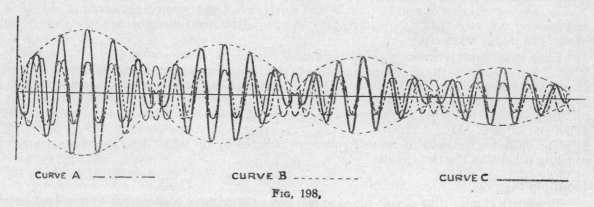

CURVE A — · — · —   CURVE B - - - - - - - - -   CURVE C ————————

FIG. 198.

The number of times per second at which the separate waves get into step is equal to the difference of the two frequencies, f_1 and f_2.

Now $f_1 = \dfrac{F}{\sqrt{1 + K}}$ and $f_2 = \dfrac{F}{\sqrt{1 - K}}$.

If K is small, $f_2 - f_1 = F\{(1 - K)^{-\frac{1}{2}} - (1 + K)^{-\frac{1}{2}}\} = F\left\{1 + \dfrac{K}{2} - 1 + \dfrac{K}{2}\right\} = KF$, approximately. (*Cf.* "F." 19.)

Therefore, the beat frequency, or the number of times per second at which the energy is transferred backwards and forwards from one circuit to another, is directly proportional to the coupling factor K, and the natural frequency F of the circuits taken individually.

This renders *plausible* the statement made in paragraph 419 with regard to tight and loose coupling. For tight coupling, higher powers of K would need to be considered in the above argument, and the approximation (K small compared with unity) is hardly justified.

423. Drawback of Radiating Two Waves.—In designing W/T circuits we have two objects always before us :—

(*a*) To radiate as much energy as is required on the wave we wish to transmit.

(*b*) To radiate as little energy as possible on any other wave.

If this second object is fulfilled, then communication from a fleet to a number of shore stations or outlying

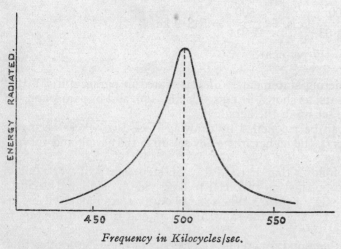

Frequency in Kilocycles/sec.

FIG. 199.

ships is possible with a minimum amount of interference.

For example, the ideal condition is illustrated in Fig. 199.

This curve, known as an "Energy Distribution Curve," represents energy radiated by a transmitter at different frequencies. It corresponds to the case of the spark transmitter with very loose coupling, in which case the two component frequencies of the complex oscillation f_1 and f_2, are very close together, and their joint effect is to give a maximum of radiation at the natural frequency of the individual circuits. The curve can be also looked upon (and in practice can be plotted accordingly) as a graph of the energy received by a receiving circuit when adjusted to different frequencies. In Fig. 199, the transmitting ship, tuned to 500 kc/s., radiates a maximum of energy on this wave, but practically none on 450 and 550 kc/s., and therefore does not interfere with other ships trying to communicate on these waves.

If, however, the coupling is tight, the current in the aerial circuit is made up of two component frequencies which differ considerably, and the energy distribution curve in this case will have two distinct maxima at these different frequencies, giving a curve as in Fig. 200.

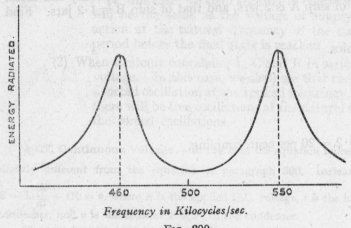

Frequency in Kilocycles/sec.

FIG. 200.

This means that the total energy available is divided, and also that interference with other lines of communication is caused.

For example, if the correct wave is 500 kc/s., and if, owing to the tightness of coupling, we radiate two waves, one 460 kc/s. and the other 550 kc/s. (a result which would be given approximately by a coupling of 17 per cent.), then we shall get an energy distribution curve as in Fig. 200, which gives bad interference on these wave frequencies. The tighter the coupling the further apart are the peaks in the Energy Distribution Curve, and the less is the energy actually radiated on the wave to which the circuits are tuned. It is found in practice that it is only for coupling of, say 5 per cent. or less, that the separate maxima merge into one and give a curve such as in Fig. 199.

In Section " A," details will be given of a method by which the interaction between the circuits is stopped soon after the oscillatory action starts, so that the aerial circuit continues to oscillate after that at one frequency only, its natural frequency.

424. Factors affecting Coupling.—For the type of coupling normally employed, *viz.*, mutual coupling, the results of paragraph 337 can be applied to give methods of varying the amount of coupling, or the coupling factor K. K depends on two factors :—

(a) How close the mutual coil is to the primary coil.

(b) How many turns of mutual coil are used.

If the mutual coil is pushed closer to the primary coil, or if the inductance in the mutual coil is increased and that in the aerial coil decreased to maintain the same total value in the aerial circuit, the mutual inductance M between the primary and the mutual is increased, and K, which is equal to $\dfrac{M}{\sqrt{L_1 L_2}}$, is increased.

From the expression $\sqrt{L_1 L_2}$, which depends on the total inductance used in the primary and aerial circuits, we learn that, with a given primary and aerial capacity, the higher the wave frequency, the less must L_1 and L_2 be, and hence, for a given adjustment of the mutual coil, K is increased.

Also, if two ships, one with an aerial of large capacity and one with an aerial of small capacity, are both transmitting on the same wave and using the same value of M, then the one with the larger

The current in the circuit is therefore also oscillatory and decreases ultimately to zero due to damping losses. The form of the expression is the same as that in paragraph 390.

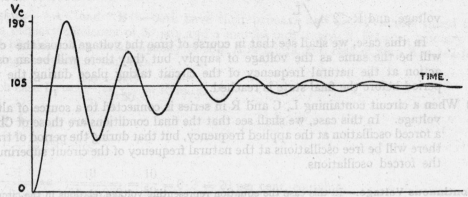

FIG. 202.

The figure above illustrates the varying voltage across the condenser in the case taken. The non-oscillatory case is similar to paragraph 174.

★428. **Alternating Voltage.**—In this case the equation becomes

$$E \sin \omega't = v + L \frac{di}{dt} + iR.$$

The frequency of the applied E.M.F. $\left(\frac{\omega'}{2\pi}\right)$ is taken to be different from the natural, or resonant, frequency

which are practically equal) of the circuit $\left(\frac{\omega}{2\pi}\right)$. In this case we shall derive the differential equation in a form which can be solved directly for current i.

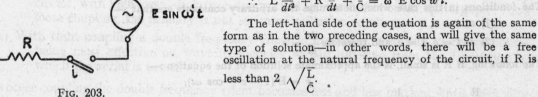

FIG. 203.

The full solution of the equation is quoted only, and is :—

Differentiating the equation above as it stands :—

$$L \frac{d^2i}{dt^2} + R \frac{di}{dt} + \frac{dv}{dt} = \omega' E \cos \omega' t.$$

Now $v = \frac{q}{C}$ and $\frac{dv}{dt} = \frac{1}{C} \frac{dq}{dt} = \frac{i}{C}$.

$$\therefore L \frac{d^2i}{dt^2} + R \frac{di}{dt} + \frac{i}{C} = \omega' E \cos w' t.$$

The left-hand side of the equation is again of the same form as in the two preceding cases, and will give the same type of solution—in other words, there will be a free oscillation at the natural frequency of the circuit, if R is less than $2\sqrt{\frac{L}{C}}$.

The particular solution obtained from the right-hand side of the equation represents the forced oscillation.

$$i = I' \sin(\omega't - \phi) + I e^{-at} \sin(\omega t - \theta),$$

where

$$I' = \frac{E}{\sqrt{R^2 + \left(\omega'L - \frac{1}{\omega'C}\right)^2}},$$

$$\tan \psi = \frac{\omega'L - \frac{1}{\omega'C}}{R}$$

$$= \frac{R}{2L} \text{ and } \omega = \sqrt{\frac{1}{LC} - \frac{R^2}{4L^2}}$$

The first term in the equation for i represents the forced oscillation, at the frequency of the applied E.M.F., and the second term represents the free oscillation, at the natural frequency of the circuit, which dies away at rate determined by the damping factor $\dfrac{R}{2L}$.

The initial current wave form is therefore a complicated one, composed of the two wave forms given.

With the initial conditions that—

    (1) at $t = o$, $i = o$.
    (2) at $t = o$, $v = o$.

and an impressed resonant frequency, i.e., such that $(\omega')^2 = \dfrac{1}{LC}$, a simple solution can be obtained if the damping of the circuit is small. This last condition means, of course, that R may be neglected in the expression for ω, making

$$\omega = \omega' = \frac{1}{\sqrt{LC}}.$$

In this case the solution reduces to the form

$$i = \frac{E}{R} \sin \omega t \left(1 - e^{-\frac{R}{2L}t} \right).$$

By integrating, v = voltage across condenser,

$$= \frac{E}{\omega CR} \left\{ \frac{R}{2\omega L} e^{-\frac{R}{2L}t} \sin \omega t - \left(1 - e^{-\frac{R}{2L}t} \right) \cos \omega t \right\}.$$

After the free oscillation dies away, only the forced oscillation, at the frequency of the applied E.M.F., remains, and the oscillatory action in the circuit may be said to settle down to its " steady state " in accordance with the theory of Chapter V.

We have now investigated the theory of free oscillations in an R, L, C circuit with no applied voltage, a constant applied voltage, and an alternating applied voltage, and in each case the free oscillatory action takes place at the natural frequency of the circuit, and lasts for a time determined by the damping losses, provided that

$$R < 2\sqrt{\frac{L}{C}}$$

The same result applies to a six-phase alternator, and this uniformity of the power output throughout the cycle is one reason for arranging the circuits so that the load may be balanced. The other principal reason is that since the sources are all exactly alike and so have the same resistance, the heating loss for a given total current output is a minimum when the currents are equally divided.

431. Two-Phase, Three-Wire System.—This arrangement is shown diagrammatically in Fig. 206 (a). The two sources are represented by S_1 and S_2 and are connected to load circuits L_1, L_1, . . . etc., and L_2, L_2, . . . etc., by means of the wires A and B and the **common return wire C.** The two sources are always so arranged that when the voltage wave is positive and is plotted above the line in Fig. 205 (a), then the wires A and B respectively are positive to the common return wire C.

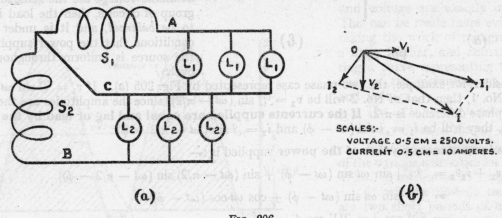

FIG. 206.

Thus, A will be positive to C during the first half of the cycle shown in Fig. 205 (a), and B will be positive to C during the second and third quarter cycles. The current from the source 1 passes out along the A wire and back along the C wire; current from 2 leaves by the wire B and also returns along C. Thus the current in C will be the sum of the two currents supplied by 1 and 2, due regard being paid to the time phases. This sum is most conveniently found by the vector method as in Fig. 206 (b). Here, OV_1 and OV_2 represent the voltage waveforms No. 1 and No. 2 of Fig. 205 (a). The currents supplied depend upon the impedances of the circuits L_1, L_1, . . . etc., and L_2, L_2, . . . etc. Each current will lag or lead on the voltage by the characteristic angle of the circuit, and will be equal to the voltage divided by the impedance. In Fig. 206 (b) the current taken by L_1, L_1, . . . etc., is represented by OI_1, and is of magnitude 65 amps., lagging by 15°. The voltage being 5,000, this assumes an impedance of L_1, L_1, . . . etc. of 5,000/65 = 77 ohms. Similarly, the current OI_2 is 22 amps., lagging by 40°; the loads L_2, L_2, ... etc., being assumed to have an impedance of 227 ohms. Other values of the impedances of the circuits would, of course, take correspondingly different currents. The current in the wire C is the sum of OI_1 and OI_2, viz., OI; found by completing the parallelogram OI_1II_2.

The load will be balanced when OI_1 and OI_2 are equal and make equal angles with OV_1 and OV_2 respectively. In that case the current in the C wire is $\sqrt{2}$ times the current in either of the wires A or B.

With the three-wire arrangement of Fig. 206 (a), load circuits could be connected between the wires A and B as at L_3, L_3, . . . etc., in Fig. 207 (a), the common return wire not being used. The voltage available between the wires A and B, *i.e.*, the amount by which A is positive to B, will be the *difference* between the amount by which A is positive to C, and the amount by which B is positive to C. That the difference must be taken is clear when it is remembered that for this arrangement the two sources are so connected that when the voltages are positive the wires A and B respectively are positive to the wire C. If one voltage is negative. the voltage between the wires A and B will be arithmetically the sum of the two instantaneous voltages. This, however, is automatically allowed for by taking the algebraical difference and making due allowance for the signs. This difference of the two voltages is found, as in Fig. 207 (b), by reversing the voltage OV_2 and adding,

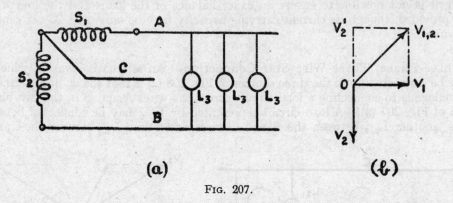

(a)   (b)

FIG. 207.

by completing the rectangle $OV_1V_{1,2}V'_2$. The value of $OV_{1,2}$ is clearly $\sqrt{2} \times OV_1$ and the voltage available between the wires A and B is $\sqrt{2}$ times the voltage of each source, and in phase is 45° ahead of the voltage of source 1.

432. **Three-Phase, Four-Wire Star Connection.**—This arrangement is shown in Fig. 208 (a) and is similar to the two-phase, three-wire connections described in the previous paragraph. The three sources 1, 2, and 3 are connected to the loads L_1, L_1, ... etc. ; L_2, L_2, ... etc., and L_3, L_3, ... etc., by the wires A, B and C, and the current returns along the common wire D. The connections to the source are so made that when the voltage is positive and plotted above the line in Fig. 205 (b), the wires A, B or C respectively are positive to the common return wire, D. The current in the common return wire will then be the sum of the three currents supplied to the three load

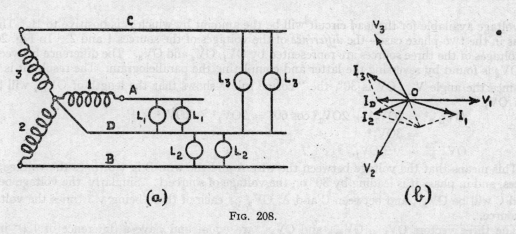

(a)   (b)

FIG. 208.

circuits. The currents may have any values, depending upon the load circuits, and the sum of them is found by the vector diagram of Fig. 208 (b), where two of the currents are assumed to be lagging and one leading. The voltage vectors OV_1, OV_2 and OV_3 are equal and spaced $2\pi/3$ (120°) apart. The three currents are OI_1, OI_2 and OI_3, the last being the one leading on the voltage OV_3. The current in the common return wire is OI_D, found by means of the construction shown in broken lines.

For a balanced load the currents OI_1, OI_2 and OI_3 would be equal in magnitude and spaced 120° apart, since each would lag by the same angle ϕ on the voltage maintaining it. The sum of three equal vectors 120° apart is zero, and under those conditions, therefore, there would be no current in the wire D, and if a balanced load could be ensured it would be unnecessary to provide this common wire. In practice, where the method of connecting the load circuits shown in Fig. 208 (a) is employed, it is not possible to ensure an exact balance of the loads and the fourth wire must actually be provided, though its current carrying capacity may be only, say, 25 per cent. of that of the other wires.

433. Three-Phase, Three-Wire Star Connection.—An alternative way in which the load circuits may be connected up to the three sources of Fig. 208 (a) is that shown in Fig. 209 (a). This is exactly analogous to connecting a load circuit across the wires A and B in the two-phase, three-wire system of Fig. 207 (a). A load circuit represented by $L_{1,2}$ may be connected between the A and B wires, another $L_{2,3}$ between the B and C wires, and a third $L_{3,1}$ between the C and A wires.

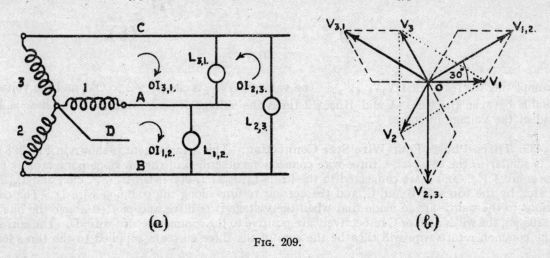

(a) **(b)**

Fig. 209.

The voltage available for the load circuit will be the amount by which A is positive to B. This will be—as in the two-phase case—the *difference* of the voltages of the sources 1 and 2. In Fig. 209 (b), the voltages of the three sources are represented by OV_1, OV_2 and OV_3. The difference between OV_1 and OV_2 is found by reversing the latter and completing the parallelogram. The resultant is $OV_{1,2}$ and since the angle $V_{1,2}OV$ is 30°, the " cosine rule " shows that the length of $OV_{1,2}$ will be $\sqrt{3}$ times OV_1.

$$OV_{1,2}{}^2 = 2OV_1{}^2 + 2OV_1{}^2 \cos 60° = 2OV_1{}^2 + 2OV_1{}^2 \times \tfrac{1}{2}$$
$$= 3OV_1{}^2$$
$$\therefore \quad OV_{1,2} = \sqrt{3}\, OV_1.$$

This means that the voltage between the wire A and the wire B is $\sqrt{3}$ times the voltage of the sources, and in phase it is leading by 30° on the voltage of source 1. Similarly, the voltage between B and C will be $OV_{2,3}$ and between C and A, $OV_{3,1}$; each of these being $\sqrt{3}$ times the voltage of the source.

The three vectors $OV_{1,2}$, $OV_{2,3}$ and $OV_{3,1}$ are equal and have a difference of 120° in time phase. They represent, therefore, three voltages similar to the three waveforms of Fig. 205 (b). With the arrangment of Fig. 209 (a) no use is made of the common return wire, D; it is unnecessary and only three wires are required, quite irrespective of whether the load is balanced or not.

With the arrangements of Fig. 208 (a) and 209 (a), the sources are said to be star connected because of the conventional method of representing the sources 1, 2 and 3. This convention is adopted owing to its relation to the three vectors OV_1, OV_2 and OV_3 of Figs. 208 (b) and 209 (b). The load circuits of Fig. 208 (a) are also said to be star connected, but those of Fig. 209 (a) are different and are described as " mesh " connected, or " delta " connected (paragraph 265).

In diagrams, the loads are often shown connected in the form of the Greek capital letter Delta, as the sources are in Fig. 112 (*a*).   In Fig. 209 (*b*) it may also be noted that the dotted lines drawn from the ends of the vectors OV_1, OV_2, and OV_3, together form the letter delta ; moreover, trigonometrically, it can easily be shown that these dotted lines are equal in magnitude and direction to the vectors $OV_{1,2}$, $OV_{2,3}$, $OV_{3,1}$ respectively.   They are, therefore, vectors themselves, and this **vector delta diagram** may be used as an alternative way of producing Fig. 209 (*b*).

The usefulness of the **vector delta diagram** for star connected sources may also be extended to include star connected loads.   When the latter are balanced the relation between the phase and line voltages at the load end must clearly be represented by a vector diagram of the same nature as that applicable to the sources ; the delta diagram drawn about O as in Fig. 209 (*b*) hence represents the three equal voltages across the phase loads, and the line voltages respectively.

When the loads are unbalanced, the phase voltages become unequal ; the relation between the phase voltages is determined by the position of the point O, which may be assumed capable of wandering and taking up any position inside or outside the delta diagram, the framework of which represents the constant line voltages.   Unbalanced loads often present complex problems ; many of them may be simply solved graphically by suitable use of the delta diagram (paragraph 442).

It should be noted that with balanced loads the vector sum of the phase voltages is zero, and forms a closed polygon when plotted, namely a triangle.   With unbalanced loads a closed figure will not be produced, and a meaning can usually be found for the " closing side " of the polygon.

Attention is called to the use of numerical sub-scripts in this work.   It is a help always to write the sub-scripts in cyclic order, 1, 2, 3, 1, etc. ; this symmetrical notation is particularly useful in calculations involving algebraic equations (paragraph 442).

The arrangement of Fig. 209 (*a*) is the one most commonly used in the large three-phase alternating current power transmission systems.   The connections which have been spoken of here as the wires A, B and C become the three conductors of the power transmission lines and are often spoken of as the three " lines."

434. The Relation between the Line Current and the Load Current with Mesh Connections.—Referring to Fig. 209 (*a*), the current from source 1 is positive when flowing out along the A wire.   The voltage across the load circuit is positive when the wire A is positive to B, and the positive direction of the current in $L_{1,2}$ will therefore be from the wire A to the wire B.   Similarly, the positive currents in the sources 2 and 3 are out along the B and C wires respectively, and in the load circuits $L_{2,3}$ and $L_{3,1}$ from wire B to wire C and from wire C to wire A respectively.   Thus, the current along the A wire will be the current in the $L_{1,2}$ circuit (from A to B) minus the current in the $L_{3,1}$ circuit (from C to A).   Similarly, the current in the B wire is the current in the load circuit $L_{2,3}$ minus the current in $L_{1,2}$; the current in the C wire is the current in $L_{3,1}$ minus the current in $L_{2,3}$.   The voltages maintaining each of the load currents are the voltages $OV_{1,2}$, $OV_{2,3}$ and $OV_{3,1}$ of Fig. 209 (*b*).   Each current can be calculated when these voltages are given and the details of the circuits are ascertained.   In Fig. 210 the three-load circuit voltages $OV_{1,2}$, $OV_{2,3}$ and $OV_{3,1}$ and the three-load circuit currents $OI_{1,2}$, $OI_{2,3}$, $OI_{3,1}$ have been drawn in for one particular arrangement of circuits ; all three currents being assumed to be lagging.   The current in the A wire is $OI_{1,2}$ minus $OI_{3,1}$, viz., OI_1; found by reversing $OI_{3,1}$ and completing the parallelogram as shown by the dotted lines.   This will also be the current in source 1.   Similarly, the current in the B wire and in the source 2 will be OI_2 and in the C wire and source 3, OI_3.

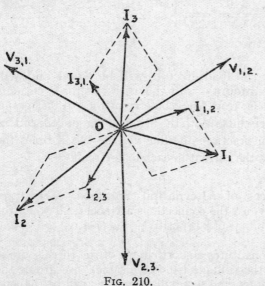

FIG. 210.

Thus, if the voltage of the sources is known, the voltage between the wires—generally known as the " **line voltage** "—can be found. It is $\sqrt{3}$ times the voltage of the source and leads by 30°. Then, if the details of the circuits are known the circuit currents can be found and from them the currents from each source can be determined. In the numerous practical cases in which these calculations are necessary it is generally the line voltage that is known, which eliminates one step in the calculations.

To take a numerical example, suppose that the line voltage is 110 R.M.S. volts and that the load circuits consist of :—

$L_{1,2}$ .... Lamps and radiators equivalent to a non-inductive resistance of 1·8 ohms.

$L_{2,3}$ .... An inductive circuit of impedance 2·5 ohms and having an angle of lag of 45°.

$L_{3,1}$ .... An inductive circuit of reactance 0·8 ohm and resistance 1·25 ohms.

What will be the currents in the three lines, and their phases relative to the voltages of the three sources ?

Here the line voltages are each 110 and may be drawn in as in Fig. 210. The current $OI_{1,2}$ will be of magnitude $110/1 \cdot 8 = 61 \cdot 1$ amperes and will be in phase with $OV_{1,2}$. The current $OI_{2,3}$ will be of magnitude $110/2 \cdot 5 = 44$ amperes and lags on the voltage $OV_{2,3}$ by 45°. The current $OI_{3,1}$ will be of magnitude $110/\sqrt{(0 \cdot 8)^2 + (1 \cdot 25)^2} = 73 \cdot 9$ amperes and the angle of lag will be $\tan^{-1} \dfrac{0 \cdot 8}{1 \cdot 25} = 32° 37'$. Drawing in these three currents to scale and completing the parallelograms gives $OI_1 = 93 \cdot 7$ amperes ; $OI_2 = 105$ amperes, and $OI_3 = 96$ amperes, and the phase angles relative to the voltages of the source as 21° 25', 23° 10' and 28° 30'.

These results may be checked by considering the power supplied from the sources and the power expended in the load circuits (paragraph 436).

The former is :—

$$\frac{110}{\sqrt{3}}\left\{ 93 \cdot 7 \cos 21° 25' + 105 \cos 23° 10' + 96 \cos 28° 30' \right\} = 17,000 \text{ watts.}$$

The power expended in the circuits will be :—

$$\frac{110^2}{1 \cdot 8} + \frac{110^2 \cos 45°}{2 \cdot 5} + \left\{ \frac{110}{\sqrt{(0 \cdot 8)^2 + (1 \cdot 25)^2}} \right\}^2 1 \cdot 25$$
$$= 17,000 \text{ watts,}$$

so checking the previous calculations.

With a balanced load, the currents taken by the load circuits will be equal and will differ in phase from the line voltages by equal amounts. In this case the three currents from the three sources will be equal and—as can be seen from the geometry of the parallelograms then arising—will be $\sqrt{3}$ times the current in the load circuits. With the arrangement of connections of Fig. 209 (a)—the one most commonly met with in practice—the line voltage is $\sqrt{3}$ times the voltage of each source and the line current is $\sqrt{3}$ times the current in each load circuit.

435. The Mesh Connection of Three Sources of Alternating Voltages.—The three sources may be connected in series as in Fig. 211, provided the connections are such that when the voltage of 1 is positive, A is positive to B ; when the voltage of 2 is positive, B is positive to C ; and when the voltage of 3 is positive, C is positive to A.

It appears at first sight that this arrangement constitutes a short circuit of the three sources. This is not so, however, because the time-phase of the voltages is not the same. Regarding the three sources as a closed circuit, the available voltage tending to circulate current will be the sum of the three voltages OV_1, OV_2 and OV_3 of Fig. 209 (b)—which is obviously zero. Thus, at every instant, the tendency of one voltage to drive current in one direction is balanced by the tendency of the other two to drive current in the opposite direction. Or, referring to Fig. 205 (b), the sum of the three curves is zero for every instant of time throughout the cycle.

This arrangement is used in practice to a considerable extent where relatively low voltages are required. Fig. 211 shows mesh connected sources joined to equal and similar star connected impedances. (Cf. paragraph 266.)

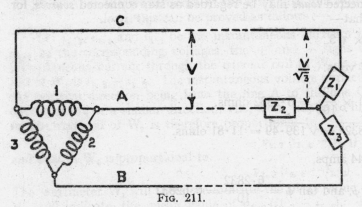

FIG. 211.

436. The Power Supply with Three-Phase Circuits.—Each individual load circuit will have a definite power factor, and if $I_{1,2}$, $I_{2,3}$ and $I_{3,1}$ are the three **phase currents**, $\phi_{1,2}$, $\phi_{2,3}$ and $\phi_{3,1}$ are the angles of phase displacement and V is the **line voltage,** then the power supplied is :—

$$V\{I_{1,2}\cos\phi_{1,2} + I_{2,3}\cos\phi_{2,3} + I_{3,1}\cos\phi_{3,1}\}.$$

If the load is balanced all the currents will be the same (I_c) and all the angles will be the same (ϕ) and the power will be $3VI_c\cos\phi$. Moreover, with a balanced load, the **line current** (I) is $\sqrt{3}$ times the current in each load circuit and so the power is :—

$$\frac{3VI}{\sqrt{3}}\cos\phi = \sqrt{3}\,IV\cos\phi.$$

Under these circumstances **cos ϕ may be spoken of as the power factor of the system,** but unless the loads are balanced this term has to be defined as the ratio of the actual power supplied to the circuits to the sum of the volt-amperes for the three circuits.

437. Numerical Examples.

Example 56.

A three-phase system supplies 25 kW. at a P.F. of 0·8, the line pressure being 250 volts. Calculate the **line current** (I_L) and the **phase current** when the load is (a) star connected ; (b) mesh connected.

(a) STAR CONNECTED.

Power $= \sqrt{3}\,V_L\,I_L\cos\phi$ $\therefore$ $25{,}000 = \sqrt{3} \times 250\,I_L \times 0\cdot8$

$\therefore I_L = \dfrac{25{,}000}{250 \times \sqrt{3} \times 0\cdot8} = \dfrac{25}{0\cdot3464} = 72\cdot16$ amperes.

$\therefore$ **Line current** $= 72\cdot16$ amps., and **Phase current** $= 72\cdot16$ amps.

(b) MESH CONNECTED.

Phase current $= \dfrac{72\cdot16}{\sqrt{3}} = 41\cdot67$ amps. ...... (paragraph 434).

$\therefore$ **Line current** $= 72\cdot16$ amps., and **Phase current** $= 41\cdot67$ amps.

Example 57.

Three coils, each having a resistance of 10 ohms and an inductance of 0·02 H. are connected (a) in star, (b) in mesh, to a three-phase 50 cycle supply, the line voltage being 500 volts. Calculate, for each case, the line current and the total power absorbed.

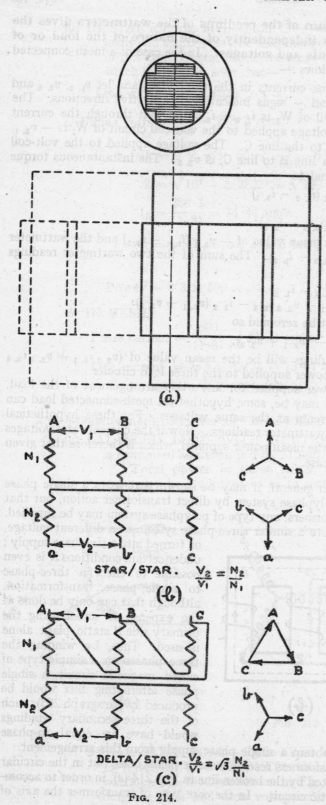

STAR/STAR. $\frac{V_2}{V_1} = \frac{N_2}{N_1}$

(b)

DELTA/STAR. $\frac{V_2}{V_1} = \sqrt{3}\,\frac{N_2}{N_1}$

(c)

FIG. 214.

the coil is usually vertical, the parts of the magnetic circuit encircled by the coils being known as the cores, legs or limbs, the remainder of the magnetic circuit being known as the "yoke." Fig. 214 (*a*) represents a vertical section of this type of transformer, showing a plan view of one of the vertical cores with a winding on it.

Because of the general appearance of the transformer, the coil windings may be realistically represented by diagrams of the nature of Fig. 214 (*b*) and (*c*). The primary and secondary windings of each phase enclose the same limb of the core of the transformer, the magnetic circuit for the flux produced in one limb being completed through the other two.

The phase relationship of the flux produced in each limb is the same as that of the respective voltages ; at any instant **the vector sum of the upward and downward flux in space is zero** (*cf.* paragraph 263). In effect this means that the flux in any limb is that which would be produced if each of the phases were transformed by separate transformer action. Fig. 213 represents diagrammatically the state of affairs at two particular instants of time for phase No. 1 (*cf.* Fig. 110, paragraph 263). Fig. 213 (*a*) shows the instant of *maximum flux*, the flux being equal numerically to the sum of the equal fluxes produced simultaneously in the other two phases. Fig. 213 (*b*) represents the instant of *zero flux* in phase 1, and this is also the instant at which the flux due to phases 2 and 3 produces mutual cancellation in the limb of phase 1.

Owing to the many different kinds of transformation which can be effected with polyphase supplies, there are very many ways in which power can be supplied to the primary and taken from the secondary. It is not possible in this work to give a complete discussion of all of them, and Figs. 214 (*b*) and (*c*) must only be taken as representing two simple connections.

Fig. 214 (*b*) shows the primaries and secondaries both star connected. The **star/star connection** is the most economical one for high voltages, and finds its greatest application with three-phase core type transformers used for supplying relatively small power loads. Both *neutrals* are available for earthing or for giving a balanced four-wire supply.

Fig. 214 (*c*) is a diagrammatic representation of the connections representing mesh connected primaries and star connected secondaries, a type of connection further shown in Fig. 215. The **delta/star connection** is widely used for stepping down to supply a four-wire load which may be balanced or unbalanced, and for stepping up to supply a high-tension transmission line. Alternatively, the secondary neutral may be earthed, as in Fig. 215 (*a*) where the secondary load is automatically balanced.

440. Numerical Example 58.—Pressure is supplied to a three-phase, core-type transformer at 20,000 volts and transformed down to 2,000 line volts at a frequency of 50 cycles. The high-tension winding is delta-connected and the low-tension star-connected—Fig. 214 (*c*). The core is made up of three packets of plates, one of 25×17 cm. and two of 4×17 cm. Assuming a maximum flux density of 12,000 lines per sq. cm., calculate the number of turns in each winding.

As the high-tension winding is connected in delta the voltage across each winding = 20,000 volts. The low-tension winding, being connected in star, will have a voltage per winding

$$= \frac{2,000}{\sqrt{3}} = 1,154 \text{ volts} = E_2.$$

Consequently, the ratio of transformation

$$T = \frac{E_2}{E_1} = \frac{N_2}{N_1} = \frac{1,154}{20,000} = 0 \cdot 0577.$$

Total area of each core ....(Fig. 214 (*a*))

$$= (25 \times 17) + 2 (4 \times 17) = 560 \text{ sq. cm.}$$

Allowing 10 per cent. for insulation between plates, the active area of each core $= 0 \cdot 9 \times 560 = 504$ sq. cm.

The instantaneous value of the secondary E.M.F. in each phase is given by the rate of change of flux linkage. With the usual symbols, and assuming no leakage flux,

$$e_2 = - N_2 \frac{d\phi}{dt} \text{ where } \phi = \phi_{\max.} \sin \omega t$$

$$\therefore \quad e_2 = - N_2 \omega \phi_{\max.} \cos \omega t \times 10^{-8} = \mathscr{E}_2 \cos \omega t \quad \ldots\ldots\text{in volts.}$$

where $\mathscr{E}_2 = - N_2 \omega \phi_{\max.} \times 10^{-8}$ ......in volts,

or in R.M.S. values, and putting $\omega = 2\pi f$,

$$E_2 = 2\pi f N_2 \phi_{\max.} \times 10^{-8} / \sqrt{2} = 4 \cdot 44 f N_2 \phi_{\max.} \times 10^{-8}.$$

$$\therefore \quad N_2 = E_2 / 4 \cdot 44 f \phi_{\max.} \, 10^{-8}$$

$$\therefore \quad N_2 = \frac{1154 \times 10^8}{4 \cdot 44 \times 50 \times 504 \times 12000} = 86 \text{ turns per winding,}$$

and $N_1 = \dfrac{N_2}{T} = \dfrac{86}{0 \cdot 0577} = 1,490$ turns per winding.

441. Three-Phase Power Rectifiers.—Fig. 215 represents a three-phase power rectifier employing separate diode valves, and a three-phase supply connected using the delta/star connection; an alternative diagrammatic representation of the connections of the windings is given in Fig. 215 (*b*).

For convenience this figure is included here, but the student will find it useful to study it in conjunction with Section " H " on " Power Supplies."

In practice, the three diode valves may be replaced by mercury vapour rectifiers, in which the three anodes may be included for convenience within the same valve envelope.

The action is similar to that of a full wave rectifier (" H " 3) electrons being drawn across the valves whenever their respective anodes are positive to the filaments. In operation, the top plate

$$\therefore \quad \left.\begin{array}{r} -50 + j\,50\sqrt{3} = -I_1\,50j - I_2\,50 \\ 100 = I_2\,50 - I_3\,50j \end{array}\right\}$$

Hence

$$I_3 = 2j - jI_2 \dotfill (4)$$

and

$$I_1 = -j - \sqrt{3} + jI_2 \dotfill (5)$$

$$\therefore \text{ from (3) } -j - \sqrt{3} + jI_2 + I_2 + 2j - jI_2 = 0$$

$$\therefore \quad I_2 = \sqrt{3} - j \text{ or } \bar{I}_2 = 2 \text{ amps.}$$

and by substitution in (4) and (5)

$$I_3 = 0 \cdot 268j - 1 \quad \text{or} \quad \bar{I}_3 = 1 \cdot 035 \text{ amps.}$$

$$I_1 = 0 \cdot 732j - 0 \cdot 732 \quad \text{or} \quad \bar{I}_1 = 1 \cdot 035 \text{ amps.}$$

Hence   P.D. across $Z_2 = 100$ volts.

and   „ $Z_3 = 51 \cdot 75$ volts.

and   „ $Z_1 = 51 \cdot 75$ volts.

The vector diagram may now be completed ; $O'a$ and $O'b$ represent the two equal phase voltages, $O'c$ representing the voltage across Z_2. The vector currents are shown by dotted lines, their vector sum being zero and represented by a closed polygon. The condenser current I_1 leads V_1 by 90°, I_3 lags behind V_3 by 90°, and I_2 is in phase with V_2.

This example shows clearly the effect of departure from the condition of balanced loads represented by the point O.

Example 60.

Three impedances of 20 ohms each and each having a reactance of 12 ohms are connected in star to a three-phase supply with 400 volts between the lines. Find the power taken and the power factor. Find the three equal impedances which if placed in mesh on the same circuit would take the same power at the same power factor. (I.E.E., November, 1932.)

Answer.—6·4 kW. at 0·8 p.f. lagging ; $Z = 60$; $X = 36$.

Example 61.

What are the advantages of the three-phase, 4-conductor system for a distribution network ?

In such a system there is a balanced three-phase motor load taking 200 kW. at a power factor of 0·8 lagging, while lamps connected between phase conductors and the neutral take 50, 70 and 100 kW. respectively. The voltage between phase conductors is 430 volts. Calculate the current in each phase conductor and in the neutral wire of the feeder supplying these loads. (Univ. Lond., 1938, El. Power.)

Answer.—510, 587, 699, neutral 174 amps.

Example 62.

A three-phase supply with the neutral point earthed and with a constant P.D. of 430 volts between lines, supplies the following unbalanced loads connected in delta : 65 kVA power factor 0·7 leading between lines 1 and 2, 100 kVA power factor unity between lines 2 and 3, and 75 kVA power factor 0·6 lagging between lines 3 and 1. Give a graphical representation of the line and phase voltages and currents, and find, graphically or otherwise, the current in each line conductor of the supply system. (C. & G. Final, 1929.)

Answer.—64 amps., 380 amps., 407 amps.

THE DECIBEL AND THE NEPER.

1. **Historical.**—The " decibel " is the 1/10th part of a " bel " (after Alexander Graham Bell, inventor of the telephone sounder), a unit in which one may express power ratios, and gain or loss ratios of related quantities such as current and voltage. It originated in line telephony in 1923, when the American Telephone and Telegraph Company introduced a new unit, then called a " transmission unit "; this was to replace an older conception based on a ratio comparison between the decrease in signal strength produced by the given telephone line, and that produced by a " mile of standard cable." In 1924, an international advisory committee on long distant telephony in Europe, together with the representatives of the Bell system, agreed to recommend their countries to adopt as standards

EITHER the " **bel**," a unit based on logarithms to the base 10, and equal to 10 of the American Company's " transmission units,"

OR the " **neper** " (after Napier), a unit based on Naperian logarithms to the base **e**.

The growth in popularity of the decibel, since 1929, has been so great that it is now almost a household word throughout all branches of Electrical Engineering and Acoustics.

2. **Definitions.**

THE DECIBEL :—Two powers P_1 and P_2 are said to differ by N " bels " when—

$$\frac{P_1}{P_2} = 10^N \ i.e. \ N = \log_{10} \frac{P_1}{P_2} \ \ldots\ldots\ldots \text{ in bels.}$$

Or in words—" The logarithm to the base 10 of the ratio of the powers, gives the gain or loss in bels." If $P_1 = P_2$, then N = O.

In practice, a unit of one bel is found to be inconveniently large, and the 1/10th part of it—the decibel—is more often used. Using the smaller unit we have—

$$\frac{P_1}{P_2} = 10^{0 \cdot 1N} \text{ or } N = 10 \log_{10} \frac{P_1}{P_2} \ \ldots\ldots\ldots \text{ in decibels.}$$

The basic power ratio is $10^{0 \cdot 1}$, that is, $1 \cdot 259$.

THE NEPER :—Two powers P_1 and P_2 are said to differ by N " nepers " when—

$$\frac{P_1}{P_2} = (e^2)^N \doteqdot 10^N$$

$$\therefore \ \left(\frac{P_1}{P_2}\right) = e^N \ i.e. \ N = \tfrac{1}{2} \log_e \frac{P_1}{P_2} \ \ldots\ldots\ldots \text{ in nepers.}$$

Any ratio in db. may be readily converted to nepers, for example 60 db.—

We have $\log_{10} \frac{P_1}{P_2} = 6$ bels.

$$\therefore \ \tfrac{1}{2} \log_e \frac{P_1}{P_2} = 2 \cdot 3026 \times 6 \times \tfrac{1}{2} = 6 \cdot 907 \text{ nepers.}$$

The neper is used in some European Countries, but is less commonly encountered than the decibel.

3. **Cables, Amplifiers and Attenuators.**—With these units, if the signal strength of a cable signal is 1/10th of that at the transmitting end, the loss is 1 bel. With two similar cables in series, the received signal would be 1/100th of the transmitted one, and the loss would be two bels.

In any amplifier, if the output power is 100 times the input, the " gain " is two bels or 20 db ; with two such amplifiers used in series, the gain in power ratio would be 10,000 : 1, or 40 dbs.

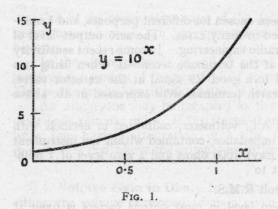

$$y = 10^x$$

FIG. 1.

If an increase of intensity by 10 times produces a given effect at the ear, and a further increase of 10 times, that is to say a total of 100 times, will produce twice the effect at the ear. Mathematically, this implies that the ear responds logarithmically to sounds of different intensities (*i.e.*, powers), or that a logarithmic graph will be obtained if " sound intensity " if plotted along the -y-axis, and " sensation of loudness " plotted along the -x-axis. The curve is similar to that obtained on plotting $y = 10^x$, Fig. 1. In a graph of this nature, equal percentage increases in the value of y give equal increments along the -x-axis. Considering the output of wireless receivers, the justification of the decibel notation is that a change in output from 8 to 40 milli-watts (7 db.) would seem to the ear identical with the change from 40 to 200 milli-watts, since the power ratio is again 5 : 1.

It is interesting to note that, in addition to the aural response to power being logarithmic, the ear also responds logarithmically with respect to pitch (*i.e.*, frequency). The graph of frequency plotted against " musical interval " along the -x-axis would be similar to that of Fig. 1. Tones separated by an octave have a frequency ratio of 2 and are detected by the ear as being similar musical intervals. The various C's on a piano would appear equally spaced along the -x-axis of a graph like that of Fig. 1.

Fig. 2 shows an amplifier fidelity curve. It represents the differential amplification of all frequencies in the usual A/F range. Ideally, an amplifier should amplify all frequencies equally well, and, in that case, the fidelity curve would be a straight line. This curve shows that with reference to the output at 500 cycles, frequencies below 200 cycles are not equally amplified. The graph gives a true representation of the fidelity with which the amplifier treats the various frequencies. At one time, these graphs were plotted using a voltage ratio scale along the y-axis ; since the ear is logarithmic in action, curves of that nature cannot represent truly the aural effect, and give a wrong impression of the performance of the apparatus. For example, at 4000 cycles, the full curve shows the voltage ratio as being 80 per cent., or 1·25 taking the reciprocal ; corresponding to this voltage ratio, from the table we obtain approximately 2 dbs., and the dotted curve accordingly passes through the point -2 db.

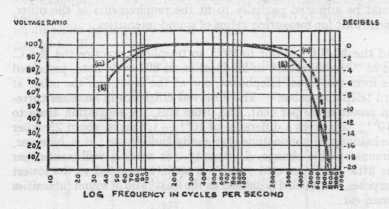

FREQUENCY-RESPONSE CURVES OF AN AMPLIFIER

(a) IN DECIBELS
(b) IN VOLTAGE RATIOS

FIG. 2.

9. Power in Sounds—Decibel Level—Tone Control.—The sensitivity of the ear varies with the frequency and also with the " level " at which the sound is produced. For any normal person there is a minimum sound intensity for each frequency, below which nothing is heard. Fig. 3 is due to Fletcher and Munson ; the lower curve shows the relative variation in level of the "threshold of audibility" over the ordinary A/F band. The level at 1000 cycles is arbitrarily marked 0 and is taken as a zero or datum level.

Ordinary conversation is approximately 60 db., above the threshold of audibility. The curves may be termed "equal loudness curves," and show the relative insensitivity of the ear to low notes when the intensity level is low. In the case of the curve 0, a just audible tone at 100 cycles has a sound power about 38 db. above a similar one at 1000 cycles.

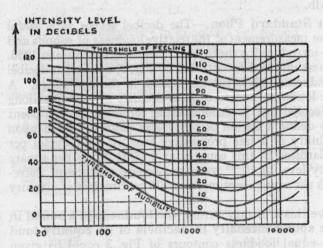

INTENSITY LEVEL IN DECIBELS

LOG. FREQUENCY IN CYCLES PER SECOND

FIG. 3.

At an intensity level of 60 db. at 1000 cycles, an equally loud tone at 100 cycles would only differ in power by about 12 db. For very intense sounds over about 90 db., the ear appears almost uniformly sensitive over the above frequency range. Still more intense sounds are felt rather than heard, and there is, in fact, a boundary called the "threshold of feeling." From the practical point of view it follows, that a voice cannot sound natural unless it is reproduced at its natural level. When this is not possible, or desirable, the volume control is turned up and the intensity level is raised; although the relative power content may remain the same, the increased sensitivity of the ear to the lower notes produces the well-known and unpleasant sensation of "booming." In a large auditorium, a surfeit of low tones masks the higher ones and impairs the general intelligibility of speech. For this reason, in large public address systems, a volume control should always be operated in conjunction with a "tone control."

It will be noted that the 50 db. curve is the one which is flattest over the greatest range of frequencies, and it is sometimes considered that this is the optimum level of reproduction.

Sound powers have, so far, been described in relative terms. It is, however, possible to put each sound power on an absolute basis. It has been measured that the average power of ordinary speech is somewhere between 10 and 15 micro-watts ; on this basis G.W.C. Kaye calculated that the continuous talk of a Wembley Stadium football crowd of 100,000 persons represented only enough energy to light a small electric lamp throughout the period of the game. It was similarly calculated that the acoustic disturbance created by a ship's syren amounts to about 6 micro-watts per square centimetre at a distance of about 115 ft. This represented a total dissipation of energy by sound of about 1/3rd of a horse power. The peak power of the loudest sound in conversation has been stated to be of the order of 5000 micro-watts, the power of the faintest sound being in the region of 0·01 micro-watts ; this represents a range of about 57 db. The power corresponding to the datum line of audibility itself has been variously estimated by different observers. Although there is no general agreement about the exact figure, the number 10^{-16} watts per square centimetre, for a free progressive wave of frequency 1000 cycles per second, is now usually quoted by American Research workers as the datum line. With this level as a basis, the level of ordinary conversation appears as about 100 db. (not 60 db. as quoted above), assuming the average power of ordinary speech to be 10 micro-watts.

Musical sounds have a much greater power range than speech sounds. The peak power produced by a large orchestra may be of the order of 100 watts, and the noisiest drum can produce peaks of power of 25 watts.

Noises may, similarly, be expressed in terms of decibels above a datum. Measurements have been made over a complete scale of noise levels, from that of an aeroplane engine (110 db.) including

TABLE I—continued.

Frequency (f) in kilocycles per second.	Wave-length (λ) in metres.	LC value (mic.-jars).	Frequency (f) in kilocycles per second.	Wavelength (λ) in metres.	LC value (mic.-jars.)
909·1	330	27·58	166·7	1,800	820·7
882·3	340	29·28	162·2	1,850	866·9
857·1	350	31·03	157·9	1,900	914·4
833·3	360	32·83	153·8	1,950	963·2
810·8	370	34·68	151·5	1,980	993·0
789·5	380	36·58	150·0	2,000	1,013
769·2	390	38·53	142·9	2,100	1,117
750·0	400	40·53	136·4	2,200	1,226
731·7	410	42·58	130·4	2,300	1,340
714·3	420	44·68	125·0	2,400	1,459
697·7	430	46·84	120·0	2,500	1,583
681·8	440	49·04	115·4	2,600	1,712
666·7	450	51·29	111·1	2,700	1,847
652·2	460	53·60	107·1	2,800	1,986
638·3	470	55·95	103·4	2,900	2,130
625·0	480	58·36	100·0	3,000	2,280
612·2	490	60·82	96·77	3,100	2,434
600·0	500	63·33	93·75	3,200	2,594
588·2	510	65·88	90·91	3,300	2,758
576·9	520	68·49	88·24	3,400	2,928
566·0	530	71·15	85·71	3,500	3,103
555·6	540	73·86	80·00	3,750	3,562
545·4	550	76·62	78·95	3,800	3,658
535·7	560	79·44	76·92	3,900	3,853
526·3	570	82·30	75·00	4,000	4,053
517·1	580	85·21	71·34	4,200	4,468
508·5	590	88·17	70·59	4,250	4,575
500·0	600	91·19	66·67	4,500	5,129
461·5	650	107·0	63·83	4,700	5,595
428·6	700	124·1	63·16	4,750	5,715
400·0	750	142·5	60·00	5,000	6,333
375·0	800	162·1	54·54	5,500	7,662
352·9	850	183·0	50·00	6,000	9,119
333·3	900	205·2	46·15	6,500	10,702
315·8	950	228·6	42·86	7,000	12,412
300·0	1,000	253·3	40·00	7,500	14,248
285·7	1,050	279·3	37·50	8,000	16,211
272·7	1,100	306·5	35·29	8,500	18,301
260·9	1,150	335·0	34·29	8,750	19,393
250·0	1,200	364·8	33·33	9,000	20,517
241·9	1,240	389·5	31·58	9,500	22,861
240·0	1,250	395·8	30·00	10,000	25,330
232·6	1,290	421·5	27·27	11,000	30,650
230·8	1,300	428·1	25·00	12,000	36,476
222·2	1,350	461·6	24·19	12,400	38,948
214·3	1,400	496·5	23·08	13,000	42,808
212·8	1,410	503·6	21·43	14,000	49,647
206·9	1,450	532·6	20·00	15,000	56,993
202·7	1,480	554·8	18·75	16,000	64,846
200·0	1,500	569·9	17·65	17,000	73,204
193·5	1,550	608·6	16·67	18,000	82,070
187·5	1,600	648·5	15·79	19,000	91,442
181·8	1,650	689·6	15·00	20,000	101,321
176·5	1,700	732·0	12·00	25,000	158,314
172·4	1,740	766·9	10·00	30,000	227,973
171·4	1,750	775·7			

TABLE II.

Frequency (f) in megacycles per second Mc/s.	Wave-length (λ) in metres (below one metre in cm.)	Frequency (f) in megacycles per second Mc/s.	Wave-length (λ) in metres (below one metre in cm.)	Frequency (f) in megacycles per second Mc/s.	Wave-length (λ) in metres (below one metre in cm.)
30·0	10·0	45·4	6·6	93·8	3·2
30·3	9·9	46·2	6·5	96·8	3·1
30·6	9·8	46·9	6·4	100·0	3·0
30·9	9·7	47·6	6·3	103·0	2·9
31·3	9·6	48·4	6·2	107·0	2·8
31·6	9·5	49·2	6·1	111·0	2·7
31·9	9·4	50·0	6·0	115·0	2·6
32·3	9·3	50·8	5·9	120·0	2·5
32·6	9·2	51·8	5·8	125·0	2·4
33·0	9·1	52·7	5·7	130·0	2·3
33·3	9·0	53·6	5·6	136·0	2·2
33·7	8·9	54·6	5·5	143·0	2·1
34·1	8·8	55·6	5·4	150·0	2·0
34·5	8·7	56·6	5·3	158·0	1·9
34·9	8·6	57·7	5·2	167·0	1·8
35·3	8·5	58·8	5·1	176·0	1·7
35·7	8·4	60·0	5·0	187·0	1·6
36·1	8·3	61·2	4·9	200·0	1·5
36·6	8·2	62·5	4·8	214·0	1·4
37·0	8·1	63·8	4·7	231·0	1·3
37·5	8·0	65·2	4·6	250·0	1·2
38·0	7·9	66·6	4·5	273·0	1·1
38·5	7·8	68·2	4·4	300·0	1·0
39·0	7·7	69·8	4·3		
39·5	7·6	71·5	4·2	(f) in Mc/s.	(λ) in cms.
40·0	7·5	73·2	4·1		
40·6	7·4	75·0	4·0	333·0	90
41·1	7·3	77·0	3·9	375·0	80
41·7	7·2	79·0	3·8	429·0	70
42·3	7·1	81·1	3·7	500·0	60
42·9	7·0	83·4	3·6	600·0	50
43·5	6·9	85·8	3·5	750·0	40
44·1	6·8	88·2	3·4	1,000	30
44·8	6·7	91·0	3·3	1,500	20
				3,000	10
				30,000	1

W/T TEXT BOOKS, WORKS OF REFERENCE AND JOURNALS.

The following is a list of selected works which may serve as a guide to any officer or rating who wishes to study other aspects of Radio Engineering, or who desires to read other books in conjunction with the Admiralty Handbook.

The selection is in no way an exhaustive one, and works of a highly specialised nature have been purposely excluded.

TEXT BOOKS.

" Radio Engineering." By F. E. Terman. (McGraw-Hill. 1937.—30s.)

" Principles of Radio Engineering." By R. S. Glasgow. (McGraw-Hill. 1936.—24s.)

" Modern Radio Communication." Vols. I & II. By J. H. Reyner. (Pitman. 1935.—5s. and 7s. 6d., from the publisher.)

" Principles of Radio Communication." By J. Morecroft. (Chapman & Hall. 1933.—37s. 6d.)

" Short Wave Wireless Communication." By A. W. Ladner & C. R. Stoner. (Chapman & Hall. 1936.—15s.)

" Foundations of Wireless." By A. L. M. Sowerby. (Iliffe & Sons. 1936.—4s. 6d.)

" Wireless Receivers." By C. W. Oatley. (Methuen Co. 1932.—2s. 6d.)

" Wireless Engineering." By L. S. Palmer. (Longmans Green & Co. 1936.—21s.)

" Theory of Radio Communication." By the Post Office Engineering Department. (H.M.S.O. 1934.—7s.)

ELEMENTARY TEXT BOOKS

" Wireless—Its Principles and Practice." By R. W. Hutchinson. (London University Tutorial Press. 1935.—3s. 6d.)

" Physical Principles of Wireless." By J. A. Ratcliffe. (Methuen Co. 1929.—2s. 6d.)

" The Outline of Wireless." By R. Stranger. (Newnes, 1931.—8s. 6d.)

" Tuning in Without Tears." By Frank Boyce. (Pitman. 1936.—2s. 6d.)

TEXT BOOKS OF AMATEUR RADIO SOCIETIES.

" A Guide to Amateur Radio." (By Radio Society of Great Britain. Yearly.—6d.)

" The Radio Amateur's Handbook." (American Radio Relay League. Yearly.—5s. 6d.)

HISTORICAL WORKS.

" Radio Communication—History & Development." The Science Museum Handbook. (H.M.S.O. 1934.—2s. 6d.)

NUMERICAL EXERCISES IN RADIO ENGINEERING.

" Problems in Radio Engineering." By E. T. A. Rapson. (Pitman. 1935.—3s. 6d.)

" Classified Examples in Electrical Engineering—Vol. II. Alternating Current." By S. G. Monk. (Pitman. 1933.—3s. 6d.)

MORE ADVANCED TEXT BOOKS ; WORKS OF REFERENCE.

" Radio Engineering Handbook." By R. Henney. (McGraw-Hill. 1935.—30s.)

" Wireless." By L. B. Turner. (Cambridge University Press. 1931.—25s.)

" Phenomena in High Frequency Systems." By A. Hund. (McGraw-Hill. 1936.—30s.)

" Measurements in Radio Engineering." By F. E. Terman. (McGraw-Hill. 1935.—24s.

" Thermionic Vacuum Tubes." By E. V. Appleton. (Methuen Co. 1931.—3s.)

" Atmospheric Electricity." By B. F. J. Schonland. (Methuen Co. 1932.—2s. 6d.)

" Electromagnetic Waves." By F. W. G. White. (Methuen Co. 1934.—3s.)

JOURNALS.

" Wireless World." (Iliffe & Sons. Weekly.—4d.)
" Wireless Engineering." (Iliffe & Sons. Monthly.—2s. 6d.)
" Proceedings of the Institute of Radio Engineers." (New York.)
" Journal of the Institution of Electrical Engineers." (Published Monthly.—10s. 6d.)
" Electronics." (Published Monthly. New York.)
" The Post Office Electrical Engineers' Journal." (Published by the Electrical Review. Quarterly.—1s.)

INDEX.

Para.

I

Imaginary numbers	341
Impedance	289, 294, 295
Impedances, series and parallel	348
Induced E.M.F.	136, 280
Induced magnetism	83
Inductance :	
analogy with inertia	139
in A.C. circuit	278
in parallel circuit	311
in parallel with R	307
in series with C and R	295
in series with R	287
mutual	135, 143
natural, of aerial	411
of solenoid	152
self	134, 149
types of	151, 153
units of	142, 143, 183
Inductances :	
cores for	383
in parallel	150, 286
in series	149, 286
iron core	154
receiving	154
tapped	382
transmitting	154
Induction :	
electromagnetic	136
field of aerial	408
magnetic	83
motors	268
Inductive coupling	332
reactance	284
Inductor :	
alternator	208
frequency meter	376
Infra-red rays	14
Iron cores	154
Instruments :	
A.C. measuring	374
D.C. measuring	184
rectifier	186, 187
Insulators	38
Intensity, field	84, 97
Interpoles	220, 240
Ionisation	36
Ions	36, 108

J

"j" $(\sqrt{-1})$	339
Jar	168
Joule	51

K

Kilocycle	15
Kilowatt-hours	57
Kirchoff's Laws	72

Para.

L

Lagging, phase	281
Lamination	205, 350, 363, 383
Lamps, incandescent	75
Law, Faraday's	141, 143
Kirchoff's	72
Lenz's	147
Ohm's	58
Leading, phase	281
Leclanche cell	111
Left-hand rule, Fleming's	130
Lenz's Law	147
Light rays	14
Lines of force	104
Line, voltage and current	436
Liquids, conduction through	108
nature of	24, 26
Logarithmic decrement	301, 386, 397
Longitudinal wave	5
Loops	306
Loose coupling	163, 419
Losses :	
in aerials	400
in condensers	176
in D.C. machines	231
in transformers	358

M

Magnetic :	
energy of current	157
flux	86
hysteresis	89, 231
induction	83
leakage	359
pole strength	77
reluctance	92
saturation	82, 383
Magnetic field	78
strength	84
Magnetism	76–93
Magneto generator	223
frequency meter	376
Magneto-motive force	92
Matter, constitution of	24
Maxwell	87
Measurement of resistance	71, 190
Measuring instruments :	
A.C.	374
D.C.	184
Megacycle	15
Megger, bridge	190
Menotti-Daniell cell	111
Mesh connected sources	435
Mesh connection	265, 433, 434
Meters, frequency	375
Microfarad	168
Microhenry	143
Millivolt per meter	104
Mixed couplings	332
Modulus of complex number	343
Molecular theory of magnetism	82
Molecules	52
Motion wave	2

INDEX.

	Para.
Motor :	
alternating current	267
alternator	249
booster	250
generator	248
starter for	246
Moving coil measuring instruments	187
Moving iron measuring instruments	188, 374
Mutual :	
inductance	135, 143
induction	136
reactance	337

N

Natural frequency	391
Negative ion	36, 108
Neutral axis of dynamo	217
Neutral line	439
NiFe cell	127
Nodes	306
Nucleus	32
Number	339
atomic	34
of oscillations in wavetrain	398

O

Ohm, International	60
Ohm's Law	58
for A.C. circuits	289
Open-core transformer	372
Open circuit test	370
Open oscillator	408
Operator "j"	339
Optimum coupling	336
Oscillation constant	392
Oscillations :	
forced	333
free	333, 387, 421, 426
number in wave train	398
Oscillators :	
closed	407
open	408
Oscillatory circuit	388
damped oscillations in	389
damping factor of	396
damping losses in	400
effective resistance of	406
log. dec. of	397
natural frequency of	391
with A.C. supply	427
with D.C. supply	427

P

Parallel :	
A.C. circuits	307
circuits, selectivity	322
condensers in	178, 293
inductances in	150, 287
plate condenser	166, 170, 182
resistances in	66
resonant circuit	312, 317
Para magnetism	83, 88

	Para.
Percentage coupling	163
Period	3
Permanent magnets	76
Permeability	77, 88, 383
tuning	154
Permittivity	96
Persistency	396
Phase difference	275, 276
of condenser	330
voltage and current	436
Phasing :	
in parallel circuit	315, 319
in series circuit	300
Phon	App. A, 10
Pitch, sound	8
Plain aerial spark system	418
Polarisation in cells	110
Pole, magnetic	76
winding	202
Polyphase A.C.	262
inter-connection of phases	265
Positive ions	36
Potential	54, 102
difference	49, 51, 102
Potentiometer	74
Power	56, 69
factor	327, 330
of coil	302
in A.C. circuits	324
rectifier, three-phase	441
to charge, condenser	172
Primary cells	107
Proton	31

Q

"Q," selectivity	302
Quantity of electricity	47, 95

R

Radiation :	
field	408
of two waves	421
resistance	405
Radio frequency	272
Rate of change of current	279
Rating of alternator	331
of dynamos	234
Ratio of L to C :	
in parallel circuit	315, 319
in series circuit	300
Ratio, transformation	852
Ray, types of æther	14
ultra-violet	14
Reactance :	
capacitive	291
inductive	284
mutual	337
positive and negative	291
Real numbers	339
Receiving condensers	180
inductances	154
Rectifier, instruments	186, 187

INDEX.

	Para.
Rectifiers, three-phase	441
Reed frequency meter	376
Regulation of dynamo	230
of transformer	362
Rejector circuit	313, 317, 321
Reluctance	92
Resistance	58
effective, of circuit	406
equivalent series	310
in A.C. circuit	277
in parallel A.C. circuits	307, 309, 316
in series A.C. circuits	287, 294, 295, 300
measurement of	190
of spark gap	402
radiation	405
specific	62
temperature coefficient of	63
variation of, with frequency	378
Resistances in parallel	66
in series	65
Resistivity	61
Resonance	296, 299, 312, 317
sharpness of	302
Resonance curves :	
parallel circuit	320
series circuit	301
Resonant current	296, 312, 317
Resonant frequency :	
in parallel circuit	312
in series circuit	296
Retentivity	83
Reversal of motor	236
Reverse current switch	121
Right-hand rule, Fleming's	147, 193
Ring, gramme	211
Rings, slip	203
Root mean square value	273
with super-imposed D.C.	274, 275
Rotary converter	254
advantages and disadvantages	261
Rotating field	267
Rotor, alternator	207, 208
Rule, Fleming's left-hand	130, 235
right-hand	147, 193

S

	Para.
Saturation, magnetic	82, 383
Screening, electromagnetic	386
electrostatic	104, 386
Secondary :	
batteries	113
E.M.F. of transformer	352
Sediment	122
Selectivity and " Q "	302, 322
adjacent channel	302
in W/T circuits	301
Self-capacity of coils	381
Self-inductance (see Inductance).	
Self-induction	137
Separately-excited dynamo	223
Series, acceptor circuits in	303
condensers in	177, 293
inductances in	149, 286

	Para.
Series, resistances in	65
resonant circuit	296
wound dynamo	221, 228
wound motor	244
Short circuit test	370
Shunt	67
for ammeter	377
wound dynamo	222, 224
wound motor	243, 244
Sine curve	195
Single phase A.C.	429
Skin effect	380, 401
Slip	268
rings	203
Solenoid	81, 91, 152
Solids	24, 26
Sound	6
Spark gap, resistance of	388
Sparking in dynamo	219
Spark transmission	18
Specific inductive capacity	96
Specific resistance	61, 62
Spectrum, visible	14
Speed regulation of motors	239
Squirrel cage motor	268
Star connection	265, 433
Starters, motor	246
Stator, alternator	207
Stiff tuning	300
Structure, atomic	31
Surface, equi-potential	104
Sulphating	123
Supersonic frequency	Prefatory Note
Switch :	
reverse current	121
reversing, for series motor	236
Symbols used in text	Tables II to V
Synchronous motor	264, 270
Systems of units	105, 183

T

	Para.
Table of æther waves	Table VI
of dielectric strength	175
of S.I.C. values	169
of symbols used in text	Tables II to V
of units	183, Table VII
Tapped inductances	382
Thermo-couple instruments	374
Three-phase A.C.	263
balanced load in	265
unbalanced load in	442
Three-phase circuits, power in	438
power rectifier	441
transformer	439
Three-wire system	431, 433
Tight coupling	163, 419
Time constant :	
of C, R circuit	174
of L, R circuit	158
Top capacity coupling	332
Toroid	91
Toroidal transformer	377

INDEX.

	Para.
Torque, electrodynamic	216, 237
Train, wave	389, 398
Transformation ratio	352
Transformer, aerial ammeter	377
air core	373
auto-	371
design in receivers	384
equivalent circuits of	369, 348
open core	372
power	349
testing	370
three-phase	439
toroidal	377
Transient conditions	338, 426
Transmitting condensers	182
inductances	154
systems, comparison of	19
Transverse wave motion	5
True watts	327
Tuning of transmitting circuits	415
Two-phase A.C. system	431

U

Ultra-violet rays	14
Unbalanced three-phase systems	442
Undamped waves	12
Units :	
electromagnetic	77, 105, 183
electrostatic	95, 105, 183
of capacity	168
of E.M.F.	51
of inductance	142, 143
of quantity	31, 95
practical	51, 105, 183

V

Valve transmission	19
Variable condensers	180
Variometer	154
Vector polygon	256, 442
Vector representation of A.C.	276, 285, 295, 308

	Para.
Velocity of æther waves	13
of sound waves	9
Virtual value of A.C.	273
Visible spectrum	14
Volt	51, 52
International	60
Voltage control of alternators	251
Voltmeters, A.C.	374
D.C.	184

W

Watt and watt-hour	57
Wattless component	278
Watts, true and apparent	327
Wattmeter in three-phase circuit	438
Wave :	
æther (electromagnetic)	13, 408
amplitude	3
classification of wireless	Prefatory Note
continuous (undamped)	12
cycle	3
damped	12
frequency	3
H/F, I/F, S/F, etc.	Prefatory Note
longitudinal	5
motion	2
period	3
sound	6
train	12, 389, 398
transverse	5
water	2
Wavelength	3, 394
Weight, atomic	30, 34
Wheatstone's bridge	73, 190
Wound rotor motor	269

X

X-rays	14

Y

Y-connection	265

S.O. Code No. 20—101—1—38

Printed under the authority of HIS MAJESTY'S STATIONERY OFFICE
BY THE WHITEFRIARS PRESS LTD. LONDON AND TONBRIDGE

2973 Wt 1934A 12M 9/41 W. P. Ltd. Gp 8.